HENRY HOLT EDITIONS IN PSYCHOLOGY

Gustav Fechner
Elements of Psychophysics
   Translated by Helmut E. Adler
   Edited by Davis H. Howes and Edwin G. Boring

Kenneth R. Hammond, Editor
The Psychology of Egon Brunswik

Oskar Pfungst
Clever Hans (The Horse of Mr. von Osten)
   Edited by Robert Rosenthal

John B. Watson
Behavior: An Introduction to Comparative Psychology
   Edited by Richard J. Herrnstein

GUSTAV THEODOR FECHNER (1801–1887)

Elements
of
Psychophysics

Volume I

Gustav Fechner

TRANSLATED BY
HELMUT E. ADLER
Yeshiva University
and the American Museum of Natural History

EDITED BY
DAVIS H. HOWES
Boston University

EDWIN G. BORING
Harvard University

With an introduction by Edwin G. Boring

A HENRY HOLT EDITION IN PSYCHOLOGY

HOLT, RINEHART AND WINSTON, INC.

NEW YORK • CHICAGO • SAN FRANCISCO • TORONTO • LONDON

Contents

203501

Editor's Preface

A major landmark in the history of scientific psychology was the publication in 1860 of G. T. Fechner's *Elemente der Psychophysik*. The character of this work and the many dimensions of its influence are well known from the accounts of historians of psychology and of other fields, especially Professor Boring's chapter on Fechner in his *History of Experimental Psychology*. But anyone who has wished to gain at first hand an acquaintance with Fechner's book has faced a formidable obstacle if English were his native tongue, for Fechner's text is difficult and long. Not many psychologists who pay tribute to Fechner as one of the founders of their field have been able to read its 350,000 words through from beginning to end.

An English translation of the *Elemente* thus has long been desirable. More than one psychologist has begun the task, including the present writer, but it proved too heavy to be undertaken casually by a psychologist as an adjunct of his regular responsibilities. It appeared that a satisfactory translation required a concerted effort. With the centennial of the *Elemente* approaching, Professor Boring and I resolved to mark that event with a joint effort to secure its translation.

In 1960, the centennial year, a grant from the National Institutes of Health (MH-4321) provided funds to pay for a translation. Boring and I began a long search for a translator with the triple qualifications that he speak native German, be a trained psychologist, and have the time for the task. We were rewarded by finding Dr. Helmut Adler, of Yeshiva University and the American Museum of Natural History, who was both willing and able to undertake the project.

Dr. Adler has labored diligently to provide an English version that is readable and yet faithful to the original, twin goals not easily mated. Professor Boring, besides contributing an introduction on Fechner, the man and his book, gave the manuscript the benefit of his editorial skill. Correction of the the proofs fell to me.

And so at last the English-speaking reader can see at least the first part of Fechner's major work on the measurement of mental processes. The translation of the second volume remains an undertaking for the future.

Boston, Mass.
October 1965

D. H. H.

Editor's Introduction

Gustav Theodor Fechner

1801—1887

Gustav Theodor Fechner's *Elemente der Psychophysik* of 1860 stands at the head of the new science of psychology. Actually the history of thought and of science is continuous, and new ways of thinking emerge only gradually as they make possible the discovery of new knowledge in the vast sea of ignorance and also the escape of the natural philosopher from the restraints of established habits of thinking.

The new experimental psychology, when it was being "founded" in the middle of the nineteenth century, already had a long past. It had a past in mental philosophy, which stems from Aristotle, if you wish, or more directly from Descartes (1650), who divided the world of experience into matter (extended substance) and mind (unextended substance). That is a dualism that has troubled psychologists for 300 years, a dualism that Fechner condemned in his philosophical war defending spiritualism against materialism. For the most part, on the philosophical side, the line of descent to the new psychology had been through the British empiricists — Hobbes, Locke, Berkeley, Hume, James Mill, John Stuart Mill. All these men, being empiricists, wrote in the atmosphere of an accepted dualism: sense-stimulation in the material world gives rise by way of the nerves to sensations, which, patterned and structured by association, constitute the furniture of the mind. Berkeley, however, reversed the genetic order and held that experience, being primordial, is given in the mind and that the conception of matter is derived from experience. John Mill's view was similar and so was Fechner's, but Fechner's formulation of the psychophysical relation nevertheless suggests the conventional view of the period that stimulus is prior to sensation, being the independent variable in the psychophysical experiment, and that sensation is measured as to its magnitude only indirectly by reference to the stimulus. He might be said to be epistemologically a dualist and metaphysically a panpsychist. The natural world, he said, is like a circle that can be viewed from the outside or from the inside and yet remains always the same circle.

The other line of descent for the new psychology is through physics and physiology. At first physics, with its standard problems of optics and acoustics, seemed nearer to the analysis of experience than did physiology. It was

This Introduction reprints with numerous modifications the greater part of the first half of the chapter on Fechner in E. G. Boring, *A History of Experimental Psychology*, 2d ed., Appleton-Century-Crofts, 1950, 275–283. It is reproduced with the permission of the publishers.

Newton, a physicist, who in 1704 made the fundamental analysis of visual sensation into the spectral colors. It was Pierre Bouguer, another physicist, who in 1729 determined the discriminatory threshold for illumination, and C. E. J. Delezenne, also a physicist, who in 1827 measured the first thresholds of pitch discrimination. At this time the physiologists entered the field through the independent discovery by Charles Bell in 1811 and François Magendie in 1822 that sensory and motor nerves constitute different systems, since they are connected with the spinal cord at different roots. That discovery invited physiologists to the separate study of the problems of sensation and of movement, and Johannes Müller, sometimes called "the father of experimental physiology," in 1826 contributed to the body of sensory fact and theory the doctrine of specific nerve energies, the conception that the quality of excitation differs in sensory nerves for each of the five senses. It was another physiologist, E. H. Weber, who in 1834 worked out the discriminatory thresholds for the tactual sense and formulated the generality that this threshold is proportional to the magnitude of the stimulus for which it is observed, a rule that has come to be called Weber's Law. Then, while Fechner was at work on psychophysics in the 1850s, H. L. F. v. Helmholtz, a physiologist, destined to become a famous physicist, turned his attention to the sensory problems of vision, publishing his huge and now classical three volumes of physiological optics in 1856–1866, as well as his other classical handbook on the sensations of tone in 1863.

In this atmosphere Fechner conceived and wrote *Elemente der Psychophysik*. Scientific experimental psychology was then all ready to emerge into the world of learning as a new discipline. Did Fechner "found" it? It is hard to say. That was not what he was trying to do. He wanted to confound materialism by disclosing empirically the relationship between mind and body. Did Helmholtz "found" the new science? That is not what he was trying to do. He supported this novel enterprise, but mainly he was concerned with the facts and measurement of visual and acoustic phenomena. Wilhelm Wundt was indeed endeavoring to "found" a new science, but he was younger and had little to say about the matter until 1863, nor very much before 1874, when his soon-to-be-famous text appeared, the first of its six editions.

Actually this matter of "founding" is moot but also unimportant. The growth of a science is inevitably gradual and continuous. "Founders" are created by the student of history as distance-markers to show how far history has come and as other signs of the road to show where there is a fairly sudden, yet never very sudden, change of direction. Great men and their unexpected quick insights are for the most part created ex post facto as mnemonic aids for the student of history. In this same manner Fechner himself, 10 years after the event, looked back on his own thinking as he had lain in bed on the morning of October 22, 1850, and chose that moment for the insight that created psychophysics. Great men and crucial dates are useful as they effect an analysis of history, for history, being descriptive, is necessarily analytical.

Gustav Theodor Fechner was a versatile man. He first acquired a modest fame as professor of physics at Leipzig, but in later life he was a physicist only as the spirit of science penetrated all his work. In intention and ambition he was a philosopher, especially in his last 40 years of life, but he was never famous, or even successful, in this fundamental effort that is, nevertheless, the key to his other activities. He was a humanist, a satirist, a poet in his incidental writings, and an estheticist during one decade of activity. He is famous, however, for his psychophysics, and this fame was rather forced upon him. He did not wish his name to go down to posterity as a psychophysicist. He did not, like Wundt, seek to found experimental psychology. He might have been content to let experimental psychology as an independent science remain in the womb of time, could he but have established his spiritualistic "day view" of reality as a substitute for the current materialistic "night view." The world, however, chose for him; it seized upon the psychophysical experiments, which Fechner meant merely as contributory to his philosophy, and made them into an experimental psychology. A fascinating life to those who wish to know how Great Men are made!

Fechner was born in 1801 in the parsonage of a little village in southeastern Germany, near the border between Saxony and Silesia. His father had succeeded his grandfather as village pastor. His father was a man of independence of thought and of receptivity to new ideas, who shocked the villagers by having a lightning rod placed upon the church tower, in the days when this precaution was regarded as a lack of faith in God's care of his own, and by preaching — as he urged that Jesus must also have done — without a wig. One can thus see in the father an anticipation of Fechner's own genius for bringing the brute facts of scientific materialism to the support of a higher spiritualism, but there can have been little, if any, direct influence of this sort, for the father died when Fechner was only 5 years old. Fechner, with his brother and mother, spent the next 9 years with his uncle, also a preacher. Then he went for a short time to a *Gymnasium* and then for a half year to a medical and surgical academy. At the age of 16 he was matriculated in medicine at the university in Leipzig, and at Leipzig he remained for the rest of his long life — for 70 years in all.

We are so accustomed to associating Fechner's name with the date 1860, the year of the publication of the *Elemente der Psychophysik*, and with the later years when he lived in Leipzig while Wundt's laboratory was being started, that we are apt to forget how old he was and how long ago he was beginning his academic life. In 1817, when Fechner went to Leipzig, Lotze, later the philosopher-pioneer in speculative physiological psychology, was not even born. Herbart had just published his *Lehrbuch*, but his *Psychologie als Wissenschaft* was still 7 years away in the future. In England, James Mill had barely completed the *History of India* and presumably had not even thought of writing a psychology. John Stuart Mill was 11 years old; Bain was not born. Phrenology had only just passed its first climax, and Gall was still writing on the functions of the brain. Flourens had not yet begun his researches on the brain. Bell, but not Magendie, had discovered the Bell-Magendie law. It was really, as the history of psychology goes, a very long time ago that Fechner went as a student to Leipzig.

It happened that E. H. Weber, the Weber after whom Fechner named "Weber's Law," went to Leipzig in the same year as *Dozent* in the faculty of medicine and was made in the following year a junior professor of comparative anatomy. After 5 years of study, Fechner took his degree in medicine, in 1822. Already, however, the humanistic side of the man was beginning to show itself. His first publication (1821), *Beweiss, dass der Mond aus Jodine bestehe*, was a satire on the current use of iodine as a panacea. The next year he wrote a satirical panegyric on modern medicine and natural history. Both these papers appeared under the nom de plume "Dr. Mises," and "Dr. Mises" was reincarnated in ironical bursts altogether 14 times from 1821 to 1876. Meanwhile Fechner's association with A. W. Volkmann had begun. Volkmann came to Leipzig as a student in medicine in 1821 and remained, later as *Dozent* and professor, for 16 years.

After he had taken his degree, Fechner's interest shifted from biological science to physics and mathematics, and he settled down in Leipzig, at first without official appointment, for study in these fields. His means were slender, and he undertook to supplement them by the translation into German of certain French handbooks of physics and chemistry. This work must have been very laborious, for by 1830 he had translated more than a dozen volumes and nearly 9000 pages; but it was work that brought him into prominence as a physicist. He was also appointed in 1824 to give lectures in physics at the university, and in addition he undertook physical research of his own. It was a very productive period. By 1830 he had published, including the translations, more than 40 articles in physical science. At this time the properties of electric currents were just beginning to become known. Ohm in 1826 had laid down the famous law that bears his name, the law that states the relation between current, resistance, and electromotive force in a circuit. Fechner was drawn into the resulting problem, and in 1831 he published a paper of importance on quantitative measurements of direct currents, a paper which made his reputation as a physicist.

The young Fechner in his thirties was a member of a delightful intellectual group in the university community at Leipzig. Volkmann, until he went to Dorpat in 1837, was also a member of this group, and it was Volkmann's sister whom Fechner married in 1833. The year after his marriage Fechner was appointed professor of physics. It must have seemed that his career was already determined. He was professor of physics at only 33, with a program of work ahead of him. He was settled in a congenial social setting at one of the most important universities. We shall see presently how far wrong the obvious prediction would have been. Fechner for the time being kept on with his physical research, throughout the still very fertile decade of his thirties. "Dr. Mises," the humanistic Fechner, appeared as an author more than half a dozen times. Toward the end of this period there is, in Fechner's research, the first indication of a quasi-psychological interest: two papers on complementary colors and subjective colors in 1838, and the famous paper on subjective afterimages in 1840. In general, however, Fechner was a promising younger physicist with the broad intellectual interests of the German professor.

Fechner, however, had overworked. He had developed, as James diagnosed the disease, a "habit-neurosis." He had also injured his eyes in the research on afterimages by gazing at the sun through colored glasses. He was prostrated, and he resigned, in 1840, his chair of physics. He suffered great pain and for 3 years cut himself off from everyone. This event seemed like a sudden and incomprehensible ending to a career so vividly begun. Then Fechner unexpectedly began to recover, and, since his malady was so little understood, his recovery appeared miraculous. This period is spoken of as the "crisis" in Fechner's life, and it had a profound effect upon his thought and his subsequent interests.

The primary result was a deepening of Fechner's religious consciousness and his concern with the problem of the soul. Thus Fechner, quite naturally for a man with such an intense intellectual life, turned to philosophy, bringing with him a vivification of the humanistic coloring that always had been one of his attributes. His forties were, of course, a sterile decade as regards writing. "Dr. Mises" published a book of poems in 1841 and several other papers later. The first book that showed Fechner's new tendency was a book about the mental life of plants, published in 1848. For Fechner, in the materialistic age of science, to argue about the minds of plants, even before Darwin had made the mental life of animals a crucial issue, was for him to court scientific unpopularity, but Fechner now felt himself possessed of a philosophic mission and he could not keep silence. He was troubled by materialism, as his book on life after death in 1836 had shown. His philosophical solution of the spiritual problem lay in his affirmation of the identity of mind and matter and in his assurance that the entire universe can be regarded as readily from the point of view of its consciousness, a view that he later called the "day view," as it can be viewed as inert matter, the "night view." Yet the demonstration of the consciousness of plants was but a step in a program.

Three years later (1851) a more important work of Fechner's appeared. It was called *Zend-Avesta*, and its subtitle declared it was about the things of heaven and the future. Oddly enough this book contains Fechner's program of psychophysics and thus bears an ancestral relation to experimental psychology. We shall return to this matter in a moment. Fechner's general intent was that the book should be a new gospel. The title means practically "a revelation of the word." Consciousness, Fechner argued, is in all and through all. The earth, "our mother," is a being like ourselves but very much more perfect than ourselves. The soul does not die, nor can it be exorcised by the priests of materialism when all being is conscious. Fechner's argument was not rational; he was intensely persuasive and developed his theme by way of plausible analogies, which, but for their seriousness, resemble somewhat the method of

Dr. Mises' satire on the comparative anatomy of the angels (1825), where Fechner argued that the angels, as the most perfect beings, must be spherical, since the sphere is the most perfect form. Now, however, Fechner was in dead earnest. He said later in 1861 that he had then called four times to a sleeping public which had not yet been aroused from its bed. "I now," he went on, "say a fifth time, 'Steh' auf!' and, if I live, I shall yet call a sixth and a seventh time, 'Steh' auf!' and always it will be but the same 'Steh' auf!'"

We need not go further into Fechner's philosophy. He did call a sixth and a seventh time, and there are seven books from 1836 to 1879 that show the persistence and the extent of Fechner's belief in his own gospel. As it happened, the public never "sprang out of bed," not even at the seventh call. His philosophy received some attention; many of these books of his were reprinted in later years; but Fechner's fame is as a psychophysicist and not as a philosopher with a mission.

It was one thing to philosophize about mind and matter as two alternative ways of regarding everything in the universe, and another thing to give the idea such concrete empirical form that it might carry weight with the materialistic intellectualism of the times or even be satisfactory to Fechner, the one-time physicist. This new philosophy, so Fechner thought, needed a solid scientific foundation. Thus he has told us that it was on the morning of October 22, 1850, while he was lying in bed thinking about this problem, that the general outlines of the solution suggested themselves to him. He saw that the thing to be done was to make "the relative increase of bodily energy the measure of the increase of the corresponding mental intensity," and he had in mind just enough of the facts of this relationship to think that an arithmetic series of mental intensities might correspond to a geometric series of physical energies, that a given absolute increase of intensity might depend upon the ratio of the increase of bodily force to the total force. Fechner said that the idea was not suggested by a knowledge of Weber's results. This statement may seem strange, for Weber was in Leipzig and had written about this matter only in 1846. We must remember, however, that Weber himself had not pointed out the general significance of his law and may have seen its most general meaning only vaguely. He had hinted at a generality in his manner of talking about ratios as if they were increments of stimulus, and in extending his finding for touch to visual extents and to tones. He had formulated no specific law. It was Fechner who realized later that his own principle was essentially what Weber's results showed, and it was Fechner who gave the empirical relationship mathematical form and called it "Weber's Law." In recent times there has been a tendency to correct Fechner's generosity, and to give the name *Fechner's Law* to what Fechner called "Weber's Law," reserving the latter term for Weber's simple statement that the just noticeable difference in a stimulus bears a constant ratio to the stimulus.

The immediate result of Fechner's idea was the formulation of the program of what he later called psychophysics, a program that, as we have already noted, was worked out in the *Zend-Avesta* of 1851. There was still the program to carry out, and Fechner set about it. The methods of measurement were developed, the three psychophysical methods which are still fundamental to much psychological research. The mathematical forms both of the methods and of the exposition of the general problem of measurement were established. The classical experiments on lifted weights, on visual brightness, and on tactual and visual distances were performed. Fechner the philosopher proved to have lost none of the experimental care of Fechner the physicist. His friend and brother-in-law, A. W. Volkmann, then at Halle, helped with many of the experiments. Other data, notably the classification of the stars by magnitude, were brought forth to support the central thesis. For 7 years Fechner published nothing of all this. Then in 1858 and 1859 two short anticipatory papers appeared, and then in 1860, full grown, the *Elemente der Psychophysik*, a text of the "exact science of the functional relations or relations of dependency between body and mind."

It would not be fair to say that the book burst upon a sleeping world. Fechner was not popular. *Zend-Avesta* and similar writings had caused the scientists to look askance at him, and he was never accepted as a philosopher. No one suspected at the time what importance the book would come to have. There was no furor; nevertheless the work was scholarly and well grounded on both the experimental and mathematical sides, and, in spite of philosophical prejudice, it commanded attention in the most important quarter of all, namely, with the other scientists who were concerned with related problems. Even before the book itself appeared, the paper of 1858 had attracted the attention of Helmholtz and of Mach. Helmholtz proposed a modification of Fechner's fundamental formula in 1859. Mach began in 1860 tests of Weber's law in the time-sense and published in 1865. Wundt, in his first psychological publications in 1862 and again in 1863, called attention to the importance of Fechner's work. A. W. Volkmann published psychophysical papers in 1864. Aubert challenged Weber's law in 1865. Delboeuf, who later did so much for the development of psychophysics, began his experiments on brightness in 1865, inspired by Fechner. Vierordt similarly undertook in 1868 his study of the time-sense in the light of the *Elemente*. Bernstein, who had just divided with Volkmann the chair of anatomy and physiology at Halle, published in 1868 his irradiation theory, a theory that is based remotely on Herbart's law of the limen, but directly on Fechner's discussion. The *Elemente* did not take the world by the ears, but it got just the kind of attention that was necessary to give it a basic position in the new psychology.

Fechner, however, had now accomplished his purpose. He had laid the scientific foundation for his philosophy and was ready to turn to other matters, keeping always in mind the central philosophical theme. Moreover, he had reached his sixties, the age when men begin to be dominated more by their interests and less by their careers. The next topic, then, that caught the attention of this versatile man was esthetics, and, just as he had spent 10 years on psychophysics, so now he spent a decade (1865–1876) on esthetics, a decade that was terminated when Fechner was 75 years old.

If Fechner "founded" psychophysics, he also "founded" experimental esthetics. His first paper in this new field was on the golden section and appeared in 1865. A dozen more papers came out from 1866 to 1872, and most of these had to do with the problem of the two Holbein Madonnas. Both Dresden and Darmstadt possessed Madonnas, very similar although different in detail, and both were reputed to have been painted by Holbein. There was much controversy about them, and Fechner plunged into it. There were several mooted points. The Darmstadt Madonna showed the Christchild. The Dresden Madonna showed instead a sick child and might have been a votive picture, painted at the request of a family with the image of a child who had died. There was the general question of the significance of the pictures, and there was also the question of authenticity. Which was Holbein's and which was not? Experts disagreed. Fechner, maintaining the judicial attitude, was inclined to believe that they might both be authentic, that if Holbein had sought to portray two similar but different ideas he would have painted two similar but different pictures. And finally, of course, there was the question as to which was the more beautiful. These two latter questions were related in human judgment, for almost everyone would be likely to believe that the authentic Madonna must be the more beautiful. Some of these questions Fechner sought to have answered "experimentally" by a public opinion poll on an auspicious occasion when the two Madonnas were exhibited together. He placed an album by the pictures and asked visitors to record their judgments; but the experiment was a failure. Out of over 11,000 visitors, only 113 recorded their opinions, and most of these answers had to be rejected because they did not follow the instructions or were made by art critics or others who knew about the pictures and had formed judgments. Nevertheless the idea had merit and has been looked upon as the beginning of the use of the method of impression in the experimental study of feeling and esthetics.

In 1876 Fechner published an introduction to esthetics, a work that closed his active interest in that subject and laid the foundation for experimental esthetics. It goes into the various problems, methods, and principles with a thoroughness that rivals the psychophysics.

There is little doubt that Fechner never would have returned either to psychophysics or to esthetics, after the publication of his major book in each subject matter, had the world let him be. The psychophysics, however, had immediately stimulated both research and criticism and, while Fechner was working on esthetics, was becoming important in the new psychology. In 1874, the year of the publication of Wundt's *Grundzüge der physiologischen Psychologie*, Fechner had been aroused to a brief criticism of Delboeuf's discussion of psychophysics (1873). The next year Wundt came to Leipzig. The following year Fechner finished with esthetics and turned again to psychophysics, publishing in 1877 his *In Sachen der Psychophysik*, a book which adds but little to the doctrine of the *Elemente*. Fechner was getting to be an old man, and his philosophical mission was still in his mind. In 1879, the year of Wundt's initiating research in the new Leipzig psychological laboratory,

Fechner issued his seventh and last call to the somnolent world on the "day view" and the "night view." He was then 78 years old. Finally, in 1882, he published the *Revision* of the psychophysics, a very important book, in which he took account of his critics and sought to meet the unexpected demand of experimental psychology upon him. In the following years there were half a dozen psychophysical articles by him, but actually his work was done. He died in 1887 at the age of 86 in Leipzig, where for 70 years he had lived the quiet life of the learned man, faring forth, while keeping his house, on these many and varied great adventures of the mind.

This then was Fechner. He was for 7 years a physiologist (1817–1824); for 15 years a physicist (1824–1839); for 12 years an invalid (1839 to 1851); for 14 years a psychophysicist (1851–1865); for 11 years an experimental estheticist (1865–1876); for at least 40 years throughout this period, recurrently and persistently, a philosopher (1836–1879); and finally, during his last 11 years, an old man whose attention had been brought back by public acclaim and criticism to psychophysics (1876–1887) — all told 70 years of varied intellectual interest and endeavor. If he founded experimental psychology, he did it incidentally and involuntarily, and yet it is hard to see how the new psychology could have advanced as it did without an *Elemente der Psychophysik* in 1860. It is to this book, therefore, that we must now turn our attention, and that we can do best in terms of the text itself, at last after 100 years available in English translation, a centennial celebration for a man who brought psychology around a corner in its history.

E. G. B.

Boston, Mass.
October 1965

Translator's Foreword

Fechner's life and his contribution to psychology contain many contradictory elements. After a lifetime devoted to championing idealism against materialism, his lasting contribution was made to the foundation of an experimental psychology. Psychophysics — a name that he coined — was first completely described in his *Elemente der Psychophysik*; yet this book, although published in 1860, had never been translated into English, whereas his speculative writings have long been available in translation.[1] He is famous for "Fechner's Law," yet the mathematical basis for this "law" has been questioned since its beginning and grave doubts have been thrown on its generality in recent years.

Why then should we read Fechner's works today?

First, his *Elemente der Psychophysik* is important as a historical document. Some great scientific innovators, such as Darwin and Newton, clearly saw the nature of their problem and worked steadily on the solution. Others, however, and Fechner is an example, were more like Columbus, who discovered a New World while looking for ancient India. Fechner's great undertaking, his attempt to refute materialism, failed, but his psychophysics laid the foundation for the new science of experimental psychology.

Secondly, Fechner's ideas influenced so many of the "founding fathers" of psychology. These men included not only experimentalists like Helmholtz, Mach, and Wundt, all of whom recognized the importance of Fechner's work immediately, but also eventually Freud, who mentioned his debt to Fechner in a passage of his *Autobiographical Study*. It reads: "I was always open to the ideas of G. T. Fechner and have followed that thinker upon many important points."[2] In particular Freud's notion of psychic energy reflected Fechner's thinking on the conservation of energy, as presented in Chapter V of the present volume. The role Freud assigned to the unconscious in *The Interpretation of Dreams* had its acknowledged source in Fechner's writings, and Freud's draft "Project for a scientific psychology"[3] included an attempt to incorporate Fechner's law.

Thirdly, Fechner showed insights into a number of important problems of psychological theory, reflecting as they did not only much that was of importance in his day, but foreshadowing many current ideas. Fechner was not a popular writer, and his difficult style, as well as his use of the German language, have prevented his ideas from being widely known. The present

[1] See *Life after Death*, tr. Wernekke. La Salle, Ill.: Open Court Publishing Company, 1906, 1914. Also tr. Mary Wadsworth. New York: Pantheon Books, 1943. *Religion of a Scientist*, tr. and ed. by Walter Lowrie. New York: Pantheon Books, 1946.

[2] Standard edition, Vol. XX. London: Hogarth Press, 1959, p. 59.

[3] *Origins of Psycho-analysis. Letters to Wilhelm Fliess, Drafts and Notes: 1887–1902*. New York: Basic Books, 1954.

translation should contribute among English-speaking psychologists to a re-evaluation of his place in history.

Fechner's interest in psychophysics came at a relatively late period in his life. Actually he was 59 when the *Elemente* was published, although the general outline of his idea had first come to him 10 years earlier and had been published in outline in his strange philosophical-speculative work, *Zend-Avesta*.

He came to this subject after a distinguished scientific career, marked by a wide range of interests, a highly individualistic approach to everything he touched upon, and a strong humanistic flavor to his thinking. Several incidents relating to his earlier life throw light on Fechner's character.

He was largely self-taught. Although enrolled at the University of Leipzig at the age of 16 to study medicine, he attended few lectures, studying mainly from books, except, we are told, for E. H. Weber's course in physiology and a course in algebra. He received his baccalaureate by passing the appropriate examinations, but never went on to the doctorate which would have entitled him to practice medicine. As he explained later: "The title of Doctor would have given me authority to practice internal medicine, surgery and obstetrics when I had not learned to bleed an artery, to apply a plain bandage, or to perform the simplest operation connected with childbirth." The doctor's degree was bestowed on him later, when he had become famous, *honoris causa*.

Fechner's medical studies may not have led him to the doctorate, but they did inspire his attacks on the medicine of his day under the pseudonym of Dr. Mises. These satirical writings expressed the rebelliousness of the young Fechner against the accepted thinking of his contemporaries. Independence of thought and a need to see for himself rather than to follow established authority marked his work throughout a long career.

Though a son and a nephew of clergymen, he considered himself a complete atheist during his student days. He experienced a sudden conversion in 1820 on reading Lorenz Oken's *Philosophy of Nature*, of which, as he himself relates, "I understood nothing very well — how indeed could I — I admit that I did not get beyond the first chapter; but in short, I had gained at once the point of view for a great unifying conception of the world."

As a young man he associated with a group of friends, and particularly a roommate, who were distinctly unconventional. Fechner joined this group in their activities, wandered about the country with them, and almost got into trouble with the police in their company. His lifelong interest in art, music, and literature may well have represented a legacy of this bohemian period in his life, but the arrival of his mother and two of his sisters at Leipzig to share his household eventually put an end to this association.

Fechner's professional interests turned to the physical sciences. He had started to translate Biot's textbook of physics from the French and thus picked up enough physics to start lecturing at the university when the opportunity arose in 1824. He also started experiments on electricity, investing the money he earned by writing in apparatus for demonstrations and research on Ohm's law. These activities led to a travel grant to Paris where he met Ampère, Biot, and Thénard, whose textbook he had also translated. In 1831 or 1832 he was appointed associate professor (but without salary) and in 1834 full professor with a substantial salary and rights to a lifetime pension.

He had married in 1833 and settled into a busy, almost frantic, period of intellectual activity. He edited and wrote extensively; he experimented and lectured on electricity; and he published a much read philosophical treatise on life after death. At the same time he carried on an active social life in the best circles of Leipzig's intellectual society. The center of this group lay in the musical world in a city where Felix Mendelssohn was then the permanent conductor of the symphony orchestra. Robert and Clara Schumann, his niece by marriage, often joined Fechner as guests of Härtel, the publisher. Fechner's early interest in music is clearly apparent in his chapter on the psychophysics of tones.

This period of successful and creative activity was bought at the cost of considerable psychological strain. He found himself plagued by headaches that he attributed to overexertion. He had trouble channeling the constant flight of his ideas. He worried about his health. To quote his own words: "The state of my head was already so bad, that when Professor Brandes' passing away cleared the way for me to aspire to the chair of physics at Leipzig, I had great qualms about applying for this position. Even after I had been nominated, I was deterred only by special circumstances from giving it up again. I hardly felt capable of satisfying the demands that this position would make on me." The special circumstances undoubtedly referred to his then forthcoming marriage. His condition grew worse. He could not sleep, became depressed, hated to lecture. His eyesight, which had been excellent, now started to bother him. Despite, or perhaps because of, his problems with his vision, he engaged in experiments on subjective colors and afterimages. This interest, particularly in afterimages, is much apparent in his *Elemente*.

Because of his deteriorating health Fechner resigned his chair in physics in 1840 and retired on his pension, his career apparently finished. His successor was Wilhelm Weber, brother of Ernst Heinrich Weber and Eduard Weber, who were both professors at the university. Wilhelm Weber had given up his chair of physics at Göttingen in 1837 as one of seven professors who resigned in protest when the newly crowned King of Hanover suspended the constitution of that state. In 1849 Wilhelm Weber returned to Göttingen to resume his work with Gauss, but Fechner, who had recovered his health by then, did not seek to reclaim his chair. He did, however, resume lecturing at the university in 1846 — on psychophysics, on esthetics, in fact on anything that interested him at the moment.

Fechner's illness was puzzling. There were two phases. A deep depression led to a refusal to eat. Laxatives, electricity, animal magnetism, homeopathic remedies and violent counterirritants, like the herbaceous moxa, only made his condition worse. Almost dead of self-imposed starvation, he finally accepted a mixture of raw ham, chopped with spices and soaked in Rhine wine and lemon juice, concocted by a lady acquaintance to whom this dish had appeared in a dream! The second phase involved a wild flight of ideas, mutism, and photophobia. He sat in a darkened room, while his mother read to him through a funnel-shaped opening in the door. Outdoors he walked with a mask over his eyes. Then, rather suddenly in October 1843, he recovered. As he himself reported, he was able to speak again because he learned to make pauses between his sentences. His sensitivity to light was overcome when he realized that he could tolerate sudden brief exposures to normal daylight, rather than the gradual exposure to dim light he had tried many times before. The idea for *Nanna* was born when he was able to see flowers again the first time he ventured into his garden.

Great concern for his health is apparent in many passages of the *Elemente*. We find him worrying about his spleen (p. 255) (". . . a mustard plaster seemed to be good for it . . . "), counting his pulse daily (p. 259), and worrying about straining his eyes. He tells us in one of the typical personal passages in the book, that, after lifting heavy weights (p. 263), " . . . blood rushed to my head, which is one of my weaker parts, due to some earlier ailment. . . ." Always a scientist, he goes on to analyze his feelings: "This effect on the head showed itself by some sensations I cannot characterize exactly, and by an intensification of the ringing in my ears from which I habitually suffer." These health problems fortunately did not stop him from voluminous writing and experimentation.

As a person, Fechner obviously was as contradictory as his ideas and his work. His writings reflect the conflict within himself. On the one hand, there was the romantic Fechner, idealistic in his philosophy and given to speculative thinking. On the other hand, there was the scientific Fechner, painstaking and rather plodding in his work, doggedly pursuing his experiments.

Of course Fechner was a product of his era. He was well grounded in the humanities. Scattered throughout his text we find allusions to classical mythology, as, for example, his reference to the Proteus legend (p. 66). He quotes Latin, French, and English at length, assuming that his readers are capable of understanding these passages. He even quotes verbatim from an article in an American journal (p. 224). The notion that angels, as perfect beings, would have to have a spherical shape, first advanced tongue-in-cheek by Dr. Mises in his *Vergleichende Anatomie der Engel* of 1825 and then repeated, more or less seriously, in the *Zend-Avesta* of 1851, can be traced back to Pythagoras. His idea that all animate as well as inanimate matter possesses a soul can be found in Anaximenes. Erwin Schrödinger, a distinguished physicist, points out in his book, *Nature and the Greeks*,[4] that it is essential for our understanding to realize that the split between science and religion did not exist in classical Greek thought. The same could be said of Fechner.

Fechner, the idealist, was also thoroughly committed to science. Like Helmholtz, he obtained his first contact with science by studying medicine, then

---

[4] *Nature and the Greeks*. London: Cambridge University Press, 1954.

concentrated on physiology to end up finally as a physicist. Physical analogies and principles are scattered liberally throughout his book. The law of the conservation of energy is featured prominently in Chapter V and enters into his thinking at a number of other points. This doctrine of the conservation of energy had been brought together by Helmholtz in 1847, generating great excitement in scientific circles. Some allowance must be made for the state of knowledge at the time of Fechner's writing of the *Elemente* in order to understand his treatment of this topic. Fechner stressed kinetic energy, because in his day kinetic energy was considered free and available for use, whereas potential energy was thought to be bound and not readily available. To Fechner it seemed that the stimulus was transmitting kinetic energy when it excited a sense organ. The modern concept of triggering the release of stored energy in neural stimulation was not available until the nature of the nerve impulse became better known.

A most significant, but neglected, aspect of Fechner's work is the incisive manner in which he dealt with the essentials of measurement. He clearly laid out the requirements for measuring a psychological variable. In obtaining a psychological measurement of, for example, sensitivity, we can observe, "(1) its limits and (2) its mean values; . . . (3) how its variations depend on conditions; . . . [and] (4) lawful relations that remain constant during variation; the last are the most important" (p. 45).

He came to grips with the nature of measurement. The meaning of measurement is derived from the means employed to obtain it. As he expressed it: "Inasmuch as the magnitudes that are to be measured do not inhere in the nature of things, and cannot be derived or handled independently, we cannot find the essential units of measurement and a means of measuring these magnitudes in their fundamental nature. The problem is solved by arranging things so that the practical means of measurement correspond with the concrete measures of reality in such a way that the relation of magnitude of that which is to be measured turns out to correspond with the units used to measure it" (p. 47).

Even physical measures, Fechner wrote, are "in their most general and ultimate sense" derived from "the fact that an equal number of equally strong psychical impressions are due to an equal number of equally large physical causes" (p. 51). Once its nature is understood, all measurement can be shown to possess the same logical structure.

In still another matter, Fechner's approach dealt with a problem in terms that are significant for our understanding of his theory. He placed great emphasis on the nature of the underlying bodily activities mediating between stimulation and the sensation. Fechner called these mediating processes *psychophysische Thätigkeiten*, translated here as psychophysical processes. By psychophysical he really meant the neural processes, as yet unobserved, that lie between stimulus and sensation. While he hoped that these processes would eventually be quantitatively determined, he did not consider absence of knowledge of their precise nature an obstacle to exploration of the relations between stimulus and sensation. By treating these processes that occur between brain and sensation as hypothetical constructs he was able not only to build a theory of sensory measurement that worked satisfactorily, but also in his second volume to find some very wise things to say about them, for they constitute the initial term of what Fechner called inner psychophysics. As he put it: "Sensation depends on stimulation; a stronger sensation depends on a stronger stimulus; the stimulus, however, causes a sensation only via the intermediate action of some internal process of the body. To the extent that lawful relationships between sensation and stimulus can be found, they must include lawful relationships between the stimulus and this inner physical activity, which obey the same general laws of interaction of bodily processes and thereby give us the basis for drawing general conclusions about the nature of this inner activity" (p. 10).

Fechner's stress on invariance, his operational approach to measurement, and his employment of hypothetical constructs are examples of how close he was to modern modes of dealing with these problems. Elsewhere his work foreshadowed theoretical positions that inevitably strike the current reader as belonging to contemporaneous psychological theory. For example, he thought of the threshold as a probability value at least half of the time, not as something that is fixed or uniquely given. He was also keenly aware that the observer's sensations depended on the previous sequence of stimuli and the observer's attitude to them.

In Volume I, Fechner took the first steps toward a quantitative psychology and staked our claim to his being the "father of psychophysics" and the pioneer experimental psychologist. In it Fechner brought to scientists and scholars for the first time the methods of psychological measurement that still remain the basis of psychophysics, although these procedures are now supplemented by others. These methods were employed to fulfill Fechner's goal of an objective psychology as laid out in 1851 in *Zend-Avesta*. There he wrote: "If mathematical psychology is possible, it must be founded on the basis of material phenomena that underlie the psychical, because they allow a direct mathematical approach and definite measurement, as is not true with respect to the psychical. There is nothing, however, to stop us from considering the materialistic phenomena that underlie a given psychical event as a function of the psychical event and vice versa" (p. 373).

Such a program was to replace a psychology that had been primarily speculative and philosophical with a psychology that was empirical and quantitative. By 1860 Fechner had brought together a considerable body of experimental work, his own and that of others, to support his thesis. The same year also saw the first publication of an objective treatment of the learning process and the principles of conditioning, when I. M. Sechenov (1829–1905) published his doctoral thesis, elaborated three years later as his book *Reflexes of the Brain* (1863). Coincidences of that sort make one think that scientific psychology must have been ready to be born, that a period of change had arrived in mental philosophy.

Fechner's writings suffer from a good deal of diffuseness and redundancy. Too often the reader finds Fechner recognizing the temptation to "lose oneself in voluminous and extensive discussion" of a marginal issue and then doing just that. He had the habit of repeating what he had just said in two or three different ways. Never satisfied with one example, he tended to add two or three more in order to make his point sure. But the translator may not cut through to the essentials of the argument, for, in doing so, the original flavor of the work would be lost. Fechner's style is set by the writing habits of the more leisurely period in which he lived, and his repetitions have, morever, heuristic value. The present translation endeavors to render Fechner's long and involved sentence structure into readable English without losing the flavor and character of the original. Simplifications have been introduced only in the interest of greater clarity. A few errors and inconsistencies were discovered in the course of the translation. They have been corrected and the corrections explained by translator's notes wherever necessary.

One unsolved puzzle is the nature of the proposed supplement entitled "Methods and Determinations of Measurement in the Area of Psychophysics," first announced on page 60 and referred to frequently throughout Volume I. No such publication is known to exist. A passage in the preface to Volume II, page viii, may provide a clue to its fate. There Fechner mentions that he would have to wait to see whether the public would develop sufficient interest in the whole range of his investigations to allow him to let the "Methods of Measurement" appear. One may suppose that this interest did not develop. Fechner did, of course, publish voluminously on psychophysics subsequent to 1860, presumably incorporating much of the material promised for "Methods of Measurement." A complete bibliography of Fechner's writings, adding up to 175 items, is appended to Volume I of the second (1889) edition of the *Elemente*, and a short bibliography of the major works appears at the end of this Foreword. The best biography, and the one all subsequent biographers appear to have used as a basis, was written by Fechner's son-in-law, J. E. Kuntze.[5]

This translation follows the first edition of 1860.[6] The second edition (1889), edited by Wundt, is identical save for some small differences in pagination and a few errors that crept into the tabular matter. There is a somewhat greater difference in pagination between the second and the third editions (1907).

A translation of the magnitude and difficulty of the present work is undertaken only with considerable trepidation. I am happy to acknowledge the help of many competent hands in this arduous task. My first debt is to Professor Edwin G. Boring, who together with Dr. Davis Howes initiated the project of translating the *Elemente* in honor of the centenary of its publication.

---

[5]*Gustav Theodor Fechner, ein deutsches Gelehrtenleben*. Leipzig: Breitkopf & Härtel, 1892. For further references to writings about Fechner see: E. G. Boring, *A History of Experimental Psychology*, 2d ed. New York: Appleton-Century-Crofts, 1950, pp. 295–296.

[6]Gustav Theodor Fechner, *Elemente der Psychophysik*. Leipzig: Breitkopf & Härtel, 1860. Vol. I, pp. xiv and 336, Vol. II, pp. xii and 571.

Professor Boring has not only provided an introduction that illuminates, as no one else could, the setting and significance of Fechner's contribution to the origins of psychology, but has given the manuscript the inimitable benefit of his editorial hand and supplied historical references in the footnotes indicated as editor's notes. Dr. Howes has read the galley proofs and offered welcome suggestions for improvement of the manuscript. Professor Philip Sisson undertook the translation of the French passages and Mrs. Katherine G. Stabile translated the Latin quotations.

Thanks are due to Yeshiva University for the sabbatical leave granted the translator for work on this volume. The Columbia University Library graciously granted me access to their large collection of Fechneriana.

My greatest debt is owed to my wife, Leonore, who typed a good part of the manuscript and also acted as my secretary, my reader, and my conscience. If one would dedicate a translation, it would be dedicated to her.

A short bibliography of Fechner's books

Nanna oder über das Seelenleben der Pflanzen. Leipzig: L. Voss, 1848, pp. xii and 399.

Zend-Avesta, oder über die Dinge des Himmels und des Jenseits. Vom Standpunkt der Naturbetrachtung (three parts). Leipzig: L. Voss, 1851.

Vorschule der Aesthetik. Leipzig: Breitkopf & Härtel, 1876, Part I, pp. viii and 264; Part II, pp. iv and 319.

In Sachen der Psychophysik. Leipzig: Breitkopf & Härtel, 1877, pp. vi and 274.

Revision der Hauptpunkte der Psychophysik. Leipzig: Breitkopf & Härtel, 1882, pp. xii and 426.

New York, N. Y.
October 1965

H. E. A.

Author's Preface

By *psychophysics*, as will be shown in greater detail in Chapter II, I mean a theory which, although ancient as a problem, is new here insofar as its formulation and treatment are concerned; in short, it is an exact theory of the relation of body and mind. Thus one finds its novel name neither unfitting nor unnecessary.

As an exact science psychophysics, like physics, must rest on experience and the mathematical connection of those empirical facts that demand a measure of what is experienced or, when such a measure is not available, a search for it. Since the measure of physical magnitudes is already known, the first and main task of this work will be to establish the as yet nonexistent measure of psychic magnitudes; the second will be to take up the applications and detailed arguments that develop from it.

It will be seen that the determination of a psychic measure is no mere matter of academic or philosophical abstraction but demands a broad empirical basis. This basis I believe I have been able to provide adequately from the results of my own and other investigations, so that the principle of this measure is now secure. In addition, I believe that I have shown its usefulness by many applications. The empirical basis, however, still needs considerable amplification; what has up to now been shown of the applications only serves to indicate that incomparably more can be provided.

In short, psychophysics in the form in which it here appears is a theory in the first stages of gestation. Therefore one should not expect by the term *Elements* in the title of this work a presentation of the essentials of a well-founded and completely formed theory, a text on elementals. Rather it should be understood as a demonstration of a theory that still is in an elementary state. One should, therefore, not make the demands upon this work that are made of a text on the elementals of a science. Investigations, arguments, and compilations are often used that would not at all fit into such a book on an established science, but that may possibly hasten the day when such a text may be written. I believe that the coherence of investigations on specific points and the consistency of results that lie in certain directions, which one could demand, will not be missed.

But just as one should not expect a text on the elementals, so one should not look here for a collection of the total material of psychophysics, but rather only for that which is relevant to the foundation of the theory of psychophysical measurement and its applications. A great deal that forms part of psychophysics cannot be dealt with here, since it has not yet advanced to the stage where it can be included.

While a great deal of this work may already be superfluous, and a great deal lacking, one has at least grounds for leniency in this respect since there has been available almost no formal and only very scattered material evidence that I could cite as a foundation. One cannot build a house without bricks;

and, when even the plan for the house has yet to be drawn, one cannot have everything right on the first try and get it all to fit together. Every subsequent attempt of this kind is bound, on the one hand, to be more complete and, on the other, to be briefer and more precise.

Certainly I have to beg indulgence, no less with respect to the formal defects than because of factual errors that may remain in this work, particularly in the treatment of many delicate, difficult, or novel questions. These errors will tend to occur even more often in the second part of this work. In the long course of these investigations I have run into so many blind alleys and unclear details, even though adhering to certain general principles which have become progressively more solidly established (it must be remembered that the whole area has previously been buried in obscurity), that I dare not hope to have them all behind me in this edition. However, I would have been quite unable to complete these investigations had I waited for complete certainty in this regard. I still am confident this theory will be capable of further advances in this same direction, since so much, after all, has now been gradually set right and cleared up.

Finally there remains only the question of whether what is offered here and the manner in which it is presented constitute a viable and fruitful beginning. Should this be true, then let the omissions and errors not count too much; at least it will be to their merit to have evoked something better.

By no means do I want to say that the contents of this work are absolutely new, and it would be a poor recommendation if they were. Rather, in order to give their just due to justifiable priorities and to show at the same time that this work is based on somewhat more than sudden fancy, I will allude briefly and at once in this preface to some historical points that I will examine more closely at their proper time and finally again in a special historical chapter.

The empirical law that forms the main foundation of the theory of psychological measurement was advanced long ago by various scholars in diverse areas and has been formulated and experimentally proven in relative generality, particularly by E. H. Weber, who in my opinion really should be called the father of psychophysics. In addition, the mathematical functions that constitute the most general and most important applications of our principle of measurement were laid down long ago by various mathematicians, physicists, and philosophers, such as Bernoulli (Laplace, Poisson), Euler (Herbart, Drobisch), and Steinheil (Pogson), and are based on special cases that were particularly suited to psychophysics and are reproduced and accepted by other scholars. While all this did not take place in order to establish a psychological measure, nor did it attract special attention, it becomes clearly evident when the principle of this measure is enunciated below (Chapter VII) that the principle was already contained in the functions these scholars set up.

It must, therefore, be apparent that our psychological measure is, in its fresh meaning as psychological measurement, only a generalization on the one hand and only a clear expression of what had previously existed on the other.

Reference to this fact may somewhat lessen the supsicion that the announce-ment of such a measure may arouse at the start. This problem is indeed not that of squaring the circle or of perpetual motion, for it has already been solved by scholars whose names guarantee the soundness of the solution.

I would neglect a cardinal obligation if, after acknowledging my debt to the achievement of past scholars on the main substance of this work, I did not make mention of both the essential help and the encouragement given by A. W. Volkmann to my own researches. The readiness with which this alert and fine scholar enlisted himself in this investigation — which, by the way, has led him into his own pathways far beyond the dictates of the immediate needs — and the value which thereby has accrued to the empirical basis of this work have indeed put me under the greatest obligation to him.

At the same time I dare to consider it a good omen for the principles and the character of this work that they are able not only to gain support from the exact investigations of the finest scholars, but also to supply starting points for such investigations. Indeed, in addition to those theoretical and experimental researches on which it is based, and which have already been connected to it, there has been often enough in the course of this work occasion to point to future or continued investigations, which are partially necessary for further development of the theory of psychophysical measurement, partially enter into its applications, and, in spite of the fact that they are of great interest, would not have presented themselves in the absence of this theory. The psycho-physical experiment, which has so far found only an incidental place in either the physical or the physiological laboratory now demands its own laboratory, its own apparatus, its own methods. It also goes without saying that the range of these investigations will be broadened more and more the further they are developed. And so I look for the main harvest of our present investigations less in what they have yielded so far than in what they promise to yield. The present report is nothing but a paltry beginning of a start.

With regard to the manner in which mathematics has been introduced into this work, particularly in the latter part, I wish these passages to be regarded by mathematicians as if written for nonmathematicians, and by nonmathema-ticians as if written for mathematicians, for I have made an effort, not without some conflict, to be understood by the one, yet to satisfy the other. I wish the mathematicians would excuse my somewhat broad and popular explanations made in the interest of nonmathematicians, for I have had it in mind that this work would particularly interest physiologists, even though I would at the same time like to interest philosophers. Yet to assume as a matter of course that both are mathematicians is nowadays still not so permissible as it actually ought to be. I wish on the other hand that nonmathematicians would consider derivations which they cannot follow (even though those that do occur make very small demands on mathematical understanding) as mathematical fact, and now and then skip a chapter, a parenthesis, or an exposition that goes beyond their depth. If I am not mistaken, anyone will find the general course and content of this work understandable, particularly all those who have some acquaintance with mathematical equations and know the properties of logarithms, or who pay heed to the brief recapitulation at the beginning of the second part. As far as others are concerned, I would prefer that they would not bother with this work, or at least that they would not pass judgment upon it, a judgment that could in no case be insightful.

I have intentionally omitted reference to the contrast between the mathematical approach to psychological relations in this work and Herbart's. To Herbart will always belong the credit not only of having been the first to point out the possibility of a mathematical treatment of these matters, but also of having made the first ingenious attempt to carry out such an enterprise; and everyone since Herbart will in this respect have to be second. Indeed, the basic point of view underlying this attempt is essentially so different from his, that there is little necessity to emphasize their difference. As it is, it would be an idle question and out of place to seek here a decision between them, especially since that could not take place without quarreling about philosophical foundations, which must at all costs be avoided here. The choice between them, and at the same time the resolutions of these fundamental questions, I leave to the future.

Perhaps the reader also anticipates here a declaration of the position this work will take with regard to materialism and idealism, as well as to the basic question of religion, which every investigation of the relation of body and mind must necessarily touch upon. As to the former, this investigation does not propose to take a position in the controversy about the basic relation of body and mind, an issue which divides materialists and idealists. The implications and consequences of this inquiry will be biased neither in one direction nor in the other, for the work considers the empirical relationship between these two sides of existence as a functional one, which itself excludes this one-sidedness.

As far as the second matter is concerned, it would be premature to assume that we would have to take a materialistic position with regard to religious questions. It is clear that the fundamental principle particularly may, as briefly mentioned on page 3, be given a one-sided materialistic interpretation, although it represents more the background than the starting point of this work. On the surface, it appears that this principle may lead to the same conclusion with regard to the question of immortality. All I shall say here to refute this interpretation is that this whole work has been evolved on the basis of and in connection with an entirely opposing concept and interpretation of this matter. I have given expression to this view in previous writings to which I must refer in case there are any misgivings, since this is not the place to take the matter up any further.[1]

---

[1]Trans. Note: See, for example: *Zend-Avesta, oder über die Dinge des Himmels und des Jenseits. Vom Standpunkt der Naturbetrachtung.* Three parts. Leipzig: L. Voss, 1851.

The present volume contains the foundation of psychic measurement, that is to say, the establishment of its principle and the exposition of the methods, laws, and data which belong to its empirical proof; the second volume will develop the functions of psychic measurement together with their implications, which shift from the outer to the inner sphere [in the mind-body relation]. The present volume then demands more of an empirical, the second one more of a mathematical and philosophical, interest. It is mathematical insofar as the new applications, which were opened up for mathematics, in the first volume, are followed up to a certain point in the second volume; it is philosophical insofar as these applications yield relevant aspects for the comprehension of the mind-body relation.

Leipzig
December 7, 1859

Elements
of
Psychophysics

INTRODUCTION

I.

General Considerations on the Relation of Body and Mind

While knowledge of the material world has blossomed in the great development of the various branches of natural science and has benefited from exact principles and methods that assure it of successful progress, and while knowledge of the mind has, at least up to a certain point, established for itself a solid basis in psychology and logic, knowledge of the relation of mind and matter, of body and soul, has up to now remained merely a field for philosophical argument without solid foundation and without sure principles and methods for the progress of inquiry.

The immediate cause of this less favorable condition is, in my opinion, to be sought in the following factual circumstances, which admittedly only make us seek their more remote origins. The relationships of the material world itself we can pursue directly and in accord with experience, as no less the relationships of the inner or mental world. Knowledge of the former, of course, is limited by the reach of our senses and their amplifications, and of the latter by the limitations of everyone's mind; still, these researches go on in such a way that we are able to find basic facts, basic laws, and basic relationships in each of the fields, information which can serve us as a secure foundation and starting point for inference and further progress. The situation is not the same in relating the material and mental worlds, since each of these two inextricably associated fields enters into immediate experience only one at a time, while the other remains hidden. At the moment when we are conscious of our feelings and thoughts, we are unable to perceive the activity of the brain that is associated with them and with which they are in turn associated—the material side is then hidden by the mental. Similarly, although we are able to examine the bodies of other people, animals, and the whole of nature directly in anatomical, physiological, physical, and chemical terms, we are not able to know anything directly about the

1

minds that belong to the former nor of God who belongs to the latter,[1] for the spiritual side is here hidden by the material. There thus remains great latitude for hypothesis and disbelief. Is there really anything revealed, we may ask, once the covers are lifted, and if so, what?

The uncertainty, the vacillation, the argument over these factual issues has so far not allowed us to gain a solid foothold or to find a point of attack for a theory of these relationships, whose factual basis is still in dispute.

And what can be the reason for this singular condition, in which body and mind can be observed, each for itself but never together, in spite of the fact that they belong to each other? Usually we can best observe things which belong together when they occur together. The inviolability of this aspect of the relationship between the mental and material worlds makes us suspect that it is fundamental, that it is rooted in their basic natures. Is there nothing similar that can at least illustrate these facts even though it cannot get to the root of the matter?

Admittedly, we can point to one thing or another. For example, when standing inside a circle, its convex side is hidden, covered by the concave side; conversely, when outside, the concave side is covered by the convex. Both sides belong together as indivisibly as do the mental and material sides of man and can be looked upon as analogous to his inner and outer sides. It is just as impossible, standing in the plane of a circle, to see both sides of the circle simultaneously as it is to see both sides of man from the plane of human existence. Only when we change our standpoint is the side of the circle we view changed, so that we now see the hidden side behind the one we had seen before. The circle is, however, only a metaphor and what counts is a question of fact.

Now, it is not the task or the intention of this work to enter into deep or penetrating discussions on the basic question of the relationship of body and mind. Let everyone seek to solve this puzzle—insofar as it appears to him as such—in his own way. It will therefore be without prejudice for what follows, if I state my opinion here in a few words, in order not to leave unanswered some possible questions about the general beliefs that formed the starting point of this inquiry and that for me, at least, still form the background. At the same time I am providing something to go by in this field of fluctuating ideas for those who are still seeking a point of view rather than believing that they have found one, even though what I say will not contain anything essential for further progress of this work. In view of the great temptation in starting a work such as this to lose one-

[1] Trans. Note: A typical Fechner notion. God is the soul of the universe.

self in voluminous and extensive discussions of this sort, and of the difficulty, by no means slight, of avoiding them completely, I hope that I will be forgiven if I limit myself here to the following brief exposition of my position.

To begin with, however, let me add a second illustrative example to the first. The solar system offers quite different aspects as seen from the sun and as observed from the earth. One is the world of Copernicus, the other the world of Ptolemy. It will always be impossible for the same observer to perceive both world systems simultaneously, in spite of the fact that both belong quite indivisibly together and, just like the concave and convex sides of the circle, are basically only two different modes of appearance of the same matter from different standpoints. Here again one needs but to change the point of view in order to make evident the one world rather than the other.

The whole world is full of such examples, which prove to us that what is in fact one thing will appear as two from two points of view; one cannot expect to find things the same from one standpoint and from the other. Who would not admit that it is always thus and cannot be otherwise? Only with respect to the greatest and most decisive example does one deny it or fail to think of it. That is the relationship of the mental and material worlds.

What will appear to you as your mind from the internal standpoint, where you yourself are this mind, will, on the other hand, appear from the outside point of view as the material basis of this mind. There is a difference whether one thinks with the brain or examines the brain of a thinking person.* These activities appear to be quite different, but the standpoint is quite different too, for here one is an inner, the other an outer point of view. The views are even more completely different than were the previous examples, and for that reason the differences between the modes of their appearance are immensely greater. For the twofold mode of appearance of the circle or the planetary system was after all basically gained by taking two different external standpoints; whether within the circle or on the sun, the observer remained outside the sweep of the circles outside the planets. The appearance of the mind to itself, on the other hand, is gained from the truly inner point of view of the underlying being regarding itself, as in coincidence with itself, whereas the appearance of the material state belonging to it derives from a standpoint that is truly external, and not in coincidence.

---

* Examination in this case is equivalent to forming, from deductions based on external observations, an adequate concept of how the internal condition would appear upon removal of barriers to direct examination.

Now it becomes obvious why no one can ever observe mind and body simultaneously even though they are inextricably united, for it is impossible for anyone to be inside and outside the same thing at one time.

Here lies also the reason why one mind cannot perceive another mind as such, even though one might believe it would be easiest to become aware of the same kind of entity. One mind, insofar as it does not coincide with the other, becomes aware only of the other's material manifestations. A mind can, therefore, gain awareness of another only through the aid of its corporeality, for the mind's exterior appearance is no more than its material nature.

For this reason, too, the mind appears always as unitary, because there exists only the one inner standpoint, whereas every body appears different according to the multitude of external standpoints and the differences among those occupying them.

The present way of looking at these phenomena thus covers the most fundamental relationships between body and mind, as any basic point of view should seek to do.

One more item: body and mind parallel each other; changes in one correspond to changes in the other. Why? Leibniz says: one can hold different opinions. Two clocks mounted on the same board adjust their movement to each other by means of their common attachment (if they do not vary too much from each other); this is the usual dualistic notion of the mind-body relation. It could also be that someone moves the hands of both clocks so that they keep in harmony; this view is occasionalism, according to which God creates the mental changes appropriate to the bodily changes and vice versa, in constant harmony. The clocks could also be adjusted so perfectly from the beginning that they keep perfect time, without ever needing adjustment; that is the notion of prestabilized harmony. Leibniz has left out one point of view—the most simple possible. They can keep time harmoniously—indeed never differ— because they are not really two different clocks. Therewith we can dispense with the common board, the constant adjustment, the artificiality of the original setting. What appears to the external observer as the organic clock with its movement and its works of organic wheels and levers (or as its most important and essential part), appears to the clock itself quite differently, as its own mind with its works of feelings, drives, and thoughts. No insult is meant, if man here be called a clock. If he is called that in one respect, yet he will not be so called in every respect.

The difference of appearance depends not only on the difference of standpoint, but also on the differences among those that occupy it. A blind person does not see any of the exterior world from an external standpoint, though his position is just as favorable as that of a seeing person; and a nonliving clock does not see its interior in spite of its standpoint of coincidence, which is just as favorable as that of a brain. A clock can exist only as external appearance.

The natural sciences employ consistently the external standpoint in their considerations, the humanities the internal. The common opinions of everyday life are based on changes of the standpoints, and natural philosophy on the identity of what appears double from two standpoints. A theory of the relationship of mind and body will have to trace the relationship of the two modes of appearance of a single thing that is a unity.

These are my fundamental opinions. They will not clear up the ultimate nature of body and mind, but I do seek by means of them to unify the most general factual relationships between them under a single point of view.

However, as I mentioned before, it remains open to everyone to seek to effect the same end by another approach, or not to seek to accomplish it at all. Everyone's chosen approach will depend on the context of his other opinions. By arguing backwards, he will have to determine the possibility or impossibility of finding a suitable general relationship himself. At this point it is not important whether he wants to consider body and mind as only two different modes of appearance of the same entity or as two entities brought together externally, or to consider the soul as a point in a nexus of other points of essentially the same or of a different nature, or to dispense entirely with a fundamentally unitary approach. Insofar as an empirical relationship between body and mind is acknowledged and its empirical pursuit is allowed, there is no objection to trying even the most complicated kind of representation. In what follows we shall base our inquiry only on the empirical relationships of body and mind, and in addition adopt for use the most common expressions for the designation of these facts, though they are expressed more in the terms of a dualistic approach than my own monistic one. Translation from one to the other is easy.

This does not mean, however, that the theory which will be developed here will be altogether indifferent to the points of view on the basic relationships of body and mind and without influence upon them, for the contrary is true. Still, one must not confuse the effects that this theory may have some day—and that are partially beginning to take form even now—with the basis of this theory. This basis is indeed purely empirical, and every assumption is to be rejected from the start.

One may well ask whether the possibility of such a basis does not directly contradict the fact, with which we started, that the relationships of body and mind are outside the realm of experience. They are not, however, beyond experience altogether, for only the immediate relationships are beyond immediate experience. Our own interpretation of the general relation of body and mind already has had the support of common experiences with these relationships, even if they do not strike everyone who comes to this work with preconceived notions as necessary. What follows will show how we can draw quite as much on special experiences, which can serve us partly to orient ourselves in the area of mediated relationships and partly to provide a foundation for deductions regarding immediate relationships.

Indeed, we could not rest content with this general point of view, even if it were generally accepted. The proof, the fertility, and the depth of a universal law do not depend on the general principles but on the elementary facts. The law of gravitation and the molecular laws (which undoubtedly include the former) are elementary laws; were they thoroughly known and the whole range of their implications exhausted, we would have a theory of the material world in its most general form. Similarly we must seek to form elementary laws of the relationship of the material and the mental world in order to gain a durable and developed theory instead of a general opinion, and we will only be able to do this, here as elsewhere, by building on a foundation of elementary facts.

Psychophysics is a theory that must be based on this point of view. More details follow in the next chapter.

II.

The Concept and the Task of Psychophysics

Psychophysics should be understood here as an exact theory of the functionally dependent relations of body and soul or, more generally, of the material and the mental, of the physical and the psychological worlds.

We count as mental, psychological, or belonging to the soul, all that can be grasped by introspective observation or that can be abstracted from it; as bodily, corporeal, physical, or material, all that can be grasped by observation from the outside or abstracted from it. These designations refer only to those aspects of the world of appearance, with whose relationships psychophysics will have to occupy itself, provided that one understands inner and outer observation in the sense of everyday language to refer to the activities through which alone existence becomes apparent.

In any case, all discussions and investigations of psychophysics relate only to the apparent phenomena of the material and mental worlds, to a world that either appears directly through introspection or through outside observation, or that can be deduced from its appearance or grasped as a phenomenological relationship, category, association, deduction, or law. Briefly, psychophysics refers to the *physical* in the sense of physics and chemistry, to the *psychical* in the sense of experiential psychology, without referring back in any way to the nature of the body or of the soul beyond the phenomenal in the metaphysical sense.

In general, we call the psychic a dependent function of the physical, and vice versa, insofar as there exists between them such a constant or lawful relationship that, from the presence and changes of one, we can deduce those of the other.

The existence of a functional relationship between body and mind is, in general, not denied; nevertheless, there exists a still unresolved dispute over the reasons for this fact, and the interpretation and extent of it.

With no regard to the metaphysical points of this argument (points which concern rather more the so-called essence than the appearance), psychophysics undertakes to determine the actual functional relationships between the modes of appearance of body and mind as exactly as possible.

What things belong together quantitatively and qualitatively, distant and close, in the material and in the mental world? What are the laws governing their changes in the same or in opposite directions? These are the questions in general that psychophysics asks and tries to answer with exactitude.

In other words, but still with the same meaning: what belong together in the inner and outer modes of appearance of things, and what laws exist regarding their respective changes?

Insofar as a functional relationship linking body and mind exists, there is actually nothing to prevent us from looking at it and pursuing it from the one direction rather than from the other. One can illustrate this relationship suitably by means of a mathematical function, an equation between the variables x and y, where each variable can be looked upon at will as a function of the other, and where each is dependent upon the changes of the other. There is a reason, however, why psychophysics prefers to make the approach from the side of the dependence of the mind on the body rather than the contrary, for it is only the physical that is immediately open to measurement, whereas the measurement of the psychical can be obtained only as dependent on the physical—as we shall see later. This reason is decisive; it determines the direction of approach in what follows.

The materialistic reasons for such a preference we need not discuss, nor are they meaningful in psychophysics, and the dispute between materialism and idealism over the essential nature of the dependency of one on the other remains alien and immaterial to psychophysics, since it concerns itself only with the phenomenal relationships.

One can distinguish immediate and mediated relationships of dependency or direct and indirect functions relating body and mind. Sensations are in a directly dependent relationship to certain processes in our brains as far as the one is determined by the other or has the other as its immediate consequence; but sensations are merely in a mediated relationship to the external stimulus, which initiates these processes only via the intervention of a neural conductor. All our mental activity has dependent upon it an immediate activity in our brain, or is accompanied immediately by brain activity, or else directly causes the activity, of which the effects then are transmitted to the external world via the medium of our neural and effector organs.

The mediated functional relationships of body and mind fulfill completely the concept of a functional relationship only under the supposition that the mediation enters into the relationship, since omission of the mediation leads to the absence of the constancy or lawfulness of the relationship of body and mind, which exists by virtue of this mediation. A stimulus then releases proper sensations only when a living brain does not lack the living nerves to transmit the effect of the stimulus to the brain.

As far as the psychic is to be considered a direct function of the physical, the physical can be called the carrier, the factor underlying the psychical. Physical processes that accompany or underlie psychical functions, and consequently stand in a direct functional relationship to them, we shall call psychophysical.

Without making any assumptions about the nature of psychophysical processes, the question of their substrate and form we may leave undecided from the start. There is a twofold reason why we may dispense with this question right away: first, because the determination of the general principles of psychophysics will involve the handling only of quantitative relations, just as in physics, where qualitative depend on earlier quantitative relationships; and second, because we will have to give no special consideration to psychophysical processes in the first part, under the plan of work which follows immediately.

By its nature, psychophysics may be divided into an outer and an inner part, depending on whether consideration is focused on the relationship of the psychical to the body's external aspects, or on those internal functions with which the psychic are closely related. In other words, the division is between the mediated and the immediate functional relationships of mind and body.

The truly basic empirical evidence for the whole of psychophysics can be sought only in the realm of outer psychophysics, inasmuch as it is only this part that is available to immediate experience. Our point of departure therefore has to be taken from outer psychophysics. However, there can be no development of outer psychophysics without constant regard to inner psychophysics, in view of the fact that the body's external world is functionally related to the mind only by the mediation of the body's internal world.

Moreover, while we are considering the regular relations of external stimulus and sensation, we must not forget that the stimulus, after all, does not awaken our sensations directly, but only via the awakening of those bodily processes within us that stand in direct relation to sensation. Their nature may still be quite unknown, the inquiry regarding their nature may be neglected for the present (as already stated), but the fact that they do exist must be affirmed and referred to often, whenever it comes to the point of taking dead aim and following up those lawful relationships which are our immediate concern in outer psychophysics. Similarly, even though the body's activities, which are directly subject to the activity of our will and obey it, are still totally unknown, we should not forget that the effect of the will on the outer world can only be achieved via just such activities. We thus have implicitly to interpolate everywhere the unknown intermediate link that is necessary to complete the chain of effects.

Psychophysics, already related to psychology and physics by name, must on the one hand be based on psychology, and on the other hand promises to give psychology a mathematical foundation. From physics outer psychophysics borrows aids and methodology; inner psychophysics leans more to physiology and anatomy, particularly of the nervous system, with which a certain acquaintance is presupposed. Unfortunately, however, inner psychophysics has not profited so far from recent painstaking, exact, and valuable investigations in this field to the extent it should. Inner psychophysics undoubtedly will do this one day, once these investigations (and those from the different kind of attack on which this work is based) have succeeded to the point of reaching a common meeting ground, where they will be able to cross-fertilize each other. That this is not yet the case to any extent indicates only the incomplete state in which our theory finds itself.

The point of view from which we plan to attack our task is as follows: Even before the means are available to discover the nature of the processes of the body that stand in direct relation to our mental activities, we will nevertheless be able to determine to a certain degree the quantitative relationship between them. Sensation depends on stimulation; a stronger sensation depends on a stronger stimulus; the stimulus, however, causes sensation only via the intermediate action of some internal process of the body. To the extent that lawful relationships between sensation and stimulus can be found, they must include lawful relationships between the stimulus and this inner physical activity, which obey the same general laws of interaction of bodily processes and thereby give us a basis for drawing general conclusions about the nature of this inner activity. Indeed, later discussion will show that, in spite of all our ignorance of the detailed nature of psychophysical processes there exists, for those aspects which are concerned with the more important relationships of ordinary mental life, a basis which within limits already allows us to form certain and sufficient conceptions of the fundamental facts and laws which define the connection of outer to inner psychophysics.

Quite apart from their import for inner psychophysics, these lawful relationships, which may be ascertained in the area of outer psychophysics, have their own importance. Based on them, as we shall see, physical measurement yields a psychic measurement, on which we can base arguments that in their turn are of importance and interest.

III.

A Preliminary Question

For the present the discussion of all obscure and controversial questions of inner psychophysics—and almost the whole of inner psychophysics at this time consists of such questions—will be postponed along with the discussion of inner psychophysics itself. Later experience will provide us with the means for the answers. Nevertheless, one of these questions will at least have to be touched upon briefly at the start. This point, which concerns the future of the whole of psychophysics, we take up now in order to answer it to the extent that it can be answered in general, leaving everything else for later discussion.

If we classify thinking, willing, and the finer esthetic feelings as higher mental activities, and sensations and drives as lower mental activities, then, at least in this world—leaving the question of the next world quite open—the higher mental activities can go on no less than the lower without involving physical processes or being tied to psychophysical processes No one could think with a frozen brain. There can be just as little doubt that a specific visual sensation or auditory sensation can only come about because of specific activities of our nervous system. No one questions this. The idea of the sensory side of the mind is actually based on the conception that there exists an exact connection between it and corporeality. Great doubt exists, however, as to whether each specific thought is tied to just as specific a process in the brain and, if not, whether brain activity as a whole suffices for thinking and the higher mental activities in general, without the necessity for a special type or direction of physiological process in the brain in order for these processes to take place in a specific way and direction. Indeed, it seems that the essential difference between the higher and lower mental spheres (distinguished by some as soul and mind in their narrower senses) is sought precisely in this point.

If we now assume that the higher mental activities are really exempt from a specific relationship to physical processes, there would still be their general relationship, which may be granted to be real, and which would be subject to the consideration and investigation of inner psychophysics. This general relationship will, in any case, be subject to general laws, including common principles, still to be discovered. Indeed, their discovery should always remain the most important of the tasks of inner psychophysics. One of the next chapters (Chapter V) will lead us to a consideration of just such conditions.

A metaphor: thought may be regarded as part of the stream of bodily processes itself, and may be real only in terms of these processes, or it may need this stream only for steering as an oarsman steers his boat, raising only some incidental ripples with his oar. The conditions and laws of the river must be taken into account in both instances when the flow or progress of thought is concerned, though in each case from a quite different point of view, to be sure. Even the freest navigation[1] is subject to laws, as to the nature of the elements and the means that serve it. Similarly, psychophysics will find it necessary, in any case, to deal with the relationship of higher mental activity to its physical base. From what point of view, however, and to what extent, psychophysics will one day have itself to decide.

For the time being everyone should try to confine the conception and the scope of inner psychophysics as much as he can until the force and limitations of facts compel him to abandon the attempt. In my opinion, which as of now has to be considered as a mere opinion, there are no boundaries in this respect.

Indeed, I feel that the experience of harmony and melody, which undoubtedly have a higher character than single tones, is based on the ratios of the vibrations that themselves underlie the separate sensations, and that these ratios can change only in exact relationship to the manner in which the single tones are sounded together or follow one another. Thus, harmony and melody suggest to me only a higher relation, and not one lacking a special relationship of dependency between the higher mental sphere and its physical basis. Indeed everything seems to agree with this suggestion so easily pursued and extended. However, neither the pursuit nor even the assertion of this matter is relevant here at the start.

---

[1] Trans. Note: A reference to free navigation as a political problem—for example, free navigation on the Rhine.

IV.
Concepts concerning Sensation and Stimulus

In the present incomplete state of psychophysical investigations, there would be little profit in an enumeration, definition, and classification of all the psychological conditions that could at some time form their subject matter. At first we shall occupy ourselves mainly with sensory experiences in the common meaning of the word experience, making use of the following distinctions in nomenclature.

I intend to distinguish between intensive and extensive sensations, depending on whether they concern the sensory perception of something whose magnitude can be judged intensively or extensively. For example, I shall include as an intensive sensation the sensation of brightness, as an extensive sensation the perception of a spatial extent by sight or touch; and accordingly I shall distinguish between the intensive and extensive magnitude of a sensation. When one object appears to us brighter than another, we call the sensation it arouses intensively greater; when it appears larger than another we call it extensively greater. This is merely a matter of definition and implies, as generally understood, no specific measure of sensation.

With every sensation whatsoever, intensive as well as extensive, magnitude and form may be distinguished, although in the case of intensive sensations magnitude is often called strength and form quality. With sounds, the pitch, even though it is a quality of the sound, has also a quantitative aspect insofar as we can distinguish a higher from a lower pitch.

E. H. Weber—and undoubtedly quite to the point—calls the spatial sense, or the capacity or sense whereby we arrive at extensive sensations (as the term is used here), a general sense. Those senses that give rise to intensive sensations he calls special senses. The former sensations cannot, like the latter, arise from the impression of single independent nerve fibers or their respective ramifications (sensory circles), but can do so only by a coordination of the impressions of several fibers, wherein the strength and quality of the impression as well as the number and arrangement of the nerve centers are essential to fix the size and form of the extensive sensation. His discussions of this matter* are very apt contributions to the clarification of the general relationship of the senses. At present it suffices to have pointed out the foregoing difference in the circumstances on which intensive and extensive sensations depend. In fact, these brief preliminary discussions are intended only to introduce the discussion of appropriate measures of sensitivity and sensation, and therefore do not enter into the theory of sensations to any greater extent than this purpose warrants.

Because of their different natures and the different conditions upon which they depend, it is necessary to make a special examination of the laws governing extensive and intensive sensations. One might think that the magnitude of extensive sensations, or the extensive size of sensations, depended on the number of sensory circles stimulated, according to the same laws and corresponding to the way in which the magnitude of intensive sensations depends on the intensity of stimulation; but this is both incorrect to assume a priori and impossible to prove as yet. Our future investigations will preferably concern themselves, though not exclusively, with the intensive sensations, and in the main are so to be understood, unless the contrary is apparent from the added adjective *extensive* or from the context.

Next to the distinction between extensive and intensive sensations we may consider the distinctions between objective and common sensations and between the so-called positive and negative sensations. Objective sensations, such as sensations of light and sound, are those that can be referred to the presence of a source external to the sensory organ. Changes of the common sensations, such as pain, pleasure, hunger, and thirst, can, however, be felt only as conditions of our own bodies. For this relationship the reader is also referred to Weber's classic work in his treatise on touch and common sensations.[1]

As positive and negative sensations it is usual to contrast such sensations as warmth and cold, pleasure and pain, which share the characteristic that the manner of their arousal or the relation to that which gives rise to them includes an antithesis. For example, the sensation of cold originates and increases through the withdrawal of heat, whereas warmth arises through the addition of heat. The sensation of pleasure is connected with a seeking of the cause of its arousal, just as dislike is connected with the opposite tendency.

---

* *Berichte der sächs. Soc.* 1853, p. 83; abstracted in *Fechner's Centralblatt für Naturwissenschaften und Anthropologie.* 1853, No. 31.

[1] Ed. Note: E. H. Weber, *Der Tastsinn und das Gmeingefühl. R. Wagner's Handwörterbuch der Physiologie.* 1846, III, ii, 481–588.

While such designations as positive and negative sensations may be allowed in the usage of common language, one should not fail to note that the so-called negative sensations have nothing negative about them psychologically. They do not represent a lack, a lessening, a removal of sensations. On the contrary, they may be as violent, or even more so, than the so-called positive sensations, and are able to manifest themselves or give rise to just as strong positive effects on the body. For example, the sensation of freezing can cause a shaking of the whole body, and that of pain can cause crying besides other vigorous movements of the body.

The term *stimulus*, in its narrow sense, refers only to means of arousing the body, the excitation of intensive sensations. To the extent that stimuli belong to the outside world, they are external stimuli; insofar as they belong to the internal world of the body, they are internal stimuli. The former concept can be explained factually by recording external stimuli, such as light and sound; the latter concept will first need closer examination and may then perhaps be at least partially eliminated. A murmuring in our ears can start through the external influences of oscillations of the air, which a waterfall sends to our ears. A similar murmur can originate without outside influence through causes within our body. These are in general unknown; yet insofar as they produce the equivalent of the effect of an outside stimulus, they must be considered its equivalent. From this point of view it will often suit us to treat these unknown, but admittedly (according to their effects) factual, internal bodily sources of sensations under the same concepts, standpoints, and formulas as the external sources.

If the mind were affected only by external and internal excitations to the extent that their effects reach a specific part of the body, then all sensations would, as far as we grant their dependence on the body, be only results of activities of the body. Thus even the innermost conditions of the body would fall under the concept of stimuli. If, on the other hand, it is essentially the case that sensations are only accompanied by bodily activities in a functional relationship, it would not be proper to include such simultaneously conditioned sensations with directly determined sensations. Only those stimuli that serve to cause sensations should be included, if one does not wish to mix two different kinds of things. In the meanwhile we do not immediately have to come to a decision. These diverse opinions have no influence on our factual observations, as long as we consider the existence and magnitude of internal stimuli only according to their equivalent effects as compared to external stimuli and take them into account as such. At this time internal stimuli are an unknown x as to their location and quality, although they enter despite this limitation into the phenomenal sphere with a quantitative effect that is comparable to that of an external stimulus. The internal stimulus derives its name and value from this effect.

Some things, like weights, to which one would hesitate to give the meaning of stimulus in everyday life, will be classed as such without misgivings, as far as they give rise to tactile pressure, or weight, when lifted. On the other hand, a generalization of the word stimulus to the causes by which extensive sensations are evoked in us has its drawbacks, especially inasmuch as little clarity exists so far about these causes. We perceive, with our eyes closed, a black visual field of a certain extent, even without the addition of external causes, and, by specially focusing our attention, we can become conscious of a certain extent of our body surface, even without being touched by calipers or other instruments. Added outside stimulation partially sets the boundaries of these natural sensation fields, partially determines their form, and partially provides a basis for judging relative size and distance, without, however, giving rise to the sensation of space. This sensation seems to be rooted in the inborn coordination and organic connections of active nerves, or of their central endings although nothing certain has been decided about the matter so far. If it is still possible to talk of a stimulus in this connection, we could do so only with respect to the coordination of the internal excitation of these nerves. Since these, however, are probably conditions that occur simultaneously with the sensation, this expression [the sensation of space] would again become unsuitable. Experience can also, aided by movements, take part in the judging of extents—as some like to emphasize. This is not the place, however, to go any deeper into this still rather obscure matter, where only the definitions of words are concerned.

One can say, disregarding this obscurity and the question of the extent to which the term *stimulus* is appropriate, that the magnitude of the stimulus in intensive sensations is replaced in the extensive case by the number of active sensory circles insofar as the perceived extension decreases or increases as a dependent function. Thus, in relation to quantitatively dependent relationships, this number can be brought under a common, though rather general, point of view. One cannot assert in this way, however, that the law by which they are dependent is the same in both cases, or that the magnitude of the extensive sensation does not depend on other circumstances besides that number. Indeed, these points are themselves the object of important psychophysical investigations.

Under the application of most outer forces on which sensations are dependent, the sensation increases, after it once becomes noticeable, as the force acting on it is increased continually and in the same direction, and decreases with the lessening of the force continually until unnotice-able. With regard to some sensations, however, such as warmth and pres-sure on the skin, the organism is so constituted that a sensation arises only by reason of a difference from a given average or normal influence, such as the normal skin temperature or normal air pressure. This sensa-tion then increases in both directions but with different characteristics, as a sensation of warmth or cold, pressure or tension, depending on whether one increases the influence above this point or reduces it below this point. In this case one would correctly regard as the stimulus, not the absolute magnitude of the acting force, but its positive or negative deviation from the point that divides the sensations of contrasting character, the point at which no sensation exists. We could call the former a positive, the latter a negative stimulus.

As far as the interrelationship of stimulus and sensation is to be con-sidered, stimuli are always assumed to be effective under comparable circumstances, unless the contrary is expressly mentioned or can be seen from the context. This comparability can, however, be nullified by a different mode of stimulation, as well as by a differing condition of the subject or the organ at the time the stimulus impinges. The concept of differential sensitivity relates to this condition, a concept and its measure-ment that will be discussed in detail in Chapter VI.

For the sake of brevity one says of a stimulus which evokes a sensation, as well as of a stimulus difference which is accompanied by a difference in sensations, that they are felt more strongly or weakly, according to whether the sensation or difference in sensations is stronger or weaker. This is also an expression that must be allowed to serve us without giving rise to misunderstanding.

OUTER PSYCHOPHYSICS: THE PRINCIPLE OF PSYCHOPHYSICAL MEASUREMENT

V.

The Measure of Physical Activity: Kinetic Energy

No stimulus functions passively. Some stimuli, such as light and sound, can be conceptualized directly as motions, and even if this does not hold for others, such as the stimuli of weight, smell, and taste, we may nevertheless assume that these stimuli evoke or change sensations only by causing or changing some kind of activity within our body. Their magnitudes are therefore representative of the extent of physical activities that are related to sensations dependent on them in some manner.

We shall now discuss some appropriate aspects of the general measurement of physical activities, without, however, taking up here the specific ways of measuring various stimuli or the bodily activities initiated by them, since we consider such measurements, to the extent they are available, as known through physics or chemistry.

Even in everyday life one uses a particular yardstick to determine the size or strength of a physical activity. One seeks such information partly in the speed of execution of movement, partly in the magnitude of the moved mass, without, however, forming any clear concept about them. At first it seems most natural to believe that the product of size and velocity of the moved mass, that is to say, its momentum, can be taken as a measure of the magnitude of an activity. Indeed, on impact and in general in the transmission of movement, the velocity a body assumes after collision, or the size of the mass to which a given velocity can be transmitted, is proportional to the momentum of the colliding bodies. Should one want to regard this effect as determining the magnitude of activity, one would indeed find a measure for it in its momentum. Doubtless the measure will depend on the definition of bodily activity. Meanwhile, if one wants to use these terms in the sense in which they are employed in exact physics, mechanics, physiology, and even in everyday life, only kinetic energy and not momentum can serve as a measure of physical activity.

The kinetic energy of which we speak here should by no means be mistaken for the vital energy of the philosophers, for it implies an exact concept of measurement with the meaning that follows.[1]

The kinetic energy of a particle, regardless of whether it is conceived atomistically or not, is calculated by multiplying its mass m by the square of its velocity, so that the expression for the energy of a specific particle becomes mv^2.* The kinetic energy of a whole system is then the sum of the kinetic energies of its parts, and therefore in a system of three or more particles with masses $m, m', m'', \ldots$ and velocities $v, v', v'' \ldots$

$$\text{kinetic energy} = mv^2 + m'v'^2 + m''v''^2 \ldots$$

which one usually expresses in brief for any number of particles by

$$\Sigma \, mv^2$$

Care should be taken to note that the summation sign Σ means the summation not of some identical products mv^2, but of as many different kinds of products as there are particles of differing masses and velocities.

Without taking up at this time the underlying principles that apply in the introduction of this concept in measurement, we may cite some of the more obvious considerations.

In accordance with the procedures of mathematical dynamics, velocities of opposite directions must carry opposite signs. It is clear, therefore, that if one asks what would have been the total sum of activity developed in a given time in a system whose particles were vibrating actively, one would find that this sum of activities is close to zero, provided one were to make momentum the yardstick of activity. This consequence must

----

[1] Trans. Note: *Lebendige Kraft* = kinetic energy, but *Lebenskraft* = vital energy, *vis vita*, or *élan vital*.

* In mechanics, strictly speaking, the kinetic energy of a particle is understood to be only one half of the product mv^2; but some people do employ this term for the whole of the product, which is what I also am doing for convenience's sake, in that this different usage understandably has no influence on the conditions which depend on energy, but only changes its units.

follow since the velocities of the movements to and fro, having opposite signs, result when they are multiplied by their masses (always taken as positive) in products that cancel each other on summation. Such cancellation would not be proper in every case, however, for the movement one way will need as much energy as the movement the other way. On the other hand, in using kinetic energy as a yardstick, the motions both to and fro contribute to the sum of activities, since the square of a negative number is just as positive as that of a positive number.

In the second place, we may note that in measuring bodily activity by kinetic energy, one can do so only by means of the output of the body or of the work that can be accomplished by it. Thus it is that one relates kinetic energy to concepts of daily life and practical mechanics. A person or a machine must, according to common concepts of work, put out two or three times the amount of work when a weight is lifted to double or treble its height; and if the work consists of a kind other than weight lifting, then one still can always convert it to this kind of work in order to have a comparative measure.

Now, according to known laws, a rock thrown up vertically reaches a height that (apart from air resistance) does not increase in proportion to the simple velocity which one imparts to it at the moment of throwing, but to the square of this velocity, and thus varies in proportion to the kinetic energy imparted to it at the moment of throwing. This same velocity, however, which is imparted to it at once (or rather in very fast increments) when thrown, is given to it in gradual increments when lifted slowly. The height reached by lifting then depends, as does the height reached by throwing, on the kinetic energy acting on the rock, or more generally speaking, on a load or weight acted upon by gravity.

In general, aside from unimportant details, in order to climb a mountain a person must develop as much kinetic energy in upward movement as would be necessary to throw his weight to this height.

Thus, in general, the kinetic energy of a body of a given mass at a given moment can be represented, regardless of the direction of its incidental movement, by the height that this, or a similar mass at the same velocity, would reach above a given·point, by virtue of possessing this particular velocity acting against gravity. It should be noted that we are assuming that the previously active force by which the mass was accelerated is terminated, and that no new force, except that of the directly opposing gravity, is added. For every point in the upward trajectory of this body, one can represent the appropriate kinetic energy by the height above this point to which the body will travel, without contradicting the first determination, in that the constantly lessening kinetic energy more and more reduces the height above the given point which can still be reached.

In throwing something upward or lifting a load in empty space, it is only the opposing action of gravity that constantly removes something from the generated velocity, until eventually, on reaching a given height, all velocity is gone. The output cannot, therefore, go beyond this point. Instead of (or together with) this opposing action of gravity, the same effect can be found through the resistance of elasticity, friction, the so-called resistance of media, or any other resistance—for in all work a resistance must be overcome, as it must be in opposing the force of gravity. But it is due just to this fact that overcoming any given resistance (and therefore doing any work) is always comparable to throwing or lifting a given load by means of a given kinetic energy in a vacuum. All work that demands and uses the same amount of energy must be considered equal.

Let us imagine a body moving in a vacuum without resistance of a medium and opposing force. It would fly on into infinity without loss of velocity, thanks to its original velocity and therefore its kinetic energy, and would not use up any of its energy in doing so. Though we call this movement and not work—which always presupposes the overcoming of an opposing force and therefore the use of energy—the kinetic energy of this body still remains the measure of the work this body could perform, should it meet an opposing force. In many kinds of work, such as the uniform pulling of a wagon by a horse, the amount of kinetic energy remains constant, but only because resistance uses up the exact amount the wagon receives through the horse's efforts. The kinetic energy of the wagon would grow continuously, were it not that the resistance just as continuously eats up the additions.

Kinetic energy can be developed in a system through the mutual interaction of its parts, as in the system of the planets or in every organism; it can be transmitted and propagated through transmission and propagation of movement in solid or fluid media; and, finally, internally generated kinetic energy can be modified through external influences, as when the kinetic energy that a system of two heavenly bodies produces by mutual influence is affected by a third, or when the inner kinetic energy of a living organism is affected by an external stimulus.

In conclusion, as far as we can tell, not merely all creation of kinetic energy, but also its transmission, propagation, and modification depend on the interaction of its components. Organic interaction creates the kinetic energy imparted to a rock thrown by hand, energy which is then propagated to the rock by an interaction of its components with those of the hand, since every propagation of movement depends to the same extent on the interaction of the component parts.

The whole of nature is a single continuous system of component parts acting on one another, within which various partial systems create, use, and transmit to each other kinetic energy of different forms, while obeying general laws through which the connections are ruled and conserved. Since in exact natural science all physical happenings, activities, and processes, whatever they may be called (not excluding the chemical, the imponderable, and the organic) may be reduced to movements, be they of large masses or of the smallest particles, we can also find for all of them a yardstick of their activity or strength in their kinetic energy, which can always be measured, if not always directly, then at least by its effects, and in any case in principle.

The uncertainty which we have from the start about the nature of the physical happenings on whose occurrence our sensations depend and which accompany our thoughts—in short, of psychophysical processes— is at any rate not accompanied by any doubt about the measure we have to apply to them. If they still find a place in physics, there is also a place for energy as their measure; if they do not, they are of no concern to us.

This fact is important from two points of view, first insofar as it furnishes us with a basis for clarity, second insofar as it gives us a basis of lawfulness on which to build.

We know, even without awareness of the special nature of psychophysical processes, what we have to understand by their magnitude, if we are clearly to relate psychophysics with physics, physiology, and everyday life, and we can base generally valid conclusions on the universal conditions and laws of kinetic energy. As far as doubt can arise as to whether these psychophysical processes do not after all form an exception to this general application, the present investigation itself has to deal with this problem.

Let us, therefore, now consider some of the most important general conditions and laws of kinetic energy, which give us a clue in these investigations or otherwise provide us with kindred applications in this field.

A system may appear to be quiet, but still develop a great amount of kinetic energy in unnoticeably small motions, often as the effect of mighty movements, because of the capacity of energy to be transmitted and converted in various forms.

When a heavy bell is rung, one does not see its slight trembling. Yet the kinetic energy of this trembling (plus some radiated heat) represents the total energy of the blow it was struck; and if the movement of this trembling back and forth were summed in one direction the bell would be tossed a good distance.

An apparently quite unimportant or nonexistent, but in reality undoubtedly very large, kinetic energy is developed by the activity of chemical reactions. We observe no extraordinary movements when this happens, but the light and heat phenomena which accompany it, based as they are on vibrations of the ether, let us assume that the ponderable particles in this reaction are excited to vibrations, which they impart to the ether and which the ether propagates. Now just as the energy of a blow apparently disappeared in the invisible vibrations of the bell, so on the contrary can the energy of unnoticeably small vibrations burst forth in mighty visible movements through suitable mediation.

Thus the whole energy of the lumbering steamcar is only a changed form of the kinetic energy of the unnoticeably minute vibrations that are caused by the combustion of its fuel (including the ether that pervades it), from where it is transmitted to the parts of the engine and from there to the car. The energy, moreover, which appears here as visible motion, disappears in the realm of invisible movement of the fuel, so that continued tending and fueling of the combustion with a steady draught and new material are necessary to keep this process going. Even without the addition of engine and car a continuing supply of energy would be necessary, as the vibrations weaken by themselves through transmission to the environment and by radiation into the surrounding space. The addition of engine and car serves to put the kinetic energy, which otherwise would be lost uselessly, to use for specific purposes.

Thus also the kinetic energy of visible movements that man carries out externally with his arms and legs is nothing but a conversion or resultant of the minute internal motion originating in the chemistry of metabolism. Man uses up some of this internally developed energy in every kind of external work, for the energy taken up by bodies set in motion escapes, and even without visible motion man has continuous losses through transmission to the external world, excretion, and radiation. All this makes necessary continuous replacement by metabolism, in order to keep the organic machine running.

Just as the kinetic energy of minute vibrations may not be neglected as compared with the invisible movements, but rather forms a major part of the energy of the world, so the kinetic energy of movements in the sphere of the unweighable may not be neglected in comparison to the weighable. Instead this energy constitutes a main portion of the energy of the world, playing an important role in the events and achievements we perceive in the sphere of the ponderable, because of the conversion and transmission of energy from one sphere to the other.

For although we have to assume the mass of the ether particles to be vanishingly small, it is still not nothing, and is compensated for by the unimaginably great velocity we have to ascribe to them. These oscillations then develop much energy and thereby can perform considerable work when transformed into the ponderable.

Kinetic energy is neither increased nor diminished by being transmitted from one body to another, from one part of a system to another, whether ponderable or not, by impact, friction, or resistance of the medium, whatever changes its form of appearance undergoes.

It may seem that with every blow, every time there is friction with any resistance, kinetic energy disappears. The kinetic energy of all stones that fall to earth appears to be lost. The kinetic energy of a vibrating string dissipates itself constantly through air resistance. A rolling wagon could not maintain its kinetic energy undiminished because of friction with the ground, if the draught-animal did not constantly add new energy taken from its own continuing metabolic processes.

All energy that is lost as visible movement, however, can be found again, in the invisible vibrations of ponderable and imponderable parts. To these latter there corresponds a certain production of heat, so that the whole loss of energy the ponderable parts sustain by the action of a blow, of friction, and so forth, is replaced by a precisely measurable and determined heat equivalent. By suitable use of this heat exactly that quantity of kinetic energy in the realm of the ponderable, by whose disappearance the heat was produced, can be regenerated. Indeed, one of the most compelling reasons for deriving the manifestations of heat from the vibrations of a substrate, which might be compared with ponderable substrates, is the fact that a given equivalent heat takes the place of every lost quantity of energy in a ponderable substance during transmission of motion and vice versa.

A popularization of the principles of this important theory of the mechanical equivalent of heat, which will undoubtedly be welcomed by some, is contained in a discussion by Baumgartner, entitled "The Mechanical Equivalent of Heat and Its Meaning to the Natural Sciences. A lecture held at the formal meeting of the Royal Academy of Sciences on the 30th May, 1856" in Grunert's *Archiv für Mathematik*, 1858, page 261, from which I would like to quote some passages. It assumes as the unit of work 1 ft-lb [foot-pound], that is, the work necessary to lift 1 lb 1 ft, and as the unit of heat that quantity of heat which is able to raise 1 lb of water from 0°C to 1°C.

By consumption of a certain quantity of heat, a certain amount of work is produced, and vice versa. According to the results of many experiments, carried out with every precaution, in which work was partly transformed into heat and heat partly into work, and where heat of various origins was used, consumption of 1 unit of heat was equivalent to 1367 units of work and vice versa. This result is based on Austrian weights and measures.

Translated into everyday language this means: heat that warms 1 lb of water at 0 °C by 1 °C exerts the same amount of mechanical force as a weight of 1367 lb that falls 1 ft.

The transformation of heat into work and vice versa does not occur capriciously or by chance, but according to specific laws, which express the conditions under which this exchange takes place. Heat, it appears, can only be transformed into work to the extent that it flows into a body. However, this happens in the case of conducted heat only in the direction from the warmer to the cooler body, and only insofar as a temperature differential exists. This added heat, moreover, can be divided into two parts. One part serves to raise the temperature, keeping volume constant; the other part performs work as, for example, when it pushes a load. Where such is not the case, there is also no exchange of forces. This is why a mass of air cools down when it expands and thereby overcomes pressure, while its temperature remains unchanged if expansion takes place without overcoming resistance, as when it flows into empty space.

Every grain of weight of coal that is completely burned under the boiler of a steam engine or an air engine yields 0.908 unit of heat or 1241 ft-lb of work, due to the chemical process of combustion, if all its heat is used to make steam or increase air pressure and is fully transformed into work.

It would not be true to say that the total kinetic energy of the world is of completely constant magnitude. Only in action, in the movement of transmission in the propagation of movement, is there no change, providing we take into consideration the equivalent of the generated heat; but the amount does vary because of the continuous, and in the course of movement continually changing, effect of forces. If a body in its course collides with another, then the total energy of both is the same after the collision as before, provided the concussive effects of the ponderable particles are considered and the equivalent heat produced by the shock is added. On the other hand, we see the kinetic energy of every planet grow as it approaches the sun and diminish as it moves away, and that of a swinging pendulum grow on the downstroke and diminish on the upstroke. But even if in this case the kinetic energy does not stay the same, it is nevertheless restored to the same magnitude as soon as the bodies of the system, which in the first case was formed by the sun and a planet and in the second case by the sun and the earth,[2] again take up the same relative positions under the influence of the inner forces of their systems. Now one finds that, in many other systems under the influence of forces residing in them, there takes place a circular or oscillating motion of a kind such that their parts always return to a given position after a lapse of time.

[2] Trans. Note: Should be pendulum and earth.

The familiar law that universally applies to these cases is known as the law of the conservation of kinetic energy. According to it, the energy in an isolated system will always be restored to its original magnitude after any kind of preceding impulses, when the parts of the system return to their original positions. This happens regardless of the inner means and the ways by which the return takes place, which in complicated systems may indeed not always be so simple as they would be in the elementary systems we have cited.

If we hit a piece of steel, the kinetic energy imparted to the steel particles by the blow, together with the heat produced, completely represent the energy that was lost by the body striking the blow. If we are dealing with a completely elastic body, then its particles, impelled by their energy to vibrate back and forth from the moment the blow was struck, will always regain their original kinetic energy when passing through their original position of equilibrium but will not retain the energy during the whole oscillation, as they leave their original positions. If, on the other hand, we are dealing with a less elastic material such as a piece of lead, it will remain permanently deformed, and the kinetic energy of the blow that displaced the particles from their equilibrium position cannot be restored. Rather, in this case, kinetic energy is really lost [as heat], having been used, so to speak, to bring about a permanent change of position of the particles.

The law of the conservation of kinetic energy then does not prevent the energy either of a system or of a part of the infinite system of the universe from temporarily changing, increasing, or diminishing, nor from changing permanently. Only one thing is certain: the energy is restored when after any amount of preceding impulses the parts of the system return to their original positions under the influence of their inner forces. But there is no guarantee of this return in general, which in many cases does not take place. It does not even take place in the simple system of three bodies attracting each other according to the law of gravitation, except under special circumstances. As is well known, the planets of our solar system, because of the incommensurability of their periods of revolution, never return to the same position relative to each other and to the sun, but do so only approximately after long periods. The kinetic energy of our planetary system, therefore, while restored approximately, is never restored exactly.

Undoubtedly, in the infinity of the universe, the loss of kinetic energy, which one part of the infinite system sustains part of the time, or permanently, will be more or less balanced by the simultaneous increase which takes place in another part; but there is no principle which puts the decrease of one and the increase of the other in such a relationship that one could count on an exact and lasting compensation. There is still less reason to make this assumption because of the existence of another principle, which establishes a different constant relationship for kinetic energy, not permanence at the same level.

It is not the magnitude of the kinetic energy in existence, but the amount of this energy plus the energy that can still be generated by the prevalent impulse—we may call it potential energy for short, although the usual expression is tension—that is of constant magnitude for every system removed from outside influences and, therefore, undeniably the universe.

As an illustration, let us consider, in order to represent a system of material particles isolated from all external influences, a string vibrating without resistance in a vacuum and not transmitting any of its movements to the support from which it is suspended, as would be the case if it were strung between two simple fixed points. The kinetic energy of this string is variable. It falls to zero at the limits of its displacement, but here the potential energy is at the same time at a maximum. For every point the string passes from there to its equilibrium position, it generates a new quantity of kinetic energy, which is added to the previous amount until it reaches a maximum in passing the equilibrium position. At its maximum displacement this energy, now real, had been potential energy, that is to say, it was kinetic energy which had not yet been generated but, thanks to the existing impulses, could be produced. In moving from the extremes of the swing to the center position all this potential energy was turned into kinetic energy; but whatever was gained in kinetic energy was lost in potential energy. Any kinetic energy realized was now no longer available until, at arrival at the center, all potential energy was exhausted, thus making impossible any further growth of kinetic energy at its expense. From this point on, as movement continues, potential energy increases correspondingly at the expense of kinetic energy, and so forth in turn ad infinitum, so that the sum total of kinetic and potential energy of the string always stays constant. It is only that each form of energy increases alternately at the cost of the other.

What is true here of the string, is also true of the universe. Kinetic energy can grow only at the expense of potential energy and vice versa. However, all the parts of the universe do not accomplish their fluctuations of kinetic and potential energy in parallel, like the parts of a string, but rather the different parts of the universe may find themselves in quite different conditions. They only fulfill this law when considered as a whole, for any one body's loss of kinetic energy to another is not balanced by growth of its own potential energy—and vice versa, what is passed on to this body is not lost in the form of its own potential energy. The constant sum of both these energies holds only for the whole system. After all, a string can suffer a loss of all its kinetic and its potential energy by imparting its movement to the air, and come to rest in an equilibrium position; but considered in connection with the air, the sum of kinetic and potential energy for the system composed of string and air has remained the same.

This is the great principle of the so-called conservation of energy, which, while related to the law of the conservation of kinetic energy, is even more universal in its importance. This principle, while founded on long-known general principles of mechanics, was first clearly developed by Helmholtz, who pointed out its full meaning and explained its most important applications. Since then it has received the broadest consideration and use in the field of inorganic physics as well as biophysics. It applies in general only to forces that are not functions of time or velocity; but up to now no one has found reasons to doubt its general applicability in the areas of the organic and the inorganic.

This may seem strange at first. In the sphere of electricity—and of magnetism insofar as it can be traced back to electricity—there are forces that according to W[ilhelm E.] Weber's investigations depend on velocity and acceleration. But it seems that these elemental forces combine in such a way that the law remains valid in all its natural manifestations. This is self-evident for magnetic effects, and for the effects of electric currents that can be substituted for them, insofar as they can indeed be represented by the effects of forces that are independent of velocity and acceleration. In addition, Professor W. Weber has told me, in answer to my question, that in all cases whatsoever to which his investigations have led him, even beyond the extent of the above effects, he has found the law in force; even though its complete validity in the sphere of these forces still lacks an exact proof.

According to this law, kinetic energy, in a system limited to inner forces which were originally produced by outside forces or to the inner play of existing forces, can only grow further at the cost of its potential energy. This capacity to grow then lessens as the potential energy becomes exhausted by the constant growth of kinetic energy, while, on the other hand, it increases with the decrease of kinetic energy, so that there can be neither a continuous growth to an unlimited extent nor a decrease to lasting extinction in a system left to its own inner forces, although there can be an exchange of kinetic energy between increase and decrease, and transmission from one part to another. The same changes can undoubtedly take place in the system of the universe, securing thereby, generally speaking, constancy of activity of the universe within definite limits of variation.

Accordingly, the kinetic energy of a part of a system may increase without drawing on potential energy and may decrease without a corresponding increase of potential energy, as long as the kinetic energy simultaneously decreases or increases in another part of the system, on account of the transmission of kinetic energy from one part to another. Now insofar as every finite body is part of the system of the universe, this law is applicable to it only in this respect, that the constant balance of potential and kinetic energy must be true particularly with regard to its inner forces. The law applies with regard to outside forces only in relation to the larger system, of which it is part—ultimately in respect of the whole universe.

It is important to remember that the principle or law of conservation of energy tells us nothing of the course or the manner of the interchange of kinetic and potential energy, nothing of the state in which the system must be at any time in this respect. That depends rather on each system's special conditions and circumstances, which cannot be determined by a general principle, but can be learned only from experience. The principle of conservation of energy merely tells us that, in a system left to its own inner forces, the exchange of kinetic and potential energy can take place only in such a way that its sum as a whole is conserved; it is free to accomplish this exchange in an infinite number of ways. This law is binding then only from a certain, rather general, point of view. The complete course of phenomena cannot be established by it.

As free as man may be, generally there exist factual limits, which are drawn by the universal laws of nature, to the mastery his will or his mind may exert not only over external but also over internal natural forces.

Man can walk on earth wherever he wants to, and displace his center of gravity in any way; no known natural law binds him or prevents him from doing this. But he can do so only to the extent that the law of the conservation of the center of gravity is maintained, which law itself follows from the principle of equality of action and reaction. When falling or jumping from a height, with all his freedom of will he is unable to displace his center of gravity by a hairsbreadth from its trajectory, except insofar as the resistance of the air offers a small possibility. According to the above general principle no physical system can displace its center of gravity through purely internal activity, for to do so it needs external help or an external resistance. Free will, then, is able to influence the freedom of movement not in spite of but only because of that law.

It is no different with respect to kinetic energy. The will, the thought, the whole mind may be as free as it may be, yet it will be able to exercise its freedom only by means of, not counter to, the general laws of kinetic energy. As far as its course is bound to the course of psychophysical processes and these in turn are bound by the law of the conservation of energy, the mind will itself be bound by that law.

That is no misfortune; for the law of the conservation of energy is a law for the conservation of the universe, and it is no misfortune that the mind is bound to feel, to think, or to will within the limitations of this law.

A general and exact proof of the extension of the validity of this law to cover psychophysical processes has not yet been demonstrated. But it can well be asserted that all experiences (to the extent that we have been able to ascertain) agree with this law and can be interpreted without trouble only by means of it. We will therefore have to take it into consideration as long as there is no proof to the contrary.

Let us reflect on some major relationships in this respect, paying attention particularly to that which one may be most tempted to remove from the jurisdiction of this law—the sphere of higher free mental activities.

At first one might think that at least higher mental activity, if not all mental activity, could take place without being bound in the slightest by kinetic energy, its laws, growth, or decrease. But everything points against this assumption. Let us leave undecided for the time being whether there are such special relationships between physical and higher mental activities, that a specific mental activity can only originate and exist because of just as specific a physical activity. It has been established and will always have to be admitted that, at least in this world, the higher mental activities in general need a basis of physical processes as much as do the lower mental activities. They need, moreover, the energy of these processes in order to take place, and experience teaches us that they need a sufficient amount of it in order to take place intensively.

Nevertheless, one might think further that the mind furnishes from its own sources the energy for the activities of the body which are necessary for its functioning, or at least for the vigorous maintenance of its functioning. This would mean that the mind would be able to increase the energy of the universe without the kinetic energy elsewhere (or the potential energy of the body itself) having to decrease, thus negating the law of the conservation of energy, which demands a general balancing of all kinetic and potential energy in this respect. In short, it would mean that the mind could be a creator of completely fresh energy in the body.

Let us examine a few facts, which will serve as explanation and at the same time give us something to go by in coming to a decision on this question.

The manifestations and uses of energy in the brain for psychophysical activity and in other parts of the body for nonpsychophysical activities do indeed exist simultaneously in the normal course of life. We are able to think and at the same time to utilize the organs of our body in other ways, and we do so as a rule. Suppose we now increase the intensity of our thinking. Immediately we see that instead of being able to create kinetic energy from its own sources for strengthening the psychophysical processes, which it needs to augment its own, the mind takes energy from other bodily activities, and without doing so cannot amplify its activities. Suppose that just a moment ago you were engaged in heavy physical action. An unusually striking thought occupies your mind; immediately your arms fall to your sides and stay there as long as the thought, and with it the corresponding psychophysical processes, are active within, only to resume their work anew when this inner activity lessens. Whither did the kinetic energy of the arm movements go? It served to kindle the activities in the head.

Just as intensive thought necessarily interrupts all outer physical work, so a jump interrupts every train of thought. The energy needed by the legs for their jump is taken from the flow of psychophysical processes needed for thinking; and the mind does not have the power either to continue its course as before or to replace the loss of its own accord.

While we can divide disposable kinetic energy at will, we can reach a maximum for any one kind of activity only to the extent that we let other activities rest. Just as we must let one arm rest to gain maximum power for the other, so we must rest all the parts of the body in order to concentrate most energy in the head, and, vice versa, we must allow the activity in our heads to rest as much as possible in order to carry out the most energetic movements of our limbs. Thus also we see the deep thinker sit as still as possible and we never see someone who is running or lifting at the same time in deep thought. That is a contradiction; it cannot occur.

Even in voluntary functions, such as digestion, stand within limits in a relationship of balance or exchange of kinetic energy with the energy we need for thinking. Through some healthy arrangement, however, which we only acknowledge here but do not have to explain, man is not able to rob the involuntary functions of so much energy by his thinking that the normal course of functioning of the organic machine is thereby brought to a halt, nor, vice versa, to rob thinking of so much power through other functions that thought would be brought to a standstill.

Thinking is only one example, but what is true of thinking in this context is true of every mental activity. Intensive feelings, passions, or sensory perceptions may behave in this respect just as does thinking. However, in some cases the psychophysical processes are naturally tied by organic adjustments to certain external activities, rising and falling with them, while at the same time opposing all other activities. Further discussion of this principle of association of physical activities occurs in what follows.

The same relationship as that between the psychophysical and the non-psychophysical activities is found also between separate psychophysical processes. It is impossible to be lost in external perception and to think deeply at the same time, or to look and to listen attentively at the same time. In order to reflect acutely on something we have to abstract from something else; and when attention is divided, it is weakened for details. Here, it is true, one could see the play of purely psychological laws, if these facts stood by themselves, but the facts are too closely connected with the previous discussion for us not to see also in them an extension of the law of the conservation of energy to the play of purely psychophysical forces. Thought does not need to seem to draw energy from the non-psychophysical activities for its amplification since it can draw upon other ongoing psychophysical processes. The existence of psychological laws is not thereby denied, nor are these laws reduced to physical laws. We are saying only that the laws governing the course of mental and physical activities are connected to no less a degree than are these activities connected among themselves. Nor is that strange; it is the contrary that would seem strange.

The nexus of parts determines that some can be activated only in certain combinations, or rather in a specific sequence; some are activated better in one or another connection, and some are only—or more readily —activated in a given context than they are by themselves. This principle conflicts with the foregoing only to the extent that here the distribution of energy between the cooperating parts in this activity, on the one hand weakens the output of single parts and on the other is made possible—or furthered—by their combination. Reference to this principle explains many apparent contradictions with the previous principle, where activities appear to rise and fall together, rather than mutually to limit each other by their respective increases, and where they appear to come to their mutual support, string along together, or follow one another. We again find a parallel in the action of machines, and therefore there is nothing here that is contradictory to the law of the conservation of energy.

By use and practice such combinations can be strengthened, in part, or in part built up anew or dissolved in our organism. With growing practice in activating isolated parts, the possibility increases of setting them in vigorous activity. The same principle also prevails—as can easily be shown—in connection with the sphere of psychophysical and nonpsycho-physical activities.

To sum up, we may say that the production as well as the use of the kinetic energy of the psychophysical processes within us, as far as we can observe it or make deductions about it from our observations, obeys everywhere the same laws as the kinetic energy of nonpsychophysical activities within us and outside us. As free as the mind may be, it still cannot do anything contrary to this law, but only whatever is based on this law.

Now how are we to interpret facts of the following kind?

Suddenly we see a person carry out a prodigious physical or mental feat stemming from purely mental excitement, just after he had been sitting there indifferently and quiet, seemingly possessed of no great supply of kinetic energy by either psychophysical or nonpsychophysical activities. Where does this kinetic energy come from so suddenly? This vigorous activity can, moreover, undoubtedly continue under the influence of a strong will. Where can we seek the lasting source of this energy if not in the will itself?

As far as the first point is concerned, we can carry out a sudden effort in a specific direction only by suddenly concentrating in one direction previously scattered energy that was therefore strongly active nowhere. We may even have to draw upon the aid of the involuntary functions to do this. If, on the other hand, we are able to carry out even long-continued unusual feats under the influence of a strong will, which without this will would not have been possible, still the production and use of the necessary kinetic energy does not take place either contrary to the law of the conservation of energy or by the purely mental power of the will.

We find indeed that every voluntary effort exhausts us physically all the more (that is to say, it decreases the possibility of further effort) the more vigorously and the longer it is continued. This fact proves that the voluntary development of kinetic energy in our bodies is only possible at the expense of potential energy, the energy which still remains to be developed, and that it takes place according to the law of the conservation of energy, just as does the development of kinetic energy on occasions when the will is not operating. It is therefore not to be denied that under the influence of free will kinetic energy, which would otherwise not have come into existence, can really be developed, but it must be at the cost of potential energy, in other words, from the source which would give rise to it in any case, when the will does not take part. Undeniably, the will—or, psychophysically speaking, the activities that are under the control of the will—provides the occasion for the permanent transformation of potential into kinetic energy. Yet clearly the will by itself is not able to create kinetic energy without the universally valid conditions for its development.

Our body's kinetic energy generally is subject to fluctuations varying with the state of nutrition, health, wakefulness, and sleep, and consequently may rise and fall in its entirety. Under normal conditions, however, it does not seem capable of sudden strong changes as a whole, but tends rather to sudden redistributions, accomplished partially either through stimuli or through voluntary direction of attention or change of the field of activities. The idealist may trace the action of the stimuli to a mental reason, the materialist may attribute choice and attention to a material reason. We, however, take the facts as they appear directly on observation, where at one time the material side (or mode of appearance), at another the mental side provides the evidence for the changed distribution.

In a way the relations are like those of a steam engine with a complicated mechanism. Depending on how much steam the engine develops, its kinetic energy can rise high or fall low; but in normal operations neither the one nor the other will happen suddenly. One can, however, easily turn on one part of the machine and at the same time turn off another at will, by opening a valve here and shutting one there. The only difference is that in our organic machine the engineer does not sit on the outside but on the inside. Now, undeniably, more kinetic energy can really be developed at the cost of potential energy in the same interval during strong bodily exertion, than when the body is at rest—for why else the quick exhaustion and need for greater replenishment—but it is then not really the will developing this energy at a given moment for mental reasons, but rather the increase in chemical metabolic processes that the exercise initiates. When we walk faster we also breathe faster and our blood circulates faster. It is as if we increase the draught of a steam engine and thereby develop more rapidly a given quantity of effective kinetic energy at the cost of the potential energy of the fuel. If the organic machine is not quite in shape or poorly supplied, so that these chemical processes cannot take place effectively, then the strongest will cannot help.

I do not mean by this to say that the kinetic energy of the body really distributes itself like steam in an engine, but only that the law of the conservation of energy leads to corresponding results.

Ultimately the development of the kinetic energy of our bodies springs from our metabolism, according to our best guess, and since each part has its own metabolic processes, it also contains within itself its own source of kinetic energy. On the other hand, experience shows, by means of the kind of facts we have cited, that this process occurs in the whole organism in association, so that not only can no part nourish itself by itself alone, but also quantitative conditions of balance enter into the metabolic processes of the different parts, in the sense of the law of con-servation of energy. The circumstance that the metabolic processes of all parts are coordinated by the organism through the influence of circula-tion and nerve action easily explains the interaction of the metabolic processes of all these parts. In spite of the fact, therefore, that neither kinetic energy, nor a special carrier, such as steam in a steam engine, really flows directly between the various parts, distributes itself, or is drawn hither and yon by stimuli, attention, or will, we shall always permit ourselves, for brevity's sake, to speak of the distribution of kinetic energy and to use corresponding metaphors, since we know how to give them the correct meaning.

Particulars of all these conditions are not very clear, but the general case is plain and obvious in the present sense, and the preceding general hints should suffice for now. Further exposition would either lead us only to unsure ground, or would not be in order here at the start.

Kinetic energy employed to chop wood and kinetic energy used in thinking—that is, in the underlying psychophysical processes—are ac-cording to what has just been said not only quantitatively comparable, but each can be transformed into the other, and therefore both kinds of work are measurable on their physical side by a common yardstick. Just as it takes a certain quantity of kinetic energy to split a log or lift a given weight to a given height, so does it take a certain quantity to think a thought of a given intensity; and energy for one can be changed into energy for the other. This idea does not cast a slur on thinking; its dignity depends on the means, the direction, and the goal of its flow, not on the possibility or impossibility of measuring the physical activity that it needs for its course. In the same way, Columbus' voyage of discovery does not lose value and meaning by the fact that the kinetic energy of the ship which carried him could be measured as adequately as that of a casually thrown stone, or the wind, and that one could even be transformed into the other. Indeed, the physical view really obtains its value, or lack of value, from the related mental view, and because of this relationship, can neither give to it nor take away from it. What is certain is that a quiet flow of thoughts or feelings may have considerably value, yet be associated with such weak processes that if they were transformed they could ac-complish only minor or quite unimportant physical work; but it remains just as certain that when emotional life or the world of ideas flourishes at higher intensities, the underlying physical activities have to take place in a livelier fashion.

In this connection it should be noted that the conditions by which the intensity of mental activity depends on the magnitude of the underlying physical activity are equally true in reverse. However difficult it is to conceive of a thought at a certain intensity, without the development of a given kinetic energy by the underlying activity, it is equally difficult to imagine the latter developing without the occurrence of a thought of the appropriate intensity. Not that a thought of given intensity corresponds to any given quantity of kinetic energy, but rather to the kinetic energy of one of those physical processes that are able to support thought processes. Now, everyone is at liberty to seek with us the reason for each single thoughtful activity in the world in a past or more general activity, and eventually the reason for all the activity of the universe in a system that carries a highest and ultimate unit of thought and a highest and ultimate will, and that can exist only in such a way. Here, however, we do not have to engage ourselves in matters of belief, in order to make a value judgment.

We have also intentionally avoided entering at all into the dispute concerning freedom of the will. It would be just as much out of place here to drag it in as it would be to omit it. Rather, by the explicit statement that the general laws of kinetic energy merely limit its free disposal in general, freedom is given every right, which it truly deserves. The law of conservation can neither dictate whether and how we transform potential energy into kinetic energy, nor whether and in what direction it should be transmitted. In this respect the will remains completely free within the limitations set by this law. To what extent, however, there may be other limits is also a matter that does not concern us here, for an answer to the last question is altogether outside the bounds of our investigation.

VI.

The Principle of Measurement
for Sensitivity

Even when applied in the same way, one and the same stimulus may be perceived as stronger or weaker by one subject or organ than by another, or by the same subject or organ at one time as stronger or weaker than at another. Conversely, stimuli of different magnitudes may be perceived as equally strong under certain circumstances. Accordingly we ascribe to the subject or organ at one time or other a greater or lesser sensitivity.

When the sense organs are paralyzed, even the strongest stimuli are no longer felt—their sensitivity is nil. On the other hand, in some conditions of excitation of the eye or ear even the weakest light or sound stimulus brings about a vivid, even annoying, sensation—the sensitivity of the organ is tremendously increased. Between these extremes exist all possible gradations of sensitivity. There is, therefore, sufficient reason to distinguish and to compare degrees of sensitivity. The question is: how can that be done precisely, how can a real measurement be made?

The following matter should be considered. Generally the measurement of a quantity consists of ascertaining how often a unit quantity of the same kind is contained in it. In this definition, sensitivity is an abstract capacity and as little a measure as is abstract energy. But instead of measuring it by itself, one can measure something related to it, something of which it is a function, which in accord with this concept increases and decreases with sensitivity—or conversely with which sensitivity increases and decreases—and thus we obtain an indirect measure in the same way as we do with energy. Instead of measuring energy itself we measure related or dependent velocities that bodies of the same mass can acquire, or the masses that can be given the same velocities. Thus we can also try to measure either the intensity of sensations that are produced by stimuli of equal magnitude, or the magnitude of stimuli that cause sensations of equal intensity. In the first case we could say sensitivity is twice as much, if the identical stimulus produces twice the intensity of sensation; in the second case, it is twice as much if a stimulus half as strong now causes just as intense a sensation.

The first course cannot, however, be taken, because we do not as yet have a measure of sensation, and, as we shall show later, such a measure itself rests on a differently derived measure of sensitivity. On the other hand, there is nothing to prevent us from taking the second course. The magnitude of stimuli can be approached by exact measurement, and the equality of sensation may well be found by taking the necessary steps, which we will discuss later in detail. We therefore take stimulus sensitivity as inversely proportional, or, in short, as reciprocal, to the magnitude of stimuli that cause equally intense sensations, or (more generally and in order to include extensive sensations) that cause equally large sensations.

One has to admit that it is ultimately only a matter of definition if we call sensitivity exactly twice as great when only half the simulus produces the same sensation. If sensitivity were measurable on its own, we could take no such liberties, but the proportional increase would have to be determined by experience or deduction. Such, however, is not the case. Interpretation is arbitrary, and the simplest possible interpretation is preferable, as it allows the least complex application.

So considered, this measure will be an aid and should be taken to have no further significance than its usefulness in orienting ourselves in the sphere of the factual relationships of stimulus and sensation and in making it possible to relate them mathematically. It neither can nor should enable us to make any statement at all in the abstract about the magnitude of our capacity for sensations. What always remains certain is that, for any one subject at any one time, it takes twice the stimulus to cause an identical sensation as it does for another subject at another time. Instead of saying this in many words, we may express ourselves briefly with but a few: in one case sensitivity for the stimulus is half as great as in the other case. Every other numerical quantity refers to a different factual relationship in this respect and should mean no more than that.

The strength or vigor of the physical activities that the stimulus starts within us, and on which the sensation directly depends—in short, the psychophysical processes—are not involved in this measure which belongs to outer psychophysics. The question as to whether these activities are proportional to the intensity of stimuli or not is immaterial for this concept and its applications. For as a measure of stimulus sensitivity it is, after all, only applicable to a relationship of sensations and stimuli, and not to the processes that stimuli initiate within us. The question should undoubtedly be raised, but can only be decided on the basis of facts that presuppose this measure.

But it is important to avoid the following fallacy. When with twice the sensitivity for a given stimulus a half-strength stimulus is sufficient to cause a sensation of equal intensity, we cannot conclude that the same stimulus would then evoke twice the sensation. At present we cannot judge, for we do not have a measure of sensation, and later, when we do, we shall find that this relationship is by no means true.

It is important to differentiate the sensitivity for stimulus change and stimulus difference from stimulus sensitivity. These measurements, however, are subject to the same approach, except that stimulus change and stimulus difference take the place of the stimulus.

Indeed, just as a stimulus of the same, double, or treble the strength may be required to evoke sensations of equal intensities, so may the same, double, or treble the stimulus change, or the same, double, or treble the difference between stimuli, be required in order to evoke the same degree of change of sensation, or the same difference between two sensations. Stimulus change, as a stimulus difference in temporal sequence, can therefore be subsumed under the same point of view and name as the difference between two simultaneously occurring stimuli. We shall in general use this terminology from now on. This does not, of course, imply that it is immaterial whether one takes the components of a difference simultaneously or successively. By "components" we shall understand, here as well as in the future, the stimuli between which the difference exists, as shown by the corresponding sensations.

On superficial examination one might be inclined to regard measures of stimulus sensitivity, and those of stimulus difference, as reducible to each other. Given two tones of different physical intensities, we can imagine a third, of a loudness equal to the difference in loudness of the first two, and one could think for example, that the least loud tone which can just be heard and the least possible difference which can still be noticed between two tones have generally the same magnitude; but this is in fact not correct. Rather, casual observations teach us (and later, exact proof will be given) that the difference between two physical tones, lights, and so forth, in order still to be noticeable, must be all the larger, the greater their absolute intensity, while the absolute intensity that is still just perceptible remains the same.

This fact makes it necessary, it can be seen, to differentiate between stimuli and stimulus differences with regard to sensitivity and the measure of sensitivity.

To the extent that the same stimulus difference is perceived more or less readily, depending on whether it is between weaker or stronger pairs of stimuli, differential sensitivity will in general vary not only with the state of the individual, but also with the intensity of the stimulus, usually being less for stronger than for weaker stimulation. Indeed, as later investigations show, the magnitude of a difference sensation evoked by a stimulus difference depends mainly on the ratio of the stimulus differences to the stimuli and the consequent ratio of the stimuli to each other. The inquiry into the law according to which sensation differences depend on stimulus intensity—that is to say, the law according to which the degree of stimulus difference that produces a uniformly distinct difference of sensation changes with stimulus intensity—is one of the most important tasks of outer psychophysics.

The following inquiries into the various sense domains will show that, at least within certain limits, a difference between given stimuli is always equally noticeable, if it increases and decreases proportionally to its components. By this statement we mean that the relative stimulus difference and the stimulus ratio for it stay the same, however the absolute magnitude of the stimulus differences and of the stimuli may be changed.

By relative stimulus difference we are to understand in general the difference of stimuli in relation to their sum, to their average, or to one or the other of them, for it does not matter which, inasmuch as by the constancy of one ratio the constancy of the other is determined automatically. In fact, relative stimulus difference and stimulus ratio always remain so closely linked that it does not matter whether one refers to the constancy of one or of the other.

If, for example, the components 5 and 3 are both doubled, the ratio of the two remains $\frac{5}{3}$ and the relative difference between them is unchanged, whether one sets the latter at $(5-3)/(5+3) = \frac{2}{8}$ or as $(5-3)/5 = \frac{2}{5}$ or as $(5-3)/3 = \frac{2}{3}$, in that after doubling it becomes respectively $\frac{4}{16}$, $\frac{4}{10}$, and $\frac{4}{6}$, fractions which correspond with the above.

On the other hand, if the stimulus ratio is changed, the stimulus difference necessarily is changed in the same direction, but not proportionally. If, for example, the ratio $\frac{5}{3}$ of the components 5 and 3 becomes $\frac{6}{3}$ in that the component 5 is changed without the 3 being changed, the relative stimulus difference $(5-3)/(5+3) = \frac{2}{8}$ changes to $(6-3)/6+3) = \frac{3}{9}$ or from $\frac{1}{4}$ to $\frac{1}{3}$, which is a change from a ratio of $5:6$ to $3:4$.

Now, as far as the law holds that a difference is equally noticeable, if it increases or decreases in proportion to its components (that is to say, if the relative stimulus difference and the stimulus ratio remain the same), one will have to say that differential sensitivity is reciprocal to the magnitude of the stimuli, since with double the stimulation the difference must be doubled in order to yield the same sensation of difference.

It may accordingly seem appropriate to express the sensitivity for differences immediately as a proportion, that is to say, to consider it equal not insofar as the same absolute stimulus difference evokes the same difference of sensation, but insofar as the same relative stimulus difference or stimulus ratio does so, and thus to express it as a reciprocal of the one or the other. Which one is used is again only a matter of definition and has no influence on the results when a measure of sensitivity is used, as long as one continues to use the measure according to its definition. It will be shown in the context of further work that for formal reasons it will be more appropriate to measure changes in the differential sensitivity, if taken as proportions of the reciprocal of the stimulus ratio rather than of the relative stimulus difference at which the sensation of difference remains the same. On the other hand, the equality of relative sensitivity can always be referred to the constancy of either the relative stimulus difference or the stimulus ratio.

To sum up: we must always make a twofold distinction with regard to sensitivity. (1) We must distinguish sensitivity for absolute stimulus intensities and for stimulus differences; in short, absolute sensitivity and differential sensitivity, of which the first is measured by the reciprocal of the absolute stimulus magnitudes that produce sensations of equal intensity. (2) The second, however, is usually understood to be measured in one of the following two ways: in the case of differential sensitivity, we have to distinguish between an absolute and a proportional, or relative, differential sensitivity, depending on whether the reciprocal of absolute difference or the ratio of stimulus intensities is used as our measure. The first of these we will usually call the simple differential sensitivity, the latter the relative differential sensitivity.

These distinctions may appear at this point as trivial and idle, but it will be shown later that they are by no means that. Indeed the clarity of conception of the most important factual relationships depends on this distinction, and, at least partially, the lack of lucidity that has continually plagued the theory of irritability is due to the lack, so far, of a clear distinction between them.

In general, the term *sensitivity* means no more than what is otherwise referred to by the terms *irritability*, *excitability*, or *sensibility*. It is only that these terms are generally used to refer not only to the evocation of sensations, but also to the activities of outer and inner stimuli. However, insofar as all sensations depend on inner processes, one could well relate the term sensitivity to its underlying psychophysical process instead of to sensation. One could then say of absolute sensitivity, for example, that it is equally large, twice as large, or three times as large, according to whether an equally strong, half or twice as strong an outer or inner stimulus is needed to evoke the same psychophysical process.[1] But this

---

[1] Trans. Note: Fechner undoubtedly meant one third, rather than twice as strong a stimulus, for three times the sensitivity.

way of thinking is not practical, because the psychophysical process is not accessible to observation.

In other places the terms irritability and excitability are used partly as synonyms, partly as arbitrary distinctions, without these distinctions being based on a clearly defined, factual relationship. It will be convenient, however, after clarifying the concept of the different sensitivities, to introduce a distinctive usage, and I will therefore use irritability in the future solely for the absolute, and excitability for the relative differential sensitivity, with the former referring to sensations and the latter to perceived differences.

In our definitions, so far, we have focused our attention primarily on the intensive sensations, to which, strictly speaking, the concept of stimulus alone refers. Nevertheless, the measurement of sensitivity is transferable from the sphere of intensive sensations to that of extensive sensations, as is consistent with the following facts.

As is well known, E. H. Weber's experiments show that it takes a certain spread of the sharp points of calipers placed on the skin to make the distance between them just noticeable. There is nothing to stop us by using a modification of his procedure (of which I will have to say more later) from determining apparently equally large distances on different places of the skin, by means of which it can be shown that the real distance which is just noticeable (or, more generally, appears equally large) is very different at different places on the skin. It can be proven just as well, by methods to be given later, that the differences between distances which can still be noticed on different parts of the skin are of different size. Differences in the perception of spatial magnitudes and of differences in magnitude that are analogous to those between diverse parts of the skin can be found between various regions of the retina, especially between the more central and peripheral parts. One can, therefore, speak of differential sensitivity in the perception of extensive size as one can in the perception of intensive size, and distinguish them briefly as extensive and intensive sensitivity.

The absolute measure and the differential measure of the extensive sensitivity of the different places on the skin and retina will then also have to be sought in the reciprocal of equally large-appearing extents, differences in extent, or ratios of extents, just as the measure of intensive sensitivity was sought in intensities appearing equally strong in intensity differences, or in ratios of intensity. For example, one place on the skin may have twice the extensive sensitivity as another, taken absolutely, if half the distance between the caliper points appears on it as equally large.

Notwithstanding the fact that the extensive sensitivity of the parts under discussion undeniably stands in some kind of dependent relationship to the number of so-called sensory circles[2] contained in a given area, it would still be just as invalid to relate the measure of extensive sensitivity to this unknown number of sensory circles, as it would be to relate the measure of intensive sensitivity to the unknown magnitude of psychophysical processes. Undeniably a given area of the back contains many fewer of these circles than do the finger tips, and the lesser extensive sensitivity of the back compared to that of the finger is based just on this fact. However, the concept of extensive sensitivity also takes account of the fact that due to its biological arrangement and state, one organ may in this respect be constituted differently from another. Were one to reduce all measurement of sensitivity to the different numbers of sensory circles, this concept of differential sensitivity would probably fall by the wayside. In any case one would have no data available, and thus the whole measure would remain pure speculation, even though undeniably there exists a generally valid, if as yet unknown, relationship of dependency in this respect, which might in all cases lead to the same value. As of now, it must be admitted that measured data of the extensive sensitivity, as well as those of the intensive, when taken according to the principle provided here, have only the value of observational data, which by themselves do not provide insight into the basic relationships of sensations to their physical basis, but which, together with other data, may yet serve to contribute to the establishment of this relationship, if one consistently takes and uses them as purely observational data.

One might entertain doubts from the start—considering the great variability of sensitivity due to individual differences, time, and innumerable internal and external conditions—that it would be of any use to strive for a measure for either form of sensitivity. For one thing, something that is constantly varying is not amenable to exact measurement; for another, results do not show constancy, and therefore are valueless, since results observed with certain individuals, at a certain time and under certain circumstances, are not found again at other times and circumstances.

Indeed, it cannot be denied that in this respect there do exist difficulties of measurement in our psychophysical domain, difficulties which do not exist in purely physical or astronomical areas. But instead of the measure or the possibility of obtaining fruitful results by its means being destroyed thereby, this difference only means that the sphere of inquiry must be widened, and considerations introduced which do not exist in the other areas.

[2] Ed. Note: This sensory circle is a translation of E. H. Weber's *Empfindungskreis*.

Insofar as sensitivity is a variable, we should not seek for a constant as its measure. We may, however, look for (1) its limits and (2) its mean values; we may also investigate (3) how its variations depend on conditions; finally we may seek (4) lawful relations that remain constant during variation; the last are the most important. The methods for measuring sensitivity that will be discussed will provide not only sufficient means, but also sufficient precision, for research and investigations into all these matters.

A thorough investigation under these circumstances is necessarily more complex than it would be for a single, constant, unchanging subject, for it cannot be accomplished for one person alone and it has as yet not been carried out adequately for a single sense domain. In this respect, rather, there opens up a rich field for future research, especially for the younger generation, by means of the methods that we will now discuss. This research is by itself not difficult, yet it demands patience, attention, endurance, and faithfulness.

VII.

The Principle of Measurement
for Sensation

The preceding chapter has dealt with the measurement of sensitivity. As a measure merely of sensory capacity, such measurement should by no means be confused with the measuring of sensation itself, nor does it, in the sense used, presuppose such a measure. It merely requires observations of equal sensations, partially under the same, partially under different, stimulus conditions. Indeed, we measure here not the sensation itself, but only the stimuli or stimulus differences that produce equal sensations or equal differences between sensations. The question of whether and to what extent it is possible to measure sensation itself or mentality in general still remains open.

In fact, no such measure exists as yet, or (expressed with more caution) no such measure has as yet been accepted. Rather, the measure has been doubted or denied, until very recently, as possible at all. Even Herbart's attempt at a mathematical psychology was unable to cope with this problem, and this failure was always the most important objection to his theory—in spite of the fact that Herbart had this measure practically within his grasp, so to speak. Now, however, the principle of this measure will be described in what follows and its utility demonstrated theoretically and experimentally. As a start we will consider only sensation, for although the applications of the principle of psychological measurement reach beyond sensation, as will be shown later, sensation provides a starting point under conditions that are the least complicated and most open to direct observation.

Initially, and in general, it cannot be denied that the mental sphere is subject to quantitative considerations. After all, we can speak of a greater or lesser intensity of sensation; there are drives of different strengths, and greater and lesser degrees of attention, of the vividness of images of memory and fantasy, and of clearness of consciousness in general, as well as of the intensity of separate thoughts. In the sleeper, consciousness is totally extinguished; in the deep thinker it is increased to the highest intensity. Again, in the over-all clearness of consciousness separate images and thoughts rise and diminish. Higher mental activity, therefore, no less than sensory activity, the activity of the mind as a whole no less than in detail, is subject to quantitative determination.

The immediate judgment we can make in this context, however, is only one of more or less, or one of equality, not one of how many times, which true measurement demands and which it is our purpose to derive. Even without a true measure of sensation—and for the present it is sufficient to consider this matter in relation to sensation alone—we are able to say: this pain is stronger than that pain or this light is brighter than that. A real measure of sensation would demand that we be able to call a given sensation twice, thrice, or in general so-and-so many times as intense as another—but who could claim that as yet? We may well be able to judge equality in the area of sensations—our whole method of measuring sensitivity, of which more later in detail, or of photometric measurement, is based on it—yet with all that we still have not measured sensation.

This method does not as yet allow us to measure, but we have laid the foundation of a metric that is based on the multiplication of equal units, particularly on the judgment of equality in the area of sensation. Indeed, we will demonstrate that in principle our psychic measurement will amount to the same as physical measurement, the summation of so-and-so many multiples of an equal unit.

It would be quite in vain to try to engage in such a summation directly. Sensation does not divide into equal inches or degrees by itself, units that we can count and summate. Let us keep in mind, however, that the same problem arises for physical magnitudes. After all, do we count periods of time directly in terms of time, when measuring time, or spatial units directly in terms of space, when we measure space? Do we not rather employ an independent yardstick, a measuring rod, which for time does not consist of pure time, nor for space of pure space and for matter of pure matter alone? Measuring any of these three quantities demands something else as well. Why should the case not be the same in the mental or psychological sphere? The fact that the psychic measure has always been sought in the sphere of the purely psychic may so far have been the main reason for our inability to find it.

Seemingly there has been some confusion in this respect. Let us grant that every magnitude can refer only to an appropriate unit of measurement. In this respect we may well say that space can be measured only by a spatial unit, time only by a temporal unit, and weight only by a unit of weight. The case is quite different, however, as far as the means of measurement and the measuring operations are concerned. Inasmuch as the magnitudes that are to be measured do not inhere in the nature of things, and cannot be derived or handled independently, we cannot find the essential unit of measurement and a means of measuring these magnitudes in their fundamental nature. The problem is solved by arranging things so that the practical means of measurement correspond with the concrete measures of reality in such a way that the relation of the magnitude of that which is to be measured turns out to correspond with the units used to measure it.

Consequently, when we want to think of a psychic quantity, such as the intensity of a sensation or a drive—and in a wider sense, the intensity of attention, clearness of consciousness, and so forth—we are tied to the same kind of unit. We are not forced, however, to seek the means of measurement and the operations of measuring necessarily in the area of the purely psychical, that is, of inner perception; all we have to do is to employ these methods so that a clear relationship to a psychic unit of measurement emerges. It will never be possible to lay one sensation directly on top of another, so that the one can form the unit of the other; but by bringing in something additional to which the sensations are tied as effectively as the length of the yard is tied to the material of the yardstick, it will be possible to reach a measure for sensations.

But what can we suggest for this purpose?

Ignoring vague possibilities I shall proceed to the principle of this measure immediately.

To measure space we need the substance of the yardstick that occupies this space. In the same way something of a physical nature that underlies the psychic process is necessary for psychic units. Since, however, the psychophysical processes which form the immediate basis of a psychic quantity are not open to direct observation, we must substitute for the yardstick the stimulus, which in outer psychophysics gives rise to the psychic quantity and with which it grows and decreases in a regular manner. In addition we may hope to go on from there to the attainment of an inner yardstick for inner psychophysics.

This procedure would actually be very simple if we could take the magnitude of sensation as proportional to the magnitude of the stimulus. We would, in this case, have to assume the existence of twice as intense a sensation, when stimulation is doubled. This assumption is not valid, however. We have no right to assume a proportionality of stimulus and sensation, as long as we do not possess a measure for sensation that would guarantee the validity of this proportionality; nor will the actual measure, once it is found, confirm this proportionality. Unfortunately it is not as simple to put a stimulus to a sensation as it is to lay a material yardstick on a material distance. In the meantime, it is clear that any functional relationship between stimulus and sensation other than that of direct proportionality can mediate the measure of sensation just as well, depending on the conditions of measurement of the stimulus. All that is necessary is that the measure can be found without making any assumptions about a prior measure of sensation. If in an equation we have y expressed as a function of x, we can determine y for any value of x and vice versa, even if their relationship is quite different from that of a mutual proportional progression. All depends then on our ability to express stimulus magnitude and sensation intensity as functions of one another, regardless of their form, in order to find the magnitude of one if the other is given. We must observe the restriction, however, that this function must correspond to reality, in order for it to apply to reality. This discussion brings us back to the main difficulty: how to derive a function, corresponding to reality, prior to measuring sensations, one which would then enable us to demonstrate that a sensation stands in this one particular and no other relation to the stimulus, according to the demands of the function. In brief, it seems that in order to find the desired measure of sensation, this is the kind of measure that must be presupposed, if it is to be derived from this principle.

One must be quite clear about this difficulty in order to win a clear insight into the manner of its solution. The solution, in brief, depends on the combination of two circumstances: (1) that we derive the function relating stimulus and sensation from a function relating the elements out of which both may be assumed to have sprung; (2) that we base this function on judgments of equality in the realm of sensations, judgments which experience has proved feasible and whose execution is assured by exact methods.

A detailed explanation follows:

The difference between one stimulus intensity and another can always be taken as a positive or negative increment to some stimulus magnitude. Therefore, the intensity of a single stimulus itself can be looked upon mathematically as the sum of positive increments starting with zero, with each increment imagined as added to previous sums until the total stimulus intensity is reached. Similarly, a sensation of difference can be looked upon mathematically as a positive or negative increment to one or the other sensation and a sensation [of difference] as such would be looked upon as the sum of positive increments starting with [a difference of] zero. Now if the functional relationship between the sum of stimulus increments starting from zero and the sum of the related sensation increments is known, the problem resolves itself for every degree of the stimulus and of resulting sensation.

The three methods of measuring differential sensitivity, treated in the next chapter, will show, as had been provisionally indicated in Chapter VI, that the stimulus increment necessary for a given sensation increment or for a constant rate of increase in sensation does not remain constant, with respect to the strength of the stimulus from which it results, but increases instead with increasing stimulation. In other words, a greater stimulus increment is necessary for a stronger stimulus than for a weaker stimulus in order for the addition to be just noticeable as an increment, or to be equally noticeable. If the addition of ½ oz [ounce] adds just noticeably to the weight of 1 lb, then the same amount added to 2 lb would not be felt, but a considerably larger increment of weight would be necessary; the same would be true for 3 lb, and so forth. Exact inquiry by suitable methods leads to a general law, as I have noted in Chapter VI. This law connects stimulus increments, which vary with stimulus magnitude and always result in the same sensation increments with constant sensation increments. The derivation of the functional relation between the stimulus, as the sum of varying stimulus increments, and the sensation, as the sum of constant sensation increments, follows, as will be shown later, from these methods.

We therefore avoid the necessity of having a measure of total sensation, before its functional relation to the total stimulus can be determined, by going back to the relationship of the basic increments that can be thought of as building blocks of stimulus and sensation. Measuring these increments does not necessitate a measure of sensation, but is well within our means and can be achieved very exactly by available methods of judging differential sensitivity, such as the judgments of equality of sensations of difference and sensation increments which go together with given measures of variable stimulus increments. We then derive the functional relationship of the sum of increments and by relating it to the known stimulus determine the measure of sensation.

In principle, then, our measure of sensation will consist of dividing every sensation into equal divisions (that is, equal increments), which serve to build it up from zero. The number of equal divisions we conceive as determined, like inches on a yardstick, by the number of corresponding variable stimulus increments that are capable of bringing about identical sensation increments. We measure a piece of cloth by dividing it into equal parts as determined by the number of yards that serve to cover it. Here the only difference is that instead of covering the sensation magnitude we establish a series of sensation increments. In short, we determine the magnitude of a sensation, which we cannot do directly, by asking how many times it contains the same unit, an operation that we are able to perform directly, and we read off the result not as the number of sensations but as the stimuli that determine sensations and that are easier to read. Finally we substitute the sum of infinitesimals for the counting of an infinite number of infinitesimal increments, which we should do in principle but cannot do in reality. In this way we will find the result of our counting without having to do so in detail.

While at first sight this method of measurement may seem difficult, it is nevertheless possible to reduce it to simple and clear approaches, methods, and formulas. However, before going into details in the next chapters, some general discussion may serve to explain the principle a little further.

We find on closer examination that in their most general and ultimate sense physical measures are based on the fact that an equal number of equally strong psychical impressions are due to an equal number of equally large physical causes. The number of these physical units is determined by the number of psychical impressions, where the magnitude of the cause of the single impression, or any multiple thereof, serves as a unit. Thus, just as we can make physical measurements only on the basis of the relationship of the physical to the psychological, so we can, according to our principle, derive psychical measures on the basis of the same relationship, only applying it in reverse.

According to the general principle of continuity, no sensation commences abruptly and suddenly at full strength, above which it will not increase; instead it traverses all intermediate degrees from a level where it is not noticeable, although often in such a short time that for us the full strength of the sensation seems to come up suddenly. An increase of sensation from zero by constantly new increments to its full strength is no fiction, but is based on the nature of the matter. At the same time our noting it is the device that alone makes it possible to measure a sensation. Once its growth is completed, the sensation cannot be measured in the absence of the quantitative relationship of "more than." On the other hand, the increments making up a sensation that is still growing present an especially comprehensible "more than" relationship, by the method I intend to present further on.

In a way this artifice in the treatment of psychic magnitudes presents certain advantages that correspond to those of the device used in the treatment of spatial magnitudes. Given a curve or a surface, calculus treats it as made up of the sum of infinitesimal increments instead of treating it as a given whole. Thus, for example, one gains the greatest insight into the shape of the curve from the general expression that relates the variable increment of the ordinate to the successive constant increments of the abscissa, or the variable dy to the successive constants dx. In the same way we can understand the relative change of stimulus and sensation best by expressing it as a general function relating to the successive constant increments of the sensation the successive variable increments of the stimulus. Consequently we may form a function relating stimulus and sensation, one which could then just as well be expressed in an equation of x and y and, if we wish, by a curve. The only difference is that we will, in the future, use the letters β and γ instead of x and y. In the meantime, for the moment let us consider this statement as a preview rather than an insight.

It may well be that psychological measurement will always remain more difficult and more complex than physical measurement, both in its construction and in its application. The reason for this problem is to be found in the fact that, in general, in physical measurement equal divisions of the yardstick correspond to equal distances in the object that is to be measured, whereas commonly experience has shown that increasing magnitudes of stimulus and sensation demand constantly greater stimulus increments in order to maintain the same increase in sensation. In other words, we can compare psychological measurement with a case in which unequal divisions of the yardstick would correspond to equal divisions of the object to be measured. As already noted, this fact does not prevent us from drawing conclusions about the sum of the one from the sum of the other, when the relation between the two is known, and that is after all the main point. Magnitude of stimulus and sensation, as a whole, are now, however, no longer proportional, so that the simplest possible relation between measuring rod and object which could be thought of, and which really exists in physical measures of space, time, and weight, cannot exist for the psychological object and its physical measure. We have here the second reason why the search for a psychological measure has been delayed.

In the meantime, experiment shows that the next most simple relationship that could be imagined does obtain. While the *absolute* magnitudes of stimulus increments leading to equal sensation increments increase more and more as sensations increase, we find that, given constant sensitivity and normal or average circumstances, the *relative* magnitudes of these increments always remain constant for constant increases in sensation. Equal *relative* stimulus increments, then, correspond to equal increments in sensation if, as before, we understand by relative increase the magnitude of the absolute increase with respect to or divided by the magnitude of the stimulus.

The circumstance that with increasing sensation there is a constant increase in the absolute magnitude of stimulus increments necessary to produce equal increments in sensation becomes then itself merely a deduction, since the stimulus, as it increases with increasing sensation, must stay in the same proportion to the absolute magnitude of the stimulus of which it forms a fraction.

According to our analogy to the yardsticks of the psychical and the physical, equal divisions on the yardstick must correspond to equal divisions of the object that is to be measured. We will be able to satisfy this demand by considering the relative, rather than the absolute, stimulus increments as the actual inches or divisions. The determination and summation of continuously equal relative stimulus increments during the increase of stimulus and sensation therefore represent a summing of just as many equal associated sensation increments. It is now only necessary to relate their sum to a unit of the same kind, in order to have a measure of the total sensation.

Strictly speaking, this summation ought to be of infinitely small increments, because the associated relative stimulus increments take an exactly determinable value only for infinitely small sensation increments. After all, if we should want to examine the relative stimulus increment for a finite sensation increment all at once, we would have to consider that the stimulus during its increase itself takes various values, each of which could properly be considered the divisor of the increment in calculating the relative increase. The difficulty which seems to arise in this way may, however, be overcome in a manner which has previously been touched upon a number of times, for it is possible to write a simple mathematical function which takes care of the results of such a determination without the need of counting in detail an infinite number of infinitesimal increments. The function that is involved may be derived from the simplest application of the calculus, demanding for its understanding and application only elementary knowledge.

The ultimate link of a psychological measure rests then finally on a function that may itself be looked upon as having a mental nature, while the physical nature is linked ultimately to physical yardsticks. We must consider only that the former link could not be found by movement in the pure realm of the mental, nor could its application be limited to the mental, since it is rather, just as is physical measure, based on the relationship between the physical and the mental worlds.

The law that stimulus increments for equal increases in sensation are larger at the upper end of a stimulus scale than at the lower, has been known for a long time, since it is a matter of everyday experience.

The words of a neighbor are clearly audible in stillness or when there is little everyday noise. On the contrary, one can, as the saying goes, hardly hear one's own words (that is, one finds the increment produced by them unnoticeably small) when there is much noise.

The same difference in weight that is clearly apparent with small weights becomes unnoticeable with heavy weights.

Lights of high intensity that are quite different photometrically still appear of practically equal brightness to the eye. For example, light reflected from a mirror appears practically as bright as the source light, in spite of the fact that considerable loss takes place in reflection.

Analogous examples are easy to find in all areas of sensory perception.

Nevertheless, this general observation by itself was not enough to form the basis for a psychological measure. The more exact formulation stating that the magnitude of the stimulus increment must increase in precise proportion to the stimulus already present, in order to bring about an equal increase in sensation, was first made with some generality by E. H. Weber and supported by his experiments. I have therefore called it Weber's Law.

In certain cases to which it applied, it had, however, been formulated and proven at an earlier period, as will be seen in more detail in Chapter IX, which will be specifically devoted to this law.

The mathematical function, on the other hand, that relates stimulus intensity and sensation magnitude had been applied more than a hundred years ago by Euler, and later repeatedly by Herbart and Frobisch in special cases concerning the dependence of the perception of tonal intervals on their relation to the frequencies of vibrations. The same relation was noted even somewhat before Euler by Daniel Bernoulli, and later by Laplace and Poisson, for the dependence of *fortune morale* on *fortune physique*. Finally it was found to hold, by Steinheil and Pogson, for the dependence of different stellar magnitudes (themselves nothing but differences of sensation) on their photometric intensities. I shall come back to all these in Chapter VIII and again in a later historical chapter.

If the generality and meaning of this law and this function had been understood earlier, this psychic measure would have been recognized sooner.

Weber's Law, that equal relative stimulus increments correspond to equal sensation increments, should, because of its wide generality and the extent of the boundaries within which it is strictly or approximately valid, be looked upon as fundamental to psychic measurement theory. Yet there are restrictions to its validity, and it is subject to complications, which will be discussed carefully later. Even where this law ceases to be valid or strictly applicable, the principle of psychic measurement I have outlined retains its exactness and full validity. For any other relationship between constant sensation and variable stimulus increments (even though merely empirically determined and expressed by an empirical formula) can serve just as well as basis of a psychic measure—and may indeed have to serve in those parts of the stimulus scale where Weber's Law loses its validity. Indeed, such a formula would yield a differential equation, quite as well as Weber's Law, leading by integration to a formula that would contain an expression of the scale.

This point of view is fundamental, in that Weber's Law with its limitations is not looked upon as restricting psychological measurement, but only as a limiting device, which the general principle of measurement is able to transcend. Indeed, this principle does not even derive its validity from Weber's Law, rather the application of Weber's Law is merely subsumed by the principle.

The search for a possible generalization of psychological measurement, accordingly, will not have to be limited to an attempt at the generalization of Weber's Law. Such an endeavor would carry with it the dangerous tendency to generalize the law beyond its natural limits, or to suggest that this law had already been stretched beyond its limits in order to make a point. Actually one should be able to ask quite freely: what are the limits of the law, where does it fail to fit? For even where it does not apply, the three methods that are used to derive the measures (and thereby the measurements themselves) do apply to yield measurements.

In short, Weber's Law merely forms the basis of the most numerous and most important applications of psychological measurement, but does not constitute the general and necessary foundation. Rather, the most general and fundamental basis of psychic measurement must be sought in those methods by which the relationship of stimulus and sensation increments is determined in general, whether within or beyond the limits of Weber's Law. Everything in psychological measurement theory will depend, therefore, on the development of these methods in ever greater exactness and completeness.

We would lose a great advantage, nevertheless, if Weber's Law, with all its simplicity, were not really basic to psychophysics, if it were not precise within its wide limits and a sufficient approximation in many other instances. That is an advantage similar to what would be lost if, for example, we were not able to accept the basis of Kepler's Law in astronomy or the rules of simple refraction of lenses in discussing the theory of dioptric instruments. The conditions with regard to these laws are here quite analogous. With Kepler's Law we ignore the perturbations, in simple refraction the optical aberrations. The situation may even arise where these laws are quite invalid, as when the simple assumptions under which they are true do not obtain. Nevertheless, they will always remain basic for the major conditions with which astronomy and dioptrics are concerned. Similarly, Weber's Law may also lose its validity completely, when the average conditions under which stimuli cause sensation are greatly exceeded or abandoned; yet normally it will always be applicable.

In psychophysics, as in physics and astronomy, we will initially neglect disturbances and small deviations from our law—without forgetting their presence—in order to get to know and survey the main conditions with which we have to deal. Eventually, detailed analysis and progress of the theory will make possible the determination and calculation of these deviations.

The establishment of a psychological measure is a matter for outer psychophysics and its most immediate applications also fall into this realm. Further applications and deductions, however, necessarily impinge upon the area of inner psychophysics, and thereby bring a deeper meaning to these measures. Let us recall that the stimulus does not cause sensation directly, but via the mediation of bodily activity, which in turn is more directly related to sensation. Quantitative dependence of sensation on the stimulus can then eventually be translated into dependence on the bodily activities that directly underlie sensation—in short, the psychophysical processes—and the measurement of sensation by means of stimulus intensity will be changed to one depending on the strength of these processes. For this translation it becomes necessary to ascertain the relative dependence of the internal motions on the stimulus, and insofar as this is not possible by direct experience, to determine it otherwise in an exact manner. It will indeed be possible to carry out all these investigations in an exact manner, and these cannot in the long run—even though this goal may not yet have been reached—fail to achieve the success of quantitative determinations.[1]

While Weber's Law is only of limited validity with respect to stimulus and sensation in the area of outer psychophysics, it probably has unlimited validity in the area of inner psychophysics, if transposed to the relationship of sensation to kinetic energy or to some other specific function of the underlying psychophysical processes. This conclusion is reached since all deviations from this law, which may be observed when external stimuli give rise to sensations, are probably due to the fact that

---

[1] Ed. Note: One hundred years later, Fechner's optimism still remains to be fulfilled.

only under normal or average conditions does the stimulus release kinetic energy proportional to the amount of internal activity directly underlying sensation. We might foresee, therefore, that once we have succeeded in making this transformation to psychophysical processes in an exact way, this law will take on for the field of mind-body relations just as general and fundamental a meaning as the law of gravitation in the field of celestial movement. The law also manifests that very simple character which we are used to finding in the basic laws of the physical world.

While the psychic measure consequently can be based on Weber's Law only to a limited extent in outer psychophysics, we would deem it to be the unqualified basis of inner psychophysics. Nevertheless, for the moment these expectations are merely opinions and hopes. Their proof will have to await what the future will bring.

So much for the principle of psychic measurement in general. The following points pertain to its more specific proof and exposition.

1. We will have to discuss the methods that allow us to determine how large a relative stimulus increment is necessary, in the ascending scale of stimulus and sensation, in order to give rise to progressively equal sensation increments. These methods coincide with the methods for measuring differential sensitivity, insofar as these measures, in our sense, consist only in determining those stimulus differences that correspond to equal sensation differences. Since such measures are of importance and interest by themselves, apart from the basis they furnish for a measure of sensations, they will be dealt with, at the start, without regard to these applications, which will be taken up later.

2. We will have to show with what generality and within what limits experiments according to these methods form a foundation of Weber's Law, which will itself have to be discussed. In addition to the support it furnishes to psychological measurement, this law also has great importance as one of the most general psychophysical laws.

3. We will have to discuss a fact (the threshold) and another law (the parallel law), which while not essential parts of Weber's Law still retain a real relationship to it and enter into its general derivation.

4. We will have to demonstrate how a general mathematical formulation may be derived from a basic expression of the relationship of stimulus intensity to magnitude of sensation, without making assumptions in advance about the comparability of magnitudes of sensation, and without recourse to a counting of single sensation increments.

5. This function itself will have to be formulated and discussed, and its applications will have to be examined.

6. It will have to be demonstrated that psychological measurement is possible even beyond the point where Weber's Law ceases to be valid.

7. Finally, we will have to seek the transition from outer to inner psychophysics by means of this measure.

The first three of these tasks will be treated in this volume; the others in the next.

VIII.

Methods of Measuring Sensitivity

According to the principles worked out in Chapter VI, absolute sensitivity is measured in intensive sensations by the reciprocal of the absolute stimulus intensities, and in extensive sensations by the reciprocal of the absolute extents that give rise to equally large sensations. In order to measure simple differential sensitivity, the reciprocals of those stimulus differences or differences in extent that arouse equal sensations of difference are used. Relative differential sensitivity is measured by the reciprocal of the ratios of stimuli or extents that give rise to equally large differences in sensation.

There is no way to separate simple from relative differential sensitivity, since in both cases we have to determine the two stimuli that give rise to a specific sensation of difference. One can at this point pay attention either to the absolute magnitude of the difference or to the ratio of the stimuli, measuring sensitivity by the reciprocal of the one or of the other. Each of these measures will retain its meaning. It will suffice for now, however, to discuss the methods for obtaining the former.

Making these measurements on the basis of these definitions assumes that we can actually judge with precision the equality of sensations and sensation differences under various conditions and that we can make statements about them, which at first glance does not seem so simple. However, as we have already noted, the well-known photometric methods of measurements are based on the judgment of equality of sensations, and in music one has to judge often enough the coincidence of two tones, as well as the equality of two tonal intervals—that is, differences of tones. We shall now examine some very general methods to prove the equality of differences of sensation. In fact, methods of measuring sensitivity that concern differences have been much better developed so far than those relating to absolute sensitivity. We will therefore begin with these methods primarily.

These methods will be covered here up to the point where a general insight into their nature and reciprocal relationship can be had and where the conditions necessary for their accuracy, which they share, may be seen. The main points with which we are concerned in experimentation and calculation will be described sufficiently for their application and for an understanding of the results cited in later chapters. Had I wished, however, to set forth here all the special methods of experimentation and calculation that have to be taken into account in more detailed investigations, or had I wanted to provide a theoretical basis and experimental proof for all the rules that are applicable, I would have disturbed the flow of the argument, interfering with the interests of those who are more concerned with general understanding of the methods than with their use by themselves. I prefer, therefore, for purposes of a more detailed exposition of the methods and the experimental series based on them, to refer to a supplement to this work entitled "Methods and Determinations of Measurement in the Area of Psychophysics," which I intend to append to this work and will cite in brief under the title "Methods of Measurement." Much that here is only briefly touched upon will be found there in detail. One will also find there more precise theoretical arguments or specific experimental proofs.

1. METHODS OF MEASURING DIFFERENTIAL SENSITIVITY

a. General Description

Three methods of measuring differential sensitivity are available at present, which, for the sake of brevity, I shall call:

1. Method of just noticeable differences
2. Method of right and wrong cases
3. Method of average error

To begin, let us examine the application of the three methods to the same task, specifically the accuracy with which differences of weight may be recognized. We hope to introduce these methods in this way and to bring about a preliminary, superficial understanding of them, although actually only the first two have been employed so far.

In the application of the method of just noticeable differences, a person compares the weight of two containers, A and B, by lifting them, after they have first been given slightly different loads. The difference in weight will be felt if it is large enough; otherwise it will not be noticed. The method of just noticeable differences consists in determining how much the weights have to differ so that they can just be discriminated. We may take the reciprocal of this difference as an indication of the degree of sensitivity.

In general it is practical with this method to decrease the difference from one that is easily perceptible to one that is just noticeable and also just as often to increase this difference up to the same point from an imperceptible difference and then to take the average result.

If one takes very small differences of weight one will, upon frequent repetition of the experiment, often be mistaken about the direction of the difference, so that the container that is lighter is taken to be the heavier and vice versa. The more the added weight or the greater the sensitivity, however, the greater will be the number of correct cases compared to the number of wrong or to the total number of cases. The method of right and wrong cases consists essentially in determining the extra weight that is necessary to give the same ratio of right judgments to wrong judgments or of right judgments to the total number of judgments under the various conditions for which the sensitivity is compared. The degree of sensitivity under these different conditions is indicated by the reciprocal of this excess weight.

Doubtful cases should not be omitted but should be counted as belonging half to the right and half to the wrong cases.

One may try, given the true weight of one container on the scale as a standard, to match it by a comparison weight on the basis of judgment of the senses alone. In general, in making this judgment one misses by a certain amount. This error is found when the second container, which had been judged equal to the first, is eventually placed on a scale. On frequent repetition of this experiment many errors are obtained from which one can calculate an average error. We shall consider the reciprocal of the average error obtained in this way as the sensitivity for differences of weight. This is the method of average error.

Since positive and negative errors derive to an equal extent from lack of correct perception, they are also equally useful for our measurement. In other words they are not to be subtracted from one another, but added according to their absolute value.

Just as these methods can be employed in respect of sensations of weight, so they can be used with visual sensations, auditory sensations, and so forth, as well as with extensive sensations. Extension, for example, is investigated by the method of just noticeable differences by noting how large a difference there has to be between the spreads of two pairs of compasses, judged either by sight or while resting on the skin, in order for it to be just perceptible. With the method of right and wrong cases we determine how often we are right and how often wrong in trying to estimate the slightly differing spread of two pairs of compasses. Finally, with the method of average error, we determine the average error that is made when one attempts to match the spread of one pair of compass points to that of the other.

These three methods complement each other in reaching the same goal. In the first method the boundary separating apparent differences from those that are not apparent is observed as a just noticeable difference; in the second method apparent differences are counted (which by chance sometimes turn out to be in the correct, sometimes in the wrong direction); in the third method imperceptible differences are measured.

All three methods employ, as their means of measuring sensitivity, relatively—and at times vanishingly—small differences. Later we will see that it is this fact that is most advantageous when our purpose is to seek the basis of a measure of sensation in some measure of sensitivity.

So far as we can see now, each of these methods is applicable to all the sense domains, but as yet we are far from carrying out measurements for all the senses by even one of them. By the same token, none of the three methods has as yet been applied completely to one single sense.

The method of just noticeable differences has been used in isolated instances in the past, as, for example, by Delezenne in testing the sensitivity for deviations from the purity of tonal intervals. It has been used extensively and with the best results by E. H. Weber in his investigations of sensitivity for weight, touch, and visual space perception.* As for myself, I have only undertaken a few not very extensive experiments in the areas of light intensity, visual distance, and temperature judgments by this method.

With the method of right and wrong cases, no previous work is known to me, except that of Hegelmayer,† a medical student at Tübingen, in the area of visual extent, and of Renz and Wolf‡ in the area of auditory measurement. Since both of these studies were carried out by young people under Vierordt's auspices, one may assume that he assigned this method to them, although this is not explicitly stated. As for myself, I have used it in very extensive experimentation in the judgments of weight.

In a certain sense, the method of average error is as ancient as the determination of the precision of observations by the magnitude of the accompanying error. To my knowledge, however, this method has been used only with respect to objective measures of precision of physical and astronomical observations or to the determination of the magnitude of the source of errors in these measurements.§ It has never been considered or

---

* See especially his writings on touch and common sensibility, and his *Programmata collecta*.

† *Vierordt's Arch.* 1852, XI, p. 844.

‡ *Vierordt's Arch.* 1856, XV (2), p. 185 or *Pogg. Ann.* XCVIII, p. 600.

§ For example, by Steinheil in his *Elemente der Helligkeitsmessungen*, p. 75; by Langier in *Comp. rend.* XLIV, p. 841, and so on.

used as a psychophysical method for determining the acuteness of the senses. Yet it seems to me to be one of the most useful for this purpose, and, together with Volkmann, I have used it in determining the precision of judgments of visual extent and touch.

From a practical point of view the method of just noticeable differences is the simplest and most direct of the three methods of measurement. It achieves its goal most quickly and demands the fewest calculations. Here the just noticeable difference is grasped directly in terms of equal sensations, and even though one also may need repetition to strengthen a single judgment and calculation of a mean for purposes of accuracy, one can depend on a much smaller number of cases, since each single observation itself is a result. On the other hand, in the other methods a great many right or wrong cases, or errors, must be observed, in order to come to a conclusion about the equality of sensations of difference, and this judgment needs to be mediated by a process of calculation. This method, then, appears to be the method of choice, in most instances, for preliminary determination of fundamental data or when one cannot spare much time for observation. It seems less suitable, however, for more detailed investigations and incapable of reaching the same high grade of precision as the other two methods, to which one therefore will frequently find oneself forced to turn in the course of an experiment. One of its major drawbacks is the fact that whatever is termed just noticeable leaves more room for error as a subjective judgment, than is the case with the other methods. This term is in no way absolute, since neither the first point, where a difference in sensation becomes just noticeable, nor the second, where it disappears, can be determined quite precisely. One passes through an interval of uncertainty as to whether one is aware of the sensation or not. This method turns into the method of right and wrong cases, if one does not want to set the standard for a just noticeable judgment rather high, that is, if one accepts only such differences as just noticeable, which, on repetition of the experiment, appear as noticeable without exception and with certainty. Yet of necessity, in this case, a somewhat smaller difference must frequently also appear as just noticeable, for there will always occur instances when one commits an error in judging the direction of the difference or where one remains in doubt. These instances must be taken in account in relation to the frequency of their occurrence.

Experience shows, nevertheless, that one can, so to speak, come to an agreement with oneself on what constitutes a small, yet definitely perceived difference. This criterion of difference can be repeated precisely enough in various experiments, even if it is not absolutely reproduced, and it can lead to good results on repetition of the experiments. These remarks should not be taken as lowering in any way the value of this method, for they serve only to put into the right light its advantages and disadvantages, as compared with the other methods. Without this method psychophysics would lose what is, so to speak, its most useful tool. In the hands of its masters it has proved itself by the fundamental data it has secured. Others, as well as myself, have had sufficient occasion to convince ourselves of its usefulness.

The method of right and wrong cases may well be the most tedious, and if one does not have much time or patience it is better not to start an investigation with it, since a few right or wrong cases accomplish next to nothing. Nevertheless, one can obtain very good results from a great number of cases—that is, results which agree well among themselves and that reveal lawful relationships in the area of sensations. While the aid of calculation is needed, only operations that can be carried out easily are involved. Whereas one is mainly confined to a simple difference in the method of just noticeable differences (namely, the one that is just noticeable), one can choose somewhat larger or smaller differences at will to measure differential sensitivity, when the method of right and wrong cases is used. The different number of right and wrong cases one obtains in this way can be employed to make specialized comparisons.

The method of average error also needs a large number of cases and some aid from calculations. Both of these latter methods possess the big advantage that they rely on the proven principles of probability and may even themselves add something to the development of these principles. Indeed, the interest that long practice of these methods has awakened in me has been very much sustained and increased by this possibility.

b. General Considerations and Precautions

While the methods I have just discussed briefly may seem simple at first glance and actually are so in principle, they do demand in the course of their execution many considerations and precautions. Some of these relate to the observations, some to the calculations; in part they depend on the particular method and the area of experimentation. The following rules, however, are more or less generally valid.

In all three of the methods irregular chance fluctuations play a major role. Some of these are inherent in the operations, others are based on the subjective nature of the interpretations of compared magnitudes. The difference to be determined by the method of just noticeable differences will sometimes appear to be much inflated, sometimes much reduced, if the range of these chance effects is considerable. To be sure about one's judgment one would have to choose an initial value substantially more remote than one would if these fluctuations did not exist. The value one records as just noticeable would for this reason be inflated because of these major effects of chance. In the method of right and wrong cases the influence of chance may make a weight appear much heavier at one time, much lighter at another time. In this case the influence of the heavier weight does not count very greatly compared to the influence of chance and, because the irregular chance fluctuations act, on the average, equally often in the heavier and in the lighter directions, the number of right and wrong cases becomes noticeably equal, or at least the number of right cases is diminished compared with the instance where less or no chance influences play a role. Finally, in the method of average error one can see immediately that on the average the errors must get bigger the more the magnitudes which are being compared appear larger or smaller due to chance.

In brief, the greater the role of chance, the smaller, according to all three methods, will be the value that yields the measure of sensitivity, and there is no way of achieving a measure free of these chance effects. Their average value will always remain a factor incorporated into any measurement. This effect does not prevent us from finding comparable measures of sensitivity, as long as this factor remains a constant, that is, as long as these irregular fluctuations remain equally large on the average. In fact, without these chance fluctuations the methods of right and wrong cases and of average error could not even exist. They do point up the important consideration that only those measurements of sensitivity may be considered comparable which can satisfy the assumption of an equal play of chance. This assumption demands strict uniformity of both external and internal conditions at the time of experimentation. Any change in the technique of measurement will immediately affect the play of chance and lead to a lack of comparability of the data. In the same way, we are not justified in assuming the same play of chance for different individuals or in the same individual at different times because of possible changes of internal conditions. We must therefore ask, any time we find lack of correspondence in measures of sensitivity, if we are dealing with real deviations or lack of comparability of the circumstances under which they were obtained.

In general much repetition is necessary, and, as already noted, in the methods of right and wrong cases and of average error an especially large number of determinations is needed in order to obtain reliable results. The multiplicity of observations has in this case an essentially different meaning as compared with those in physical and astronomical measurement. A physical or astronomical magnitude may already be determined quite accurately by means of a few exact measurements by the usual methods. On the other hand, in the methods of average error and right and wrong cases the large number of determinations is by itself a necessary condition for accuracy. Each individual observation has next to no meaning, and a few determinations, even if exact, do not give accuracy. The individual right and wrong cases, the individual errors, are indeed distributed quite irregularly. Fractional parts of the experiment, in spite of the fact that they may have been obtained under circumstances which appeared on the surface to be quite comparable, nevertheless may yield widely differing results. Yet one is often amazed to see how in major parts of the experiment these irregularities yield results that agree very well among themselves. The point is, that the law which in the field of probability is known as the law of large numbers is valid here. This law governs chance as long as the number of cases is large.

There is no more apt comparison of our methods than to Proteus, who appears to evade every answer by constantly changing his shape, instead of answering the questions put to him simply and willingly. Yet by sticking to the same point long enough one can force an answer from him. In the past I have wasted much time, particularly with the method of right and wrong cases, trying to draw conclusions from a few hours or days of experimentation, without being able to say anything definite. It was not until I resolved to continue trials concerned with a single point for months, one hour a day, that I achieved results which gave me cause to be content.

Apart from the inevitable influence, mentioned on page [64], that the range of chance fluctuations exerts on the size of the measured values, the effects of chance must be compensated by frequent repetition. Trials must be continued until one achieves agreement between measurements made at different times, provided variability and sensitivity stay the same. In this way the single chance deviation loses its influence and the final results become independent of chance in this respect. To make sure that such is the case, one continues or repeats each series of experiments until major parts, or replications, agree in the relevant results. Naturally deviations of so small an order of magnitude that they would be permissible as errors of observation in physical experiments must be allowed, for those chance errors that cannot be completely balanced out play the part of observational error in our methods. If minor subsets should agree one should not be satisfied, for this consistency itself may be due to chance. Probability theory gives us a way to calculate beforehand the degree of accuracy that can be expected at a given probability level from a given number of trials. On the other hand, it allows us to calculate the degree of accuracy reached, taking into account the number of observations and the degree of correspondence shown by the single trials or fractions of a series of observations.

If possible, experiments should be carried on from the start according to some prearranged plan, appropriate to a given purpose. Preliminary trials may, however, often be a great help in finding the best conditions for measurement and in finding the factors that should be taken care of in planning the experimental procedure. They have also the advantage, when practice effects are not being investigated at the same time, that they allow us to pass the first stage of practice and to avoid a part of the early variability in the main experiment. The influence of practice always remains, meanwhile, an element to be reckoned with, and it is useful to take note of it and follow its course starting with the first preliminary trials, since later trials, when practice has already partially taken place or has reached its limits, include practice only incompletely or not at all.

The widest possible systematic variation of circumstances should be brought into play in order to avoid one-sided results, or results that are valid only under particular conditions. I have often found that what seemed quite regular under given circumstances turned out quite differently under other circumstances.* I have become very cautious before calling results general, if they have not proven themselves under many very different circumstances. This rule leads to a conflict, however. As the number of combinations of conditions under which one conducts an experiment increases, the number of experiments that can be made under each single condition decreases, and one can, therefore, in general determine the measurements with respect to each single one only with less accuracy. One should therefore be just as wary of wanting to investigate everything at once, so to speak, whereby one gets nothing right, as of limiting procedures to certain fixed variables.

Taking weight-lifting experiments as an example, one can investigate how sensitivity to differences of weight changes with the magnitude of the standard. Assuming one has determined these relationships lifting the weights with one hand, would one find the same results if one lifted with the other hand, or if one lifted one weight with one hand and the other with the other hand instead of lifting both with one and the same hand? What would happen if one changed one's grip or the mode of attack or the position of the weights within the containers? Would not the speed of lifting each container, the intertrial interval, the sequence, whether the

---

* This caution is especially important with respect to constant errors, which have yet to be treated.

heavier one is lifted first or second, or the height to which they are lifted bring about differences? Would one still find the same results if trials were run with the order of the standard weights ascending from less to more or if one were to run them in reverse order? What is the influence of a fatigued versus a nonfatigued arm? What change occurs in the ratio of right and wrong cases as a function of the magnitude of the comparison weight? And so on.

A determination of all these influences really belongs to an exhaustive investigation of sensitivity for differences of weight, and in other fields of inquiry regarding sensitivity other influences will appear in their stead and would have to be investigated. Each factor in turn requires a long series of appropriate experiments in order for one to be sure of its magnitude, its direction, and its dependence on other circumstances.

Where the influence of different factors is to be compared, trials should be made with each in turn, alternating ascending and descending series and larger and smaller values, either on the same day or over a series of days. The influence of the trial sequence on the results through changes in sensitivity or for other reasons can then be either recognized, compensated for, or taken into account. In the case of weight-lifting experiments, for example, this procedure would be applied to the series of different standards, different comparisons, different intervals between lifting of weights, and so on—all the conditions under which the trials are made.

If, for example, experiments are to be conducted with a series of standard weights, one could proceed by taking first an ascending series, then a descending series, on the same day, and repeating on the next day with a descending series followed by an ascending series. One could also run through the series with only ascending trials on one day and descending the following, keeping to this alternation methodically through the whole series of days necessary to complete the experimental run.

In some experiments I have begun and ended with each one of the values in turn, instead of starting and ending at all times with the lowest or highest value, passing through the series backward and forward as if the values were arranged on a circle, where the starting point can be taken at will. Perhaps, however, the expected advantage of complete compensation of the influence of serial order is outweighed here by the disadvantage of the lessened simplicity of method, or possibly it is worthwhile only under special circumstances.

In general, different conditions must be considered in testing the influence of serial order on experiments. These conditions may partially work against one another and be in conflict, with sometimes one and sometimes the other gaining the upper hand. On the one hand, especially when practice is lacking, attention and the activity of the sense organs are only set going, so to speak, after a certain duration of the experiments, but then commence to yield a certain uniformity. On the other hand, they will become weary, tired, or under some conditions irritated by long-continued practice. Finally, within limits, the influence of practice makes itself felt from the start and often throughout a long series of experiments. Each of these influences may be made subject to special investigation. Insofar as they automatically play a role in every investigation, one should guard against the following especially.

Unless they are themselves the object of investigation, one does well to avoid major changes in these conditions (that is, one should not continue experiments until massive fatigue or irritability sets in) and should prefer experiments with gradual practice effects or where practice has reached its limits to those where practice effects are large. Since, however, a prolonged continuation of the experiments, either every day or in a series of days, presents an advantage in terms of uniformity as well as in ability to carry through the experiment in a given time, one has to look for a limit in this respect, which is best chosen according to the individual and the experimental conditions. This limit must be left to everyone's own judgment. In any case, one should count upon the exact determination and compensation of these influences rather than their avoidance, for they can in no way be excluded. A suitable methodological arrangement of the trials can take care of them. For details see the discussion of each of the methods.

As useful and as necessary as a systematic change in conditions might be, in order to explore the effect of their differences, it is understandable that their greatest possible constancy—or, insofar as this cannot be achieved, allowance for their variation—is needed in all experiments which are to be combined to yield a common result for a given set of conditions. Even if the external conditions can be controlled in this respect, the same is by no means true for the internal conditions. Sensitivity itself, as well as some other internal conditions that play a secondary role, is subject to no less a variability through causes that can neither be calculated nor removed. This fact leads to two considerations. The first is that the comparability of measurements taken at different times, even under identical external conditions, is not to be taken for granted without further investigation, if one has not convinced oneself of their comparability by the data themselves. The second, that longer series of experiments should be broken up into parts not only according to different experimental conditions, but also according to periods of time, in order to test these factors separately. In general it is better to combine calculated results of fractions of longer series than to take the result of the whole undivided series all at once.

Breaking up the experiment into parts has the advantage, in general, of allowing us to estimate the greater or lesser constancy of the results and to follow the changes due to practice, if any. Particularly it gives us a better chance of eliminating mathematically the influence of internal disturbances (which in longer series of trials often act in opposite directions) than we have when the observations are treated as a whole—as will be seen later in the special discussion on methods.

It is true that by treating the part totals mathematically, reliability is reduced more than if we had used all the results, because of the smaller number of observations. However, according to the laws of probability it can be shown that whatever reliability is lost by breaking up the run into parts is regained when the results of these parts are again combined. Thus the cited advantages of breaking up the experiment into subgroups still remain.

On the other hand, however, fractionation makes the treatment and reporting of results more cumbersome. In the methods of right and wrong cases and of average error the number of trials that are included in a subgroup exerts an influence on the value of the measures obtained, as can be demonstrated theoretically and as experience shows. This effect vanishes when the number of trials becomes large. It can be taken into account by a correction if the number of trials is few or it can be made harmless by invariably using the same number of trials.

Since every extended series of experiments continues through several days or even weeks and months, trials should be scheduled at the most regular intervals possible and in subdivisions containing the same number of trials and, if possible, equal and symmetrically arranged subtests. Strict adherence to a rigid order in this respect not only aids materially in making different days' runs comparable and preserving their relationship, but also prevents confusion and accidents in the order of experimental conditions. It also simplifies calculation and facilitates whatever use is made of the observations, whereas the usefulness of the observations suffers in every respect if they are made at one time in one order and at a second time in another, when there are now so many and now that many, now made under these conditions and then again under different conditions without rigid rules. The over-all advantage of an orderly arrangement at any time becomes the more apparent with our method, in general, the more details there are to be organized and kept in order.

In addition, for the most part I conduct trials in a series, which is continued over a period of days, at the same time of day, since possibly the time elapsed since sleeping or eating may influence the sensitivities that are to be investigated. Perhaps such an influence can be neglected, especially if the comparable circumstances are always the same. Nevertheless, this factor should first be investigated separately and caution is always advisable before such an investigation. In any case, this precaution would be subsumed under the general rule of keeping strict order in the time relationships of the trials.

Since, according to our methods, judgment should be based purely on the witness of the senses, all possible care should be taken that the judgment is not determined by the influence of one's fancy, the anticipation of the expected results—in short, by the power of imagination. On the other hand, one may not proceed blindly, so to speak, so as to avoid a possible influence of the power of imagination. Our methods offer opportunity for both these errors to occur.

The ordering of experimental conditions, the recording of the observed values, and the addition of errors or right and wrong cases (as well as all calculations based on them) should be arranged so as to preclude, if one can, other unavoidable slips. Repetition or other means of control should be instituted, on account of the mass of records, additions, and calculations involved. In the recording and use of the data themselves absolute honesty must be observed.

The keeping of these last rules is more important and more difficult than appears on first glance. According to my own and my co-workers' experience, I do not trust any sum or calculation that has not been checked by repetition or otherwise. One tends to overlook errors even on repeated recounts and recalculation, especially when done one after the other and in the same form, as easily as errors in proofreading. Care and caution in this respect cannot be stressed too much. As bothersome as repetition or other checks may become in operations that are tiresome in any case, they nevertheless are necessary in order not to prejudice the advantage of careful observations by slips in their application.

However, even before any records are taken it is easy to slip up in arranging the systematic changes in conditions, which are generally necessary, by mixing up the sequence of conditions or by keeping on through several subtests without the required change. One should therefore make it a rule to check carefully in this respect.

As to honesty in recording, one is tempted—even without wanting to falsify the results—to exclude unusual values, such as exceptionally large errors in the method of average error due to, let us say, a lapse in attention. This procedure is not based on any principle nor does it have limits, and it leads to an arbitrariness that is based only on vague impressions. Such cases should be avoided if possible, but if they do occur one should seek to compensate for them by a large number of trials. The laws of probability which govern chance (and on which the method of right and wrong cases and the method of average error must rest) anticipate the rare occurrence of extraordinary cases. There is no advantage in excluding such cases from calculations that have to be based on these laws. It is, of course, impossible for attention to remain at exactly the same degree during protracted experimental series, even though one should seek to preserve its consistency as much as possible. These unplanned variations themselves are part of chance variability, inherent in these methods, and one may not disturb the working of the law of probability, as it applies to large numbers, by arbitrary interference.

Marking down the date of the observations is important not only in the interest of general orderliness, but especially because periodic and continuing changes in sensitivity that may occur during the course of an experiment can be recognized and considered in the compilation and utilization of the results only in this way. One does well also to write down all secondary conditions, such as temperature, which might possibly have an influence on the success or comparability of the results, even when such an influence has not been proven. It is better to do too much in this respect than too little.

It is especially advantageous in our work for two or more observers to pool their investigations. They are thus able to supplement, to help, or to check each other. It is not easy for an observer to undertake by himself a successful and complete investigation of a single sense domain or of one of its important aspects. The extensive task involved makes a division necessary, just as it also makes it necessary to combine different results at other times. Under some conditions the direct cooperation of two observers (or at least of an observer and a helper) is needed because of technical reasons. Finally, in our field more than in any other it is important that results obtained by one observer be checked by one or more others, because of the danger that the results depend mainly on the observer's personality. According to the particular circumstances a division of labor can therefore take place advantageously through division of the field of observations, through common participation in the same experiment, or through independent repetition of the whole experiment.

One may perhaps say in general that in our work no result may be considered certain, even if obtained by a most reliable observer, unless it has been checked by another reliable observer, because the reliability of an observer is only a guarantee of the honesty and exactness of his records, but not of the general validity of what he has observed. This generalization holds, notwithstanding the fact that some relationships and laws are such that one can presume from the start that they are not merely a matter of personalities.

So important as the cooperative effort of several observers in a common undertaking may, according to these points of view, be said to be, it would be quite invalid to consider the possibility of experimental psychophysical measurement limited only to that aided by a co-observer or assistant. On the contrary, important as an independent check of any of these observations may be, it is just as important to carry out any observation in this area with the minimum disturbance, under the most uniform conditions possible, and with full control over the time, experimental conditions, and sequence of trials. One should try to avoid the danger that knowledge of the experimental conditions whose influence is being investigated may give a clue to the power of the imagination which would help to falsify the results. Where a helper is therefore not necessary, for one reason or another, he would also not be useful, just as any complication of a machine is harmful when it is not necessary. In the special discussion of methods of measurement we will have more opportunities to come back to this subject, with special discussion pertaining to the nature of conditions and to experiences already made in this regard. General impressions are not a sufficient base for particular rules.

c. The Temporal and Spatial Relations of the Experiments: Constant Errors

Since our method consists of the comparison of two magnitudes, a successive presentation should be preferred to a simultaneous one, especially since the latter is hardly possible, in that attention is inevitably turned to one or the other magnitude. The experiment should therefore be arranged, if possible, so that, although the observations follow each other closely, each is uninfluenced by the other, and the superposition takes place only in the memory of the observer. The ability to compare magnitudes in this way is, as E. H. Weber has already noted, very curious, and its explanation must await the future progress of inner psychophysics. At present we must base ourselves on the fact of its existence.

Because perceptions of the compared magnitudes do not coincide exactly in time, just as they do not coincide exactly in space, we find effects that influence the measurements, due to differing conditions in the perceiving organs. I will call these conditions, for short, conditions of the temporal and spatial state of the compared magnitudes. They are the source of the main difficulties in the formulation of a precisely comparable measure of sensitivity. Development of these methods must pay most attention to the detection and elimination of these difficulties through mathematical and other procedures that allow us to accomplish more than at first appears possible. So far our attention has been directed less in this direction than the subject warrants.

In general we can say about temporal relationships that they concern: (1) the time during which a magnitude is perceived, as when a weight is lifted in weight-lifting experiments, or a distance is judged in distance judgments, and so forth, (2) the time allowed to elapse between the perception of the one magnitude and of the other, (3) the temporal order, whether one or the other is first perceived, (4) the more or less frequent repetition of comparisons before one makes one's decision. In general, habit will introduce a certain uniformity of these conditions, and the influence of small differences that may occur in individual experiments will be evened out in the long run. It may be appropriate for a systematic execution of the experiments to bring about complete uniformity and comparability in this respect with the aid of a timer. Then their influences can be investigated by purposeful changes in conditions. Very little work has been done in this area so far. However, I have paid strict regard to these considerations in my weight-lifting experiments with the method of right and wrong cases.

There is no sense in my speaking at this point in generalities about the spatial relationships of the magnitudes being compared, for conditions vary even more under different methods and areas of investigation than they do for temporal relationships. Let me merely remark, in anticipation, that the paired nature of our sense organs demands special consideration, on the one hand, because it gives occasion for comparison of the degree of sensitivity of paired organs taken singly as opposed to both working in cooperation, and on the other hand, because, insofar as their cooperation is concerned, it is not easy for both to stand in the same relationship to the object being compared.

Thus there is a difference when the weight of a container is being judged and the number of right cases of the method being used changes, a difference that depends on whether the comparison weight lies in the left or the right container. This difference occurs, not because of any mystical property of right or left, but because in using one hand to lift one container, the other to lift the other, both hands quite possibly may not really possess the same sensitivity. If the same hand is used to lift both containers it can be shown that the hand, in switching from one weight to the other, automatically assumes a different position and its mode of attack relative to both containers therefore differs slightly. This fact, as I can prove by actual experiments, is not immaterial to the outcome. In judging distance by eye, using the method of average error, it makes a difference whether the standard distance, to which one tries to match the other, is to the right or left of the other, above or below it. In the corresponding experiments on the discrimination of two points on the skin it is not immaterial, when one experiments on oneself, even when using a compass with a handle, whether one holds the compass determining standard distance with the right hand and the other compass with the left, or vice versa, for in some way the manner in which the compass is applied is likely to change. And so with other cases.

To the extent that temporal and spatial conditions remain the same for a given series of trials, though they may vary when different magnitudes are being compared, they form the basis of what one may in general call a constant error in the final measure which is obtained.

When the method of right and wrong cases is used in weight-lifting experiments, the constant error is demonstrated when a large number of cases where the container with the comparison weight was lifted first is compared with an equally large number of cases where it was lifted second, while all other circumstances were the same. The ratio of right to wrong cases in the one instance will be quite different from the ratio in the other. Likewise a difference was found when in a large number of cases the heavier weight lay in the left container as compared with the cases where it lay in the right container.* When the method of average error is used for judging distances by eye or by touch, the constant error becomes apparent in that the mean distance which is judged equal to the given standard still does not agree with the standard distance even after many trials, but will differ by a considerable positive or negative amount depending in a regular manner on the spatial and temporal relationship of the distances being compared. In this connection we also find that the sum of positive errors (that is, the sum of positive deviations from the standard) often differs markedly from the sum of negative errors, instead of being equal in absolute value. This difference is a great deal larger than could be attributed to uncompensated chance errors.

One might regard these results with suspicion and attribute many of these observations to the influence of imagination. However, after one has tried out these methods oneself, he will soon be convinced that he cannot escape these constant errors, try as he may. Since the influence of imagination was practically ruled out in what I observed in this connection, I must admit that this quite unexpected occurrence of constant

---

* In addition, Renz and Wolf mention in their experiments on sound, in which they used the method of right and wrong cases, that one of them had a general tendency to perceive as louder the sound heard first, whereas the other one heard the second sound as louder. This finding shows that the influence of different temporal relationships makes itself felt here also, and in a manner which varies according to circumstances.

errors in these experiments was most puzzling to me in the beginning, and before I managed to eliminate them, most embarrassing. Even today, after much work in this area, particularly in the measurement of weight and touch, a great deal is not clear to me about their ultimate cause and only the fact itself is certain. Other observers, whom I induced to repeat my experiments, have also found results that correspond closely.

The existence of constant errors, one may note, merely complicates the measurements obtained by our methods, but does not cause them to be inexact. If the errors are really constant they can be taken out by suitable means and at the same time their amount can be exactly determined, as I show later in the discussion of the individual methods.

Unfortunately there is, strictly speaking, no constancy of constant errors. I am not as inclined on one day as on another to judge the container lifted first or standing on the left, the distance to the right or the left, as larger or smaller. Rather, the internal dispositions in this respect change in a most astonishing degree, even though external conditions are held constant. These changes are easy to follow with our methods, but we run into difficulties when it comes to achieving the ultimate in exactness, because the variability due to constant errors becomes mixed up with the purely variable error and contaminates it in the method of average error. In the method of right and wrong cases the errors enter into the measurements in still another way. The greatest care should be taken, therefore, to exclude such variability or render it as harmless as possible by the design or treatment of the observations (fractionation).

In spite of these considerations, one must not see a disadvantage in these complications of our methods as caused by the presence of constant errors, but rather an important advantage, inasmuch as the determination of constant errors itself becomes a part of the psychophysical measurements that can be made. After all, their influence is typical of the factors associated with sensations and should be measured. At the same time, however, the opportunity exists to exclude them from the measure of differential sensitivity with which we are at present concerned. Constant errors, therefore, should not merely be discarded as idle waste; they should be carefully separated from the measure of sensitivity and investigated one after another in every area, according to the conditions, laws, and variables that apply. Our methods of observation should indeed advance experimental technique in this respect, in that they reveal not only a totally unexpected general occurrence of constant errors, but also some of their sources in factors which had earlier hardly been considered. More on this will be found in my "Methods of Measurement."

In the sensitivity of these methods to experimental conditions affecting constant errors lies a proof of their discriminatory power.

The preceding comment is not nearly enough to exhaust all that is to be known and all that is to be observed by anyone wanting to use for himself the methods of experimentation I have described. Since I am obliged to reserve more exact explanations for the "Methods of Measurement," I shall limit myself in what follows to characterizing the essential points of the last two methods. I shall summarize them here briefly but will take them up more thoroughly later. In doing this I shall base my account on weight lifting with respect to the method of right and wrong cases, and on visual and tactual distance judgments with respect to the method of average error, as these are the only fields where my own experiences are at my disposal. The terms I shall use in what follows will be employed throughout with reference to the methods concerned.

d. The Method of Right and Wrong Cases as Applied to Weight-lifting Experiments

The experiments (started in the year 1855) that form the basis of the following exposition of the method of right and wrong cases were first undertaken with the simple intention of making a more exact check of Weber's Law. They were carried further in the interest of perfecting the method itself and expanded later when it became apparent that the check I had in mind demanded previous investigation of the precision of the method under various conditions and development of its experimental and technical aspects, which were not available at the time. For several years I considered it a kind of daily labor to undertake experiments to this end for about one hour a day. They were carried through, systematically, over longer periods, and were devoted to inquiry into the various specific relationships. The material amassed in this manner is by no means exhausted in this volume. The large number of trials and the multiple repetition of series of experiments for the purpose of determining important points at different times and under changed conditions, which appear in some of the following chapters, give proof of this. The work also effected a thorough practice in the use of the method.

Our method depends on the determination of the ratio of the number of right cases to the number of wrong cases or to the total number of cases, with the latter the preferred ratio. I propose to call the number of right cases r, the number of wrong [*falsch*] cases f, and their total n, so that the ratio with which we will be mainly concerned will be r/n. If, however, the results of a particular set of observations have been divided into subgroups and these enter into the calculations separately, r and n refer to the number of right cases and the total of each subgroup separately, whereas v will designate the number of subgroups, so that vn then becomes the total number of cases for a particular set of observations. When the whole series concerns several of these sets of observations that must be compared with each other (as usually is the case), then vn must, of course, be multiplied by the number of sets in order to get the total number of cases of the whole series.

Note that each judgment that remains in doubt should be counted half as belonging to the right and half to the wrong cases. In order to avoid half cases arising in this way, I count each right judgment as two right, each wrong judgment as two wrong, and each doubtful judgment as one right and one wrong, because only the ratios count in forming the fraction r/n.

P will designate the standard weight, that is, the weight of each of the loaded containers lifted for comparison, but without D, where D designates the weight increment (extra weight) that is used in a trial. We designate by h a value that is directly proportional to differential sensitivity and therefore inversely proportional to the weight increment D that would give the same r/n—in short, the measure of differential sensitivity with which we are concerned.

There are two ways in which the method may be carried out. According to the first procedure one decides which weight is heavier or lighter only after much lifting back and forth of the weighted containers. According to the second, one commits oneself firmly after each container is lifted once for comparison, or in case of doubt counts the undecided case as half right and half wrong.

In the beginning I always used the first procedure, but later I discarded all experiments done in that way and used the second course exclusively, having become convinced of its much greater advantages. It is not only that this course leads to greater uniformity than the first, but it is the only one which can also yield a basis for elimination and precise determination of the influences of time and position, which cause constant errors. Only with the second approach can these influences be pitted against one another properly, as we will see.

Of course it is easier to make a mistake respecting the direction of the difference by the second course than by the first. The total of undecided and wrong cases also turns out to be larger, even though D is constant and the total number of cases is the same. This does not, however, make the method less exact, based as it is in any case on the errors made. Any reduction of the ratio r/n, which is of as little advantage for measurement as too large a ratio, can be compensated by using a larger D. On the other hand, the second method yields more than the first in the same time, and each single pair of weight liftings can be made quite the same as the other or comparable to it.

If the first procedure is used, it is essential that the position of the heavier weight not be known, and the aid of a helper is needed in determining its position in order to rule out the influence on the judgment of preconceived notions. In the second procedure, according to the description given below, this precaution is both unnecessary and inapplicable. The reasons will become more apparent after a more detailed exposition of the whole matter.

According to the rules given on page [73], the containers should always be picked up one after the other. The dual lifting which forms the basis of judgment in the second procedure, therefore, consists of successively raising one container and then the other; hence it is made up of two simple liftings. However, since each judgment is counted double, as pointed out on page [78], the total number of cases will be determined by the number of single lifts of the weight and not the number of dual liftings.

When I pick up both containers with the same hand I call it the one-handed procedure; when I lift one with one hand, the other with the other hand, I call it two-handed. Even the one-handed procedure has been carried out by me with both hands, since right and left hand were used in alternating sequence. In every longer series of experiments it was found that the right hand was somewhat—though not much—more sensitive than the left. The one-handed procedure, however, was found to be, on the whole, not inconsiderably more sensitive than the two-handed procedure. The constant effects of time and space relationships of the containers differ considerably with one-handed, two-handed, left-handed, or right-handed procedures. This is not the place, however, to go into the details that are at my disposal in this matter.

The arrangement of the containers (together with the weights put into them) that constitute the standard weight P demanded special consideration. Only after I lost much time by experimenting with imperfect apparatus did I find a satisfactory arrangement, briefly described below, having a round handle that could be turned and a fixed series of weights that formed, as it were, a continuous solid body with the container.

It will be perhaps of some interest if I give an example—and it is indeed only one instance—of how many petty problems have to be met, and can be a cause of delay, in experiments of this kind, by describing first some of those imperfect arrangements.

To begin with I used as containers simple hollow wooden cylinders that I grasped by hand from the top. If the weights were heavy the hand had to have a firm grip so that the container would not slide from the grasp, whereas if the weights were light the hand tended to grip them softly. There was thus no assurance of a uniform grasp. After that, I had brass handles put on my containers. The handles were free to pivot around pegs at opposite sides of a diameter of each container, so that when the containers were lifted they would swivel into position by themselves because of gravity. But this arrangement soon wore loose. After that, I had the handles riveted fast, but since I had them made of thin sheet brass in order to save weight, they buckled when I started to use heavier weights and could no longer be considered comparable. Substituting stronger material and discarding all previous experiments, I then used this apparatus for almost a year to make careful and painstaking experiments. In the end, although these were not discarded altogether, they were at least considered in need of repetition and checking, as I have done since to the extent that all those earlier observations can now be considered superfluous—or perhaps may serve in their turn as an incidental check of the results of the new series. In the results that follow they are completely omitted. The reason will be found in the following circumstances. The ballast, used originally but now discarded and only checked for its weight, varied in size in proportion to its weight. Since the containers had to be wide enough to accommodate even the largest load, the smaller and even some of the larger weights tended to shift when the container was lifted. I had assumed that despite this fact the pressure of the container's weight would fall on the same point of the hand as it grasped the handle and that, therefore, no disadvantage could arise from the possible shifting of the loads in their containers. Because of the mass of attendant circumstances that had to be investigated and tested one after another, as possibly influencing the procedure, I neglected to make this factor subject to a special investigation. This neglect came home to roost. When I finally wanted to make sure and turned my investigations in this direction by making comparisons of weights purposely fixed in the middle or the sides of the container, I discovered that the results differed considerably for the two cases, not because of the difference in amount, but because of the difference in the distribution of pressure. It so happened that a container appears the heaviest when the weight occupies the center, and this difference is by no means negligible when extremes of positioning in this respect are compared. Of course the shifts that could have taken place in my experiments would have been much smaller and probably compensated each other by the great number of cases. Confirmation of this conjecture may be found in the fact that major subgroups of the results agreed with one another and also in that later experiments with improved equipment led to essentially the same results. I was nevertheless so unhappy with my previous results, and their precision and reliability in individual determinations (even though not for the data as a whole) became so risky, that I preferred to take the trouble of repeating the determinations with a new apparatus, rather than to let things rest as they were.

All experiments to which I will refer in what follows were carried out according to the second procedure—page [78]—under almost identical conditions, which I shall call the normal circumstances or conditions.

Aspects of secondary importance, which are omitted here, I shall reserve for my "Methods of Measurement." Deviations from these normal conditions were made only insofar as the outcome of these deviations was itself subject to investigation.

The final arrangement of the containers consisted merely of a kind of framework of four vertical brass bars, connected at the bottom by horizontal crossbars. The weights (lead or zinc) were rectangular and fitted precisely into the frame. They differed only in thickness, so that they were seated solidly in the frame and would not shift when lifted. The standard weight P consisted of the container, the inserted weight, and a cover, which had a small open box soldered in its middle. Two standard containers were carefully equalized. The added weight D was then placed into the box on the cover of one of the containers. This way it also was given its fixed place in the middle of the standard weight. The container's handle consisted of a wooden cylinder, 1 Paris inch[1] in diameter, which could turn around its axis. It was grasped by the whole hand.

Depending on whether a lighter or heavier cover was used, each container, together with its cover, weighed 300 or 400 gm [grams]. A weight of 300 gm then became the smallest standard P, that is, when the lighter cover and no further weights were used. The heaviest standard that I employed weighed 3000 gm; the apparatus would perhaps not have been able to bear a heavier weight in the long run. When it was not the purpose to test the outcome of the use of different standards, I normally used a standard of 1000 gm.

Weights of $.04P$ and $.08P$ served most often as added weights.

In spite of the fact that both containers had been constructed exactly alike, D was placed equally often in the one and in the other container in each series of experiments, in order to compensate for the influence of possibly unnoticed differences.

The height to which the weight could be lifted was limited by a horizontal board arranged above the laboratory table in such a way that it amounted to 2 in. 9 Paris lines.

Lifting took place with the arm stripped to shirt sleeves.

The raising was done in such a way that, if, for example, in the first pair of comparisons the left container had been lifted first, the right container would be lifted next, and so forth in alternation. A single set of experiments included 32 successive alternating pairs of weight lifts or 64 single lifts, during which D always occupied the same container. In the middle of each set (that is, after 32 single liftings of the weight), the posi-

---

[1] Ed. Note: The equivalent of 1 Paris in. is 1.066 English in.; the equivalent of 1 Paris line is 0.0888 English in.

tion of the containers was switched from right to left. The four kinds of different combinations of time and position of the extra weight D form the basis of the so-called four main cases of the method, to be discussed in detail below. Each kind was accordingly represented by 16 single liftings or cases in each set of experiments. Each day 8 to 12 such sets of 64 cases were usually run in succession, with changes in the appropriate experimental conditions (P, D, and so forth). For longer series of experiments these would be continued for approximately one month.

The time to lift a container was regulated by a metronome to take one second, putting the container down took one second, and the time between lifting and putting down also took one second. The time for a pair of weight lifts, therefore, on which one comparison or one case was based, took exactly five seconds. The same amount of time—that is, five seconds—was allowed to elapse between one pair of weight lifts and the next. This time was used for recording of the results. In the one-handed method recording was always done with the idle hand, in the two-handed method with one or the other in alternation, depending on the day.

Practice soon allows one to carry out these operations quite mechanically in rhythm with the metronome. Even the direction of attention soon becomes uniform and mechanical so that, as my data themselves show, attention does not seem noticeably weakened at the end of the daily hour of experimenting. The judgments, dependent as they are jointly on the extra weight D, the constant effects of temporal and spatial position, and the irregular effects of chance, come in irregular sequences of changing directions: Right heavier, left heavier, doubtful. They drop in one's lap, so to speak, in an objective manner, without making choice or thought necessary, as would undoubtedly have been the case in the first procedure.

The way in which the recording should be arranged so as to avoid confusion and add conveniently the right cases contained in the four main cases separately will be explained in more detail in "Methods of Measurement."

For the moment this ends our discussion of the external conditions of experimentation. I shall now pass to general principles relating to the method.

The general task of the method is to find for each of the comparisons a term r/n—or, if we divide the total into v parts, to find v values of r/n—and to derive from them the measure of differential sensitivity. These comparisons must be made under each condition for which the sensitivity for differences in weight is to be investigated. A related secondary task consists in determining the direction and magnitude of constant effects that are by-products of experimental procedure.

Now there seems to be a fundamental difficulty present from the start.

We know that, everything else being equal, the ratio r/n increases with increasing sensitivity for differences in weight. We also know, however, that twice the ratio r/n does not correspond to double the sensitivity, if we want to remain true to our previous concept of its measurement, but rather that half as heavy an added weight D, producing the same ratio r/n, would correspond to twice the sensitivity. From these general considerations we can now make the following observations.

Let sensitivity be as low as you like, one will always be able to find an addition D which is so large relative to P that almost all or all of the cases will turn out to be right. It is understandable that then even the greatest increases in sensitivity would not bring about an increase in the ratio r/n. Under these circumstances, then, we would not be able to find a suitable general yardstick for sensitivity, for even if sensitivity changes drastically the ratio would stay constant or nearly so. On the other hand, assuming a greatly increased sensitivity, a much smaller extra weight would be just as sufficient to bring the ratio r/n to approximately n/n, and we would judge the increase in sensitivity accordingly. We are therefore forced back to our previous concept of measurement as inherent in the nature of things. But how can this fit into our method?

Let us assume, for example, that I would like to compare the sensitivity of the right and the left hand for differences in weight. I would lift the same standard weight P and the same additional weight D a number of times, once with the left hand (L) and once with the right hand (R). I would then have different ratios r/n for L and R, which would allow me to judge the greater or lesser sensitivity of the one hand or the other but would not give me a measurable comparison of their sensitivities. The question is now to find the different magnitudes of D which would have to be added to lead to the same ratio r/n for L and R.

Similar questions arise if I want to investigate the sensitivity of one hand only, or the average of both hands, with different P's. Adding equal weights D results, as experience shows, in a larger r/n with a lighter P than with a heavier P, but the point in question had been to find the different D's which give a constant r/n for different P's, in order to use the reciprocal of these D's as the measure of sensitivity for these different values of P.

From this point of view the method of right and wrong cases, as used up to now, was indeed only suitable to give an indication of more or less, but not a comparable measure of sensitivity. Nevertheless, the method can be developed to yield such a measurement.

The most obvious way would be to use a procedure of trial and error.

One could vary the additional weight under the conditions being tested until identical ratios r/n were obtained. However, since it takes a great many trials to find a precise value for even one and the same D, this procedure, which would need numerous trials for each of the D's investigated, would not only be very tedious, but would not be exact even after the most wearying trials.

One could of course interpolate between closely adjacent values. For the longest time I tried to help myself in this way. However, even this approach can overcome only incompletely the disadvantages of inconvenience and inexactness. Luckily they can be surmounted simply and completely.

Every r/n that has been found for a given D can be used to find what D would be necessary to give any other r/n, as long as P and other conditions are held constant and the r/n that is taken as the basis has been derived from a sufficiently large n. The formula used is exact in principle and has stood up in experimental tests. While it is based on mathematical analysis, it is easily translated into practice. It can therefore be used to calculate the constant r/n we are seeking. Indeed, one can find the measure of differential sensitivity concerned directly in a table without calculations, given any ratio r/n based on a sufficiently large n.* This measure corresponds to the concept we developed previously and I shall show immediately how it is used, but first a few words on the reasoning that led up to this formula.

In studying the theory of probability, to which my interest in the development of our methods drove me again and again, the following considerations occurred to me: (1) according to our procedure the measure of sensitivity for differences could be represented by the value usually designated by h, which, according to Gauss, affords a measure of the precision of observations, as long as precision depends only on the sensitivity for the perception of differences under comparable modes of procedure; (2) a mathematical relationship should exist between the experimentally determined ratio r/n and the product of the above-mentioned measure h and the weight increment D for which r/n was determined—that is, between r/n and hD—which should allow us to derive hD from r/n and hence, after division by D, the measure of differential sensitivity h.

It only remained in the first place to determine this relationship theoretically, in the second to prove it experimentally, and in the third to

---

* When a large number of trials is divided into parts n is reduced and one loses precision in each of the parts, but one makes up for this later when the partial results are again combined.   See p. 70.

turn it to practical use in our method. These three tasks I have, I believe, solved satisfactorily, and with this the method of right and wrong cases should have reached the status of a real method of measurement.

As far as the mathematical derivation is concerned, it is inserted as a separate section below, since for practical purposes of application of the method it is not necessary to understand the mathematics. The experimental proof consists essentially in showing that, when a certain value of r/n is found for a given value of D, then the value r/n (calculated according to our mathematical relationship) associated with another D standing in a certain ratio to the first D, can be duplicated experimentally, provided sensitivity is constant. Small deviations springing from uncompensated chance errors are of course allowed. Alternatively, in another form of the same proof, we could show that under constant conditions of sensitivity, but with another D, the experimentally determined values of r/n would correspond to calculated values of hD which are proportional to D according to our table, based on our mathematical relationship.* As evidence, I have at my command a very extended experimental series, which I shall communicate in "Methods of Measurement." We will encounter some of these data in Chapters IX and XII.

Thus this matter can be presented in a purely practical way, so that anyone, even without insight into the reasons for the rules which must be applied and even without a mathematical background, will be able to make use of this method to make measurements. He will also be able to do this with confidence, for its mathematical derivation has had the benefit of a check by a famous mathematical authority and the check by experience has also been decisive.

Formulation and Mathematical Derivation
of the Computational Rules for the Method of Right
and Wrong Cases

There exists as yet no a priori principle that determines how the ratio r/n should vary with the magnitude of the standard weight P, when the additional weight D is held constant. Rather, this should be looked upon as a matter for a law that should be determined experimentally. It is possible, on the other hand, to state a priori, according to the principles of probability, how the ratio r/n must vary (assuming a large n) when the standard weight P is held constant and the added weight is varied (with differential sensitivity h remaining the same), or if, in general, anything is changed that determines the apparent gain in weight, which will be represented here once and for all by D. The same principles hold

---

* Since the differential sensitivity with which we are concerned varies with P (but not with D as long as D remains small), experiments under the same conditions of sensitivity call for constant P.

good in this case as those by which one can determine the variation of the relative number of errors of observation with a change in their magnitude, assuming constant precision of observation. The relationship of r/n to Dh with which we are concerned cannot, however, be represented by a finite expression, but has to be expressed as an integral, which for practical purposes must be tabulated, as has been done below.

The integral expression, designated from now on by Θ, which comes into play here is the same as that which expresses the relative number or probability of errors within the limits of a given magnitude. The only exception is that half the weight increment $D/2$ is substituted for the error term usually designated by Δ. We write

$$\Theta = \frac{2}{\sqrt{\pi}} \int_0^t e^{-t^2}dt$$

where π is Ludolf's number[2], e the base of natural logarithms, $t = h\Delta = hD/2$, and h the measure of precision in Gauss' sense. The value of t corresponding to a given Θ is tabulated in various places, such as in the *Berlin astronom. Jahrb.* for 1834, pages 305 ff, to $t = 2.0$; as well as in a special lithographed table, now out of print, to $t = 3.0$. Therefore, given Θ corresponding to r/n one can consider t or $hD/2$ determined at the same time.

We will now proceed immediately to prove the following equations, which are fundamental to our method and by which Θ can be derived from r/n.

$$\frac{r}{n} = \frac{1+\Theta}{2}; \frac{f}{n} = \frac{1-\Theta}{2}; \frac{r}{f} = \frac{1+\Theta}{1-\Theta}$$

and therefore

$$\frac{2r}{n} - 1 = 1 - \frac{2f}{n} = \Theta$$

It is sufficient to consider only the relationship between r/n and Θ as follows. One derives the value of Θ from the observed r/n by means of the equation $(2r/n) - 1 = \Theta$, looks up the corresponding value of $t = hD/2$ in a table of the integral Θ, and then divides this value by $D/2$ in order to find h. Alternatively, one may divide by D, if one takes h in the method of right and wrong cases to be only one half as large as it is in the method of errors (as we shall proceed to do). In order to avoid the separate conversion of the observed value of r/n into the value of $(2r/n) - 1$ for each observation, I have converted the table of the integral Θ, which gives the relationship between $\Theta = (2r/n) - 1$ and t, to read directly in r/n and t. The fundamental table given is derived in this way.

---

[2] Trans. Note: Ludolph (or Ludolf) van Ceulen, 1540–1610. Dutch mathematician; professor of fortification at Leiden; known for computations of the value of π (Ludolphian or Ludolph's number), which he finally carried to 35 decimal places. In Fechner's time the decimal equivalent of π was in general referred to as Ludolph's number.

The mathematical derivation of the relationship of r/n and Θ has passed the inspection of Professor [A. F.] Möbius [1790–1868], to whom I had presented it, and can accordingly be considered mathematically unobjectionable. He has also done me the favor of substituting a briefer and more precise derivation for my somewhat clumsy one, which in the end leads to the same results. I shall therefore prefer to give his in what follows, rather than mine.

Möbius' derivation uses as an example the deviation of two parts of a straight line from equality rather than the difference of two weights. The principle is the same in one case as in the other.

In general let

$$\frac{2}{\sqrt{\pi}} \int_0^{h\Delta} e^{-t^2} dt$$

be the probability that the error of measurement falls between $-\Delta$ and $+\Delta$, where h represents, as before, the precision of measurement, and π is Ludolf's number.

Now let, for example,

$$A \qquad C \qquad B$$

be three points on a straight line, with C being close to, but not quite at, the mid-point between A and B. In n observations by the method of right and wrong cases I judge a times that C is closer to A than to B, therefore that $CB > CA$. I also judge $n - a = b$ times that C is closer to B than to A and therefore $CB < CA$. The probabilities for $CA < CB$ and $CB < CA$ vary, accordingly, as a and b, and the two probabilities themselves are a/n and b/n.

If we now let

$$A \qquad CM \qquad B$$

represent the line with M the true mid-point between A and B, and C displaced a little from M toward A, then my judgment had been correct a times and I had been in error b times. I have, in other words, believed the point C to lie between M and B b times. In each of these b estimates my assumption of the point's position was in error by more than the small segment CM beyond M and in the direction of B. I have therefore committed an error, $> CM$, in one direction each time. The probability of this error on the one hand $= b/n$ and on the other hand

$$= \frac{1}{\sqrt{\pi}} \int_{hCM}^{\infty} e^{-t^2} dt$$

where CM is to be taken as positive. Now

$$\frac{1}{\sqrt{\pi}} \int_0^{hCM} \cdots + \frac{1}{\sqrt{\pi}} \int_{hCM}^{\infty} \cdots = \frac{1}{2}$$

therefore

$$\frac{1}{\sqrt{\pi}} \int_0^{hCM} \cdots + \frac{b}{n} = \frac{1}{2}$$

and it follows that

$$\frac{1}{\sqrt{\pi}} \int_0^{hCM} \cdots = \frac{1}{2} - \frac{b}{n} = \frac{1}{2} - 1 + \frac{a}{n} = \frac{a}{n} - \frac{1}{2}$$

Finally, therefore:

$$\frac{a}{n} = \frac{1}{2} + \frac{1}{\sqrt{\pi}} \int_0^{hCM} \cdots = \frac{1}{\sqrt{\pi}} \int_{-\infty}^{hCM} \cdots = \frac{1}{\sqrt{\pi}} \int_{-hCM}^{\infty} \cdots$$

$$\frac{b}{n} = \frac{1}{2} - \frac{1}{\sqrt{\pi}} \int_0^{hCM} \cdots = \frac{1}{\sqrt{\pi}} \int_{hCM}^{\infty} \cdots = \frac{1}{\sqrt{\pi}} \int_{-\infty}^{-hCM} \cdots$$

These two expressions for a/n and b/n could also be explained as follows: in n observations of the line $ACMB$, of which only points A and B are visible, one believes in a cases that M lies somewhere between C and B (which is correct), and in b cases (falsely), that M lies somewhere between A and C. The limits of integration, however, which are $-hCM$ and ∞ for a/n and $-\infty$ and $-hCM$ for b/n, relate to these same two segments CB and AC. For if we take the direction $ACMB$ as positive and M as the origin, the abscissas of C and B become $-CM$ and MB, and the abscissas of A and C become $-AM$ and $-CM$ respectively. AM and MB, however, can be considered as infinite compared to CM.

So goes the Möbius derivation.

In order to convert the example using lines to an example using weights one will have to substitute the weight of P for AC and $P + D$ for BC. The length $AM = (AC + BC)/2$ now becomes $P + (D/2)$, the segment CM consequently corresponds to $D/2$, and $D/2$ therefore should be substituted for CM in the above expressions. Further, a/n is equal to our r/n, and b/n equals our f/n, leading to the following expressions for direct application to our method:

$$\frac{r}{n} = \frac{1}{2} + \frac{1}{\sqrt{\pi}} \int_0^{hD/2} e^{-t^2} dt$$

$$\frac{f}{n} = \frac{1}{2} - \frac{1}{\sqrt{\pi}} \int_0^{hD/2} e^{-t^2} dt$$

or if we denote the integral

$$\frac{2}{\sqrt{\pi}} \int_0^{hD/2} e^{-t^2} dt$$

by Θ for short,

$$\frac{r}{n} = \frac{1+\Theta}{2}; \frac{f}{n} = \frac{1-\Theta}{2}; \Theta = \frac{2r}{n} - 1 = 1 - \frac{2f}{n}$$

The previously mentioned fact that we take the measure of precision or sensitivity h of our method as equal to half the measure of precision of error theory, does not influence the applications within the scope of our methods, since only the relative values or t or h matter in this case. They would have to be considered, though, in case one would want to compare the absolute values of results by the method of right and wrong cases with those obtained by the method of average error, as might be done by means of the integral Θ. The same would be true for a priori calculation of the probable error or the variability of r/n or t, which does not concern us here, however.

Let us now turn to practical matters:

The procedure with which we are concerned consists simply in looking up in the following table, which I call the fundamental table of the method of right and wrong cases, the value of $t = hD$ corresponding to the experimentally determined fraction r/n (interpolating, if the value of r/n cannot be found exactly in the table). This number is then divided by D in order to determine the value of h, the desired measure of sensitivity, or one can also use the value of $t = hD$ found in this way directly for measurement, when D is constant, which is very convenient in many cases.

This rule is sufficient when no constant influences (except for the constant weight increment D) are present that could determine the judgment of the heavier weight or when these influences are already compensated by the experimental design when r/n is being determined. Where this is not the case, the constant sources of error enter into the value of t, which now depends no longer on h and D alone (where D refers only to the added weight), but also on these extraneous sources. The simple division of t by D can then naturally not allow us to find h correctly, and the value of t cannot be used instead of h as a comparable measure, even if D is constant, when these secondary sources of variability do not remain constant with D. Even then, however, a properly arranged procedure with suitable use of the fundamental table presents the simplest way of correction. I shall deal with this case separately later.

Notes: (1) Since only ratios of t or h are concerned, I am in the habit of using the numbers of the tabulated values of t as whole numbers instead of decimals. Future citation of values calculated from this table will always take this form. (2) It is only necessary to tabulate the values of r/n greater than 0.5. Should values of r/n smaller than 0.5 occur, as happens frequently under given experimental conditions when D is not too large in one of the principal cases to be discussed below, one must look up $f/n = (n - r)/n$ instead of r/n, in the column headed r/n in the table and enter the corresponding value of t with negative sign in the equations determining hD, hp, and hq, as will be shown later. (3) The table lists for $r/n = 1$ (that is, the contingency where all cases are right) an infinite value for t. Strictly speaking, this assumes an infinite number of observations. One should, in general, make D small enough and n large enough so that this case does not occur.

FUNDAMENTAL TABLE FOR THE METHOD OF RIGHT AND WRONG CASES

r/n	$t = hD$	Diff.	r/n	$t = hD$	Diff.	r/n	$t = hD$	Diff.
0.50	0.0000		0.71	0.3913		0.91	0.9481	
0.51	0.0177	177	0.72	0.4121	208	0.92	0.9936	455
0.52	0.0355	178	0.73	0.4333	212	0.93	1.0436	500
0.53	0.0532	177	0.74	0.4549	216	0.94	1.0994	558
0.54	0.0710	178	0.75	0.4769	220	0.95	1.1631	637
0.55	0.0890	180	0.76	0.4994	225	0.96	1.2379	748
0.56	0.1068	178	0.77	0.5224	230	0.97	1.3297	918
0.57	0.1247	179	0.78	0.5460	236	0.98	1.4531	1234
0.58	0.1428	181	0.79	0.5702	242	0.99	1.6438	1907
0.59	0.1609	181	0.80	0.5951	249	1.00	∞	∞
0.60	0.1791	182	0.81	0.6208	257			
0.61	0.1974	183	0.82	0.6473	265			
0.62	0.2160	186	0.83	0.6747	274			
0.63	0.2347	187	0.84	0.7032	285			
0.64	0.2535	188	0.85	0.1329	297			
0.65	0.2725	190	0.86	0.7639	310			
0.66	0.2917	192	0.87	0.7965	326			
0.67	0.3111	194	0.88	0.8308	343			
0.68	0.3307	196	0.89	0.8673	365			
0.69	0.3506	199	0.90	0.9062	389			
0.70	0.3708	202			419			
		205						

One makes use of the fundamental table most conveniently by taking $n = 100$ once and for all, that is, one determines r separately each time for 100 cases. Longer series are divided into parts of 100 each and the t values for each part are later added separately and averaged, since this treatment by parts is necessary or useful in any case for other reasons. All that is then necessary is to cross out the zero and decimal point in the r/n column in order to find the experimentally derived r's directly. One can save oneself not only the division to form r/n, but also the need for interpolation, since one can find all experimental values of r exactly tabulated.

If one chooses n different from 100, one will always run across values of r/n that cannot be found exactly in the fundamental table. One can then determine the corresponding t's easily by simple interpolation with the aid of the difference in the difference column, whereby one can miss only by about one to two units in the last decimal of the t value, up to an r/n of approximately 0.85. This error is unimportant, since the fourth decimal in this kind of observation can be regarded as a luxury in any case. With

SUPPLEMENTARY TABLE I

r/n	$t = hD$	Diff.	r/n	$t = hD$	Diff.	r/n	$t = hD$	Diff.
0.8300	0.6747		0.8825	0.8397		0.9300	1.0436	
0.8325	0.6817	70	0.8850	0.8488	91	0.9325	1.0569	133
0.8350	0.6888	71	0.8875	0.8580	92	0.9350	1.0706	137
0.8375	0.6960	72	0.8900	0.8673	93	0.9375	1.0848	142
0.8400	0.7032	72	0.8925	0.8768	95	0.9400	1.0994	146
0.8425	0.7105	73	0.8950	0.8864	96	0.9425	1.1145	151
0.8450	0.7179	74	0.8975	0.8962	98	0.9450	1.1301	156
0.8475	0.7253	74	0.9000	0.9062	100	0.9475	1.1463	162
0.8500	0.7329	76	0.9025	0.9164	102	0.9500	1.1631	168
0.8525	0.7405	76	0.9050	0.9267	103	0.9525	1.1806	175
0.8550	0.7482	77	0.9075	0.9373	106	0.9550	1.1988	182
0.8575	0.7560	78	0.9100	0.9481	108	0.9575	1.2179	191
0.8600	0.7639	79	0.9125	0.9591	110	0.9600	1.2379	200
0.8625	0.7719	80	0.9150	0.9703	112	0.9625	1.2590	211
0.8650	0.7800	81	0.9175	0.9818	115	0.9650	1.2812	222
0.8675	0.7882	82	0.9200	0.9936	118	0.0675	1.3048	236
0.8700	0.7965	83	0.9225	1.0056	120	0.9700	1.3297	249
0.8725	0.8049	84	0.9250	1.0179	123	0.9725	1.3569	272
0.8750	0.8134	85	0.9275	1.0306	127	0.9750	1.3859	290
0.8775	0.8221	87			130	0.9775	1.4175	316
0.8800	0.8308	87						
		89						

larger values of r/n, however, one would commit a greater error in this interpolation, the larger these values become. I append, therefore, a few supplementary tables to augment the last part of the table wherein the

SUPPLEMENTARY TABLE II

r/n	$t = hD$	Diff.	r/n	$t = hD$	Diff.	r/n	$t = hD$	Diff.
0.970	1.3297		0.980	1.4522		0.990	1.6450	
0.971	1.3404	107	0.981	1.4672	150	0.991	1.6728	278
0.972	1.3513	109	0.982	1.4828	156	0.992	1.7032	304
0.973	1.3625	112	0.983	1.4991	163	0.993	1.7375	343
0.974	1.3740	115	0.984	1.5164	173	0.994	1.7764	389
0.975	1.3859	119	0.985	1.5345	181	0.995	1.8214	450
0.976	1.3982	123	0.986	1.5537	192	0.996	1.8753	539
0.977	1.4110	128	0.987	1.5742	205	0.997	1.9430	677
0.978	1.4242	132	0.988	1.5961	219	0.998	2.0352	922
0.979	1.4380	138	0.989	1.6195	234	0.999	2.1851	1499
		142			265	1.000	∞	∞

values of r/n are more closely spaced, and with the aid of these one will have a sufficient basis in any case for further interpolation.

In itself there is no special advantage to the number $n = 100$. I have personally always based myself on $n = 64$ rather than $n = 100$. I have divided all my longer experimental series into parts with $n = 64$, added the t values of these parts separately, and used these sums and the means derived from them. My reason was that 64, as a power of 2, could be broken into a greater number of subdivisions than 100, and I had wanted at first to keep the way open for any kind of partitioning. Later I stayed with this number in order to make all series comparable in this respect, since, as will be noted later, the size of n which is used as a base exerts a certain influence on the magnitude of the measurements and should be kept comparable throughout. The fundamental table I normally used is therefore arranged for r corresponding to $n = 64$ in order to avoid the necessity of transforming the fraction r/n into a decimal and interpolating, as was described for the earlier tables. It is added below in case others would like to make use of the same base.

FUNDAMENTAL TABLE
$n = 64$

r	$t = hD$	r	$t = hD$
33	0.0277	49	0.5123
34	0.0555	50	0.5490
35	0.0833	51	0.5873
36	0.1112	52	0.6273
37	0.1394	53	0.6695
38	0.1677	54	0.7142
39	0.1964	55	0.7619
40	0.2253	56	0.8134
41	0.2547	57	0.8696
42	0.2844	58	0.9320
43	0.3147	59	1.0026
44	0.3456	60	1.0848
45	0.3772	61	1.1851
46	0.4095	62	1.3172
47	0.4427	63	1.5231
48	0.4769	64	∞

In order to handle my longer series conveniently, either as a whole or in larger parts, for purposes of comparison with the fractional treatment, I also constructed a table for $n = 512$, since all my series consisted of multiples of 64 cases, and 64 is $\frac{1}{8}$ of 512. Tables for $n = 64$, 2×64, or 4×64 also can be derived directly therefrom. By referring back to the table of the integral Θ cited on page [86] and by means of the equation relating r/n and Θ given on page [86], the expert will in any case be able to design tables for any base n (with the help of interpolation) without trouble. One would do well in any case, whichever base n may be chosen, to keep to the same number for all experiments. Longer series may be broken into parts of the same length and one would arrange one's table for this number once and for all.

One can make use of the fundamental table also to infer from a ratio r/n, found with a given D and P, the D which would be necessary to produce any other r/n wanted, provided the sensitivity h and, therefore, P stay constant (since h varies with P but not with D). It would merely be necessary to enter the table with the other r/n and seek the corresponding t. We can then form the following proportion: the $t = hD$ of one is to $t = hD$ of the other as one D is to the other. Conversely, one could find the values of r/n belonging to a known D from the table, given a value of D, as long as h remains constant. However, our method does not easily lead to these applications in practice, since in the end everything depends on the determination of h, or sometimes only t, as explained above.

One should not forget that this simple use of the table, as I have explained, takes place only under the conditions given, namely that the estimate of the apparently heavier weight depends only on D, apart from chance. In reality it depends also on the constant influence of temporal and spatial factors. Actually the tabulated value of t is, in this case, not merely hD, but $h(D + M)$, where M is the algebraic sum of all constant influences besides D that also determine the choice of the apparently heavier weight. Taking this factor into account, our practical task consists of combining the tests and their evaluations in such a way that we compensate for M and always come back to the same value hD that we would have found without the presence of these outside sources, by the previously mentioned simple use of the table.

As far as procedure is concerned, our normal method of execution, as we have noted, is planned with this purpose in mind. The heavier weight is switched in completely systematic manner between the four principal cases of the disparate temporal or spatial orders: (1) where it is in the left container and is lifted first; (2) where it is in the left container and is lifted second; (3) and (4) the corresponding cases for the right container. We have then, in order to keep the four principal cases clearly apart, the heavier weight:

1. At the left in the container lifted first
2. At the left in the container lifted second
3. At the right in the container lifted first
4. At the right in the container lifted second

In brief I term these four principal cases in the order given:

$$I>, II>, I<, II<$$

The numbers of right choices, added separately for each case, become

$$r_1, r_2, r_3, r_4$$

and the corresponding values of t from the table, (which can no longer be equated simply with hD) derived by forming the quotient with n, become

$$t_1, t_2, t_3, t_4$$

assuming the same n for all principal conditions.

It is easy to see that M can be compensated completely if one adds the t's of the four main cases and then divides by four. One arrives thus at

$$hD = \frac{t_1 + t_2 + t_3 + t_4}{4}$$

and division by D will yield, as before, the pure value of h. Again, as long as D is constant, one also could use hD or $4hD$ themselves as measurements.

This manner of completely compensating for the effect of M is based on the following arguments. According to the discussion on page [75], the temporal order of lifting and the spatial position of the containers influence the determination of the apparently heavier weight. I shall call the effect due to temporal sequence p, that due to spatial location q. With opposite temporal and spatial order, p and q take opposite signs. Which sign we wish to adopt for a given position is arbitrary, as long as we use the opposite for the opposite position. If we take p and q as positive for the first case, then M has the values $+p$ and $+q$ for the first, $-p + q$ for the second, $+p - q$ for the third, and $-p - q$ for the fourth of our four principal conditions. The following values hold, therefore, for the four main cases of $t = h(D + M)$:

$$t_1 = h(D + p + q)$$

$$t_2 = h(D - p + q)$$

$$t_3 = h(D + p - q)$$

$$t_4 = h(D - p - q)$$

Addition of these four values and division by four equals hD. The addition of the first and fourth (as well as the second and third) equation followed by division by two is also sufficient by itself to allow us to find hD.

The same equations are suited to the calculation of hp and hq by addition and subtraction, and thus of values for p and q. One first forms:

$$hp = \frac{t_1 - t_2 + t_3 - t_4}{4}$$

$$hq = \frac{t_1 + t_2 - t_3 - t_4}{4}$$

By dividing these values of hp and hq by the previously calculated value for

$$hD = \frac{t_1 + t_2 + t_3 + t_4}{4}$$

one obtains the ratios of p and q to D, and by multiplication of these ratios by D, the values of p and q in grams, when D is itself expressed in grams. Each hp and hq, as well as each hD, can also be determined in two ways by means of t's from two of the principal cases, and the agreement of the values so obtained can serve as a check.

Depending on the direction in which they are acting, p and q could turn out to have negative as well as positive signs in this procedure, so that their directions as well as their magnitudes are being determined simultaneously. The meaning of the sign must be interpreted by the way p and q were introduced into the basic equations.

The definitive solution of this whole question, as well as secondary points raised by it, leads then to the determination of h, p, and q by means of the following equations:

$$h = \frac{t_1 + t_2 + t_3 + t_4}{4D}$$

$$p = \frac{t_1 - t_2 + t_3 - t_4}{t_1 + t_2 + t_3 + t_4}D$$

$$q = \frac{t_1 + t_2 - t_3 - t_4}{t_1 + t_2 + t_3 + t_4}D$$

Of course, one frequently can compare measurements stopping at computation of hD, hp, hq, or $4hD$, $4hp$, $4hq$, by combining results from a number of parts with some larger multiple of those values, so long as the same number is used throughout, as the well informed can easily see.

All my determinations of differential sensitivity in weight lifting, which I shall describe later (in Chapters IX and XII), were obtained in this manner. It eliminates the effects of p and q completely and at the same time makes it possible to obtain an accurate determination of these effects. The results cited there may serve in more than one way to explain and substantiate what I have said here in general on this matter. A complete and better organized discussion of this subject will be offered in "Methods of Measurement".

In the future, when reference has to be made to signs, I shall, in agreement with the choice of signs made on page [94], take p, the influence of temporal order of lifting, as positive when the weight that is lifted first appears heavier. I shall call it negative if the second container, independently of D, appears as the heavier. I shall call the effect of the spatial factors positive, when the left-hand container appears as heavier, and negative when the right-hand container appears heavier. If I say, for example, that the influence of p was $+10$ gm, this means that, apart from the truly heavier weight, the first container appeared 10 gm heavier than the second one. Chapter XII will give us an opportunity to cite such determinations.

Even if temporal and spatial relationships stay the same, p and q may change due to internal causes, since these objective conditions can only be considered in terms of their subjective manner of appearance, which, due to unknown reasons, is highly variable.

The effect of p and q may vary considerably due to external and internal conditions. The sum total of my experiments, made under all kinds of different conditions, indicates without exception that the effect on p of heavier main weights or previous fatigue of the arms, with one-handed as well as with two-handed procedures, is to change it in the negative direction, that is, to cause p to take on lesser positive or greater negative values, or to change from a positive to a negative value. They further indicate that p and q have greater positive and lesser negative values for the right hand than the left hand in the one-handed procedure under otherwise identical conditions. They indicate finally that the magnitude and direction of these effects does not depend essentially on the size of D. Further details will not have to be considered here.

One could also try to compensate for the effect of p and q by adding the r's of the four principal conditions before calculating the t's and deriving from the over-all r/n, by means of the fundamental table, a common t that one can set equal to hD. This procedure may be satisfactory at times, but will be called incomplete compensation by me, since, as will be shown, by this method one cannot truly get back to the exact value of hD (and therefore of h) which would have been obtained in the absence of these effects.

Let us assume, for example, that the effect p operates in favor of the weight which is lifted second. Let us also exaggerate by assuming that this effect is extraordinarily, even infinitely, large. It is obvious that the addition of a finite D to one of the containers would be quite without influence on the judgment, and the container which is lifted second would always appear to be heavier. Then if the container with D is lifted as often first as it is second (as happens in our experiments) and if the cases obtained under these two orders are added together, as one might be tempted to do assuming that the influence of p is thereby eliminated, one will find that the number of right and wrong cases will turn out to be equal, just as if the sensitivity for differences in weight were zero, a case in which one would also obtain an equal number of right and wrong cases. The sensitivity for D seems to be swamped, so to speak, by the effect of this factor. If, on the other hand, the effect of the time sequence of lifting did not exist, D would make itself equally felt under both temporal conditions. It would then determine a preponderance of right cases (in proportion to its magnitude and to the state of sensitivity) with respect to the container in which it is placed. Thus one cannot consider the addition of right cases of opposite temporal sequences as equivalent to the case where there is no effect due to temporal sequence at all. Clearly the more closely one approaches this extreme, the stronger the effect of this factor. Whatever is true of p in this respect is also true of q and of the simultaneous presence of both factors. Our procedure of complete compensation, on the other hand, in which the number of r's is used separately to derive the t's for the various cases, will correctly lead to the same result with respect to hD as if there were no effect of p and q, since this effect is eliminated by this arrangement.

It can easily be seen that, just as the influence of D can vanish compared to p or q, so it must also be possible for the reverse to take place. When D is very large, the influence neither of the order of lifting nor of the position of the hand can be felt, but judgment is determined only by the position of D. As long as D is found equally often in contrasting temporal and spatial conditions, as is the case in our procedure, the number of cases in the first and second position or the right and left hand must be equally large or approach this equality with increasing D.

Although this relationship is easily shown theoretically, I must confess that I have only been led to it by experience, since with heavy standard weights the influence of p became sometimes so large that the swamping of D we have mentioned became noticeable in the experiments, even without calculations. When computation was completed the lawful relationships of differential sensitivity appeared considerably altered, since formerly I always added the right cases belonging to different temporal and spatial conditions before calculating the t values.

As can easily be seen, a procedure consisting of repeatedly lifting the containers in alternation (p. [78]), which does not allow separation of the four principal conditions, can only have this incomplete compensation as an outcome.

One might, moreover, dispense with a completely compensating procedure when concerned only with judgments of "more," "less," or "equal" and not with a true measure of differential sensitivity, and when one need assume no important changes, or nearly none, in the effects of p and q during the course of the investigation. In that case, of course, one would not only combine all four principal conditions, but would also consider it unnecessary first to transform the number directly into t values, since the same—or a larger or smaller—number of r's for a specified n with a given D would then show an equal, greater, or lesser differential sensitivity. One should not forget, of course, that this procedure remains dependent on the constancy of the effects of p and q. As has already been mentioned, any considerable amount of regular constant effects acting in opposite directions has the same consequence as considerable irregular chance fluctuations (see p. [65]), that is, it diminishes the number right (r). Therefore if the same, or even greater, differential sensitivity were to exist, the combined number r of the four principal conditions may still turn out to be less, when constant effects are larger, and therefore may give rise to false results, which would vanish only under complete compensation. Because of the great variability of influences due to inner causes (see p. [96]), even under carefully controlled comparability of external conditions, we can never be completely sure that the results to be compared have really been found under comparable circumstances. Complete compensation (that is, the separation of the four principal conditions and then translation to t values) will, while more bothersome, always guarantee greater confidence, and the mere comparison of r's can only serve for rough estimates and preliminary determinations.

The systematic employment of the same number of observations and regular alternation between the four principal conditions, without which an exact elimination and determination of the constant effects p and q cannot be made, presupposes regular changes in the position of the additional weight and constant knowledge of its position. This knowledge would necessarily influence the judgment in the first procedure given on page [78], where every determination that contributes to r is made only after repeated lifting back and forth of the container. This influence is absent in the second method, where each pair of weights lifted affects r, since one knows that this result also is determined by random effects and the spatial and temporal positions of the containers. The knowledge of the position of D therefore cannot be used for conjectures concerning a specific outcome in a pair of weight lifts, but one is obliged to go by the objective evidence of the senses. This opinion is confirmed by examining my tables of results. The results of single judgments are seen to be quite irregularly distributed and on the whole determined by the effects of p and q as often as (and sometimes more than) by the position of D. In fact, the number of wrong cases in many series greatly outnumbers the right cases under some of the principal conditions, in spite of what might be expected because of the known position of D.

Accordingly we may eliminate the assistant with this second method, although he was indispensable in the first procedure, where he had to change the position of the added weight without the observer's knowledge. In fact his presence now is not permissible, since a steady personal check on the position of the additional weight and undisturbed even attention during the course of the lifting of the weights is essential in this procedure.

As I had carried out experiments following the first procedure for some months, carefully keeping myself in ignorance of the position of the added weight, before going over to the second procedure, involving knowledge of its position, I am now well able to compare both methods. Certainly I would not have stopped at the second procedure, had I not been sufficiently convinced that the necessary knowledge of the position of the additional weight, entailed by this procedure, was without danger.

Should anyone find these explanations insufficient to exclude suspicion of the part played by conjecture in my experiments as they were carried out according to this procedure, I must refer them to "Methods of Measurement," where a more detailed exposition both of the nature of this experimental method and of the method itself, together with its results, should counter this suspicion effectively. In any case I could allow objections on these grounds only after careful personal checks of the procedures.

For purposes of computation I regularly divide the experimental series not only into the four principal conditions, but also, it should be noted, into parts according to time periods and other circumstances. In this way each single t value is based on 64 simple weight lifts or cases, which are then combined as sums or averages, instead of deriving the t of each principal condition from the total n. The reasons for this procedure have been referred to many times in a general way and will be discussed in detail in my "Methods of Measurement."

Of course calculations of this kind become rather clumsy, especially for longer series. However, they reduce harmful variations due to constant effects.

One should also take into account the fact that the value of hD derived from partial results is somewhat greater, on the average, than that calculated from the total—and the more so, the smaller the fractions that have been taken. Theoretical reasons for this fact may be given, but I shall omit them for the present. All derivations should therefore be made from partial runs having the same n, in order to keep these values comparable, and the n used should be mentioned. In my own results, which I shall quote later, this n was always 64, with regard to simple lifts, unless expressly stated otherwise.

There are also practical hints regarding the magnitude of D (which one should properly make neither too small nor too large), the testing of the significance of the results, and some other minor points, whose discussion I shall save for the "Methods of Measurement."

e. The Method of Average Error, Applied to Visual Span and Touch

In respect of the experiments, note that in judging distances visually it is better to use parallel threads or tips or distant points, rather than near compass points, to mark off the distances which are to be estimated, in order to avoid bringing into play the angles formed by the legs of a compass, unless these themselves are supposed to form the object of the experiment.

In experiments on touch I use compasses with a handle, fitted with points made from English sewing needles. I hold the compass by the handle during the experiments.* The tips are blunted very lightly or not at all, so that the distance can be determined exactly on a ruler with transverse lines. The tips are applied only gently and irritation is avoided. Most of these experiments on touch were made by myself, but for purposes of comparison I have also had an assistant apply the compass. In this case I have found smaller constant errors, but much larger variable errors, because of the less uniform application of the compass by other

---

* Using a compass without a handle and holding it by the legs when applying it to oneself results in both greater constant and greater variable error, according to some comparisons I have made myself.

hands, which gives rise to a greater play of chance. I shall discuss immediately how to keep these errors separate.

The standard distance is the length that is kept constant in estimating visual or tactual extents. The variable distance is the extent, generally somewhat in error, that is estimated to be equal to it. The difference between a variable distance and standard distance results in what I call raw error and denote by δ to distinguish it from the pure error Δ.

As noted on page [75], the average error in extent, as derived from many observations, generally deviates considerably from the standard distance, and sums of the positive and negative raw errors are not equal to each other in absolute value. One tends to be greater than the other by a considerable amount. To take this circumstance into account properly I regard the deviation of the averaged errors from the standard distance as constant error and the deviation of a single judgment from the average as the pure variable error. Consideration of both these errors is substituted for consideration of the raw error. Since each raw error is composed algebraically of the constant and a pure variable error, I call them both components of the raw error. I denote a constant error by c, a pure variable error by Δ, and the sum of pure errors for a given experimental series or fraction thereof by $\Sigma\Delta$. Only pure error is to be used to measure differential sensitivity and only from it, not from raw error, can the average error that serves to measure it be derived. Constant error depends on the constant effect of temporal and spatial position of the magnitudes to be compared, and also on the way in which subjective conditions affect the judgment.

The necessity of breaking up the raw error into its components springs from both mathematical and theoretical reasons, which I discuss in "Methods of Measurement." There are also mathematical relationships between raw error and its components that are useful to know when making use of this method. This subject also will be discussed in "Methods of Measurement," as I shall limit myself here to discussing only the most essential details of the method.

It is of fundamental importance to realize the essential independence of variable error and constant error as shown by experiments. When the distances being compared change relative position or sequence and the constant errors therefore are reversed, the raw sum of the errors may often turn out to be quite different in the two cases, but one actually obtains the same sum for the pure errors. There would be an exception if these effects were accompanied by different average irregular chance effects, but in our experience this is not frequently the case. Accordingly, it often does not seem necessary to repeat the comparison of distances by reversing position and sequence in order to determine only the variable error, although this liberty is not allowable when we are concerned with the determination of the constant errors. By combining the values obtained under different conditions of position and sequence in suitable ways, one can separate the different components according to their origin, as I show in more detail in "Methods of Measurement" and as is obvious to the expert. This procedure corresponds essentially to the one that served to determine separately the effects of p and q in the method of right and wrong cases.

In judgment of visual extents one will have to distinguish (depending on whether these distances are horizontal or vertical) the right and left, or upper and lower, position of the standard distance as compared to the variable distance. In the case of experiments on touch, the compass for the standard stimulus is grasped with the right hand and the compass for the variable stimulus with the left and vice versa, or, if one carries out the experiment with one hand on the other and so must grasp both compasses in the same hand, one compass is grasped in the upper part and the other in the lower part of the hand and vice versa. In addition I have carried out experiments on touch with time as the variable, depending on whether the standard or the variable stimulus was applied first.

When forming the average error from the pure variable error one has the choice of two kinds of average error. One, which I term merely "average error" (or, in order to distinguish it especially from the following, "simple average error") and call ϵ, is derived by taking the simple average of the pure errors according to the equation

$$\epsilon = \frac{\Sigma \Delta}{m}$$

where m is the number of errors that contribute to $\Sigma\Delta$. The other, which astronomers call "average error," but which will be called here "quadratic average error,"[3] will be denoted by ϵ_q. It is calculated by squaring separately each singular error, dividing the sum of these squares $\Sigma\Delta^2$ by their number m, and taking the square root of this quotient, according to the equation

$$\epsilon_q = \sqrt{\frac{\Sigma\Delta^2}{m}}$$

[3]Trans. Note: This error is today called the standard deviation, but Fechner's term will be retained here.

In a word, it is the root of the mean square error. Both of these average errors have, if derived from a large number of errors, a constant ratio according to the laws of probability, which can be given by

$$\frac{\epsilon_q}{\epsilon} = \sqrt{\frac{\pi}{2}} = 1.2533\ldots$$

where π is Ludolf's number, so that the quadratic average error is almost exactly $\frac{5}{4}$ of the simple error. I have convinced myself by examining a great number of experimental series that experience corresponds very closely to these relationships, and that with a sufficiently large number of determinations only very small chance deviations from this normal condition are found. Proof of this relationship is given in "Methods of Measurement." One can also derive a proof from the results on visual distance judgments given in Chapter IX. Accordingly it seems immaterial whether one employs ϵ or ϵ_q. However, there is some choice based on the fact that ϵ is much less elaborate to calculate, while ϵ_q is somewhat more securely determined from the same number of observations, so that (according to the laws of probability) 114 observations are necessary to obtain an ϵ with the same degree of significance as an ϵ_q determined from 100 observations. I still believe, as the full discussion in "Methods of Measurement" will show, that practical reasons overwhelmingly favor ϵ, considering the rather large number of observations which our method invariably demands. These practical advantages compensate for the relatively small (and with large m negligible) advantage of the significance of ϵ_q. In any case, the choice remains open to all. Whenever results are determined from a given number of observations, one is equally justified in using the pure error sum $\Sigma\Delta$ directly for measurement, as in using ϵ, thus saving oneself division by m.

One should pay special consideration to the fact that the pure sum of deviations as well as the pure average error (whether ϵ or ϵ_q) will vary slightly in size, depending on whether the deviations from which they were calculated were based on the mean of the total number of deviations or whether this number had been divided into parts, the average error determined separately for each part, the pure error reckoned separately, and the results then summed or averaged together. This procedure would be analogous to the one discussed on page [100] with respect to the method of right and wrong cases and would be based on similar reasoning. In general, with everything else the same, the sum of the deviations and the average error become larger, the less one has resorted to division into parts. For example, the sum is larger when one calculates the pure sum of deviations from 100 raw deviations as a whole, than when one divides these 100 raw deviations first into two parts of 50 each, calculates the sum of deviations separately for each part, and then combines these two. This sum will in turn be larger than if one had combined the results of four parts with 25 each, and so forth. However, this difference is trifling unless one reduces these divisions to fractions that are too small.

There are two reasons why this difference occurs. First, because of the small number of observations, the average deviation—and the corrected error calculated from it—would deviate from its true value, which is the value one would get under the same circumstances from an infinite number of observations. It can be proven by means of the theory of probability and confirmed by experience, that the mean square error always, and the simple average error generally (and always in a normal distribution) would be too small. The other reason arises from the variability of the constant error, which can never be quite excluded in longer series of experiments, thus causing the sum of deviations to become contaminated and enlarged, when observations that are subject to such variability are added together and used to derive the average error and the corrected error.

There is a correction that can be made for the first of these causes, which I call the correction for a finite m. By it the sum of deviations and the average error are treated as if the true average error had been determined from an infinite number of observations and used to calculate the corrected error. This correction has been applied for a long time to the quadratic average error when it is employed to determine the precision of physical and astronomical observations. It consists in expressing ϵ_q by

$$\sqrt{\frac{\Sigma\Delta^2}{m-1}}$$

instead of by

$$\sqrt{\frac{\Sigma\Delta^2}{m}}$$

One can immediately appreciate how this correction becomes less important and therefore how it becomes easier to neglect the larger m. The corresponding correction has not as yet been developed for the simple average error because there has been so far no practical use for it. I find that by reasoning analogous to that underlying the derivation of the correction of the mean square error, one can correct by multiplying

$$\epsilon = \frac{\Sigma\Delta}{m} \text{ by the factor } \frac{\pi m}{\pi m - 1}$$

where π is Ludolf's number. Somewhat simpler and still exactly enough, one could substitute

$$\frac{3m + 1}{3m},$$

an expression which approximates somewhat better than the more apparent expression

$$\frac{3m}{3m - 1}$$

as one can see by carrying out these calculations.*

An expert mathematician has done me the favor of checking the derivation of this correction, as will be discussed in "Methods of Measurement." The identical factor should be used to correct the sum of deviations of finite m when one stops with this sum, without calculating the average error ϵ from it. If an experimental series is treated in parts (that is, if the corrected errors are determined from the average errors of the specific parts) the correction for finite m should be applied to each part separately according to its m, not to the total number of observations of all subsets. Examples will be given in the fifth section of Chapter IX.

Where only determinations of relationships are concerned, one can save oneself the correction for finite m by using at all times the same m or by breaking up the series into runs with the same m, when different numbers of observations are made. In that case the reduction of the average error or the sum of the deviations due to a finite m would affect all runs to the same degree.

There is no correction possible for the second cause, but this error can be avoided by breaking up the total into a sufficient number of parts.

---

* Even the correction factor

$$\frac{\pi m}{\pi m - 1}$$

is only an approximation for an integral that cannot be expressed in finite form, but deviates only very slightly from it.

Since the first cause can be made harmless by a correction or by keeping to the same m throughout, I generally prefer a partial treatment to treating longer series as a whole, in order to render the second cause of error harmless. In my experiments on touch I have always broken down the runs to an m of 10 (resulting in a correction factor of $\frac{31}{30}$ for ϵ and $\Sigma\Delta$), and carried out the 10 observations in each run one directly after the other, when this could be done without too much irritation of the skin. (Some parts, particularly the forehead, do not tolerate so many experiments one after the other on the same place.)

In any case it will be necessary with the present procedure, as it was with the method of right and wrong cases, to mention when reporting results whether the run had been broken into parts and what m had been employed. In this connection I shall use m and μ with the method of average error in the same way as n and ν were used with the method of right and wrong cases. In other words, when the runs had been broken into parts, m stands for the number of observations in a single run, μ for the number of runs, so that μm represents the total observations. These will then contribute to the results applied to any one specific observed value, which would be made up of μ individual results.

Sums of deviations yielding a very small average error may make it necessary to consider two other corrections, which I call the correction for interval size and the correction for estimating the gradations. The first correction concerns the fact that recorded errors always are separated by given finite intervals, which vary with the size of the subdivisions on the ruler used to measure the errors, and that the subdivisions are estimated as decimals, which reduces the infinitely many intermediate errors to adjacent points on the scale. This fact influences the average error. The second correction relates to the fact that inaccuracies occur in measuring the errors themselves on the scale. The correction for the first factor rests on the purely mathematical principles of the theory of error and can be determined a priori. The second demands experimental investigation of the way errors of estimating the subdivisions of a particular unit on the scale behave. An interesting investigation of this factor is reported by Volkmann in the *Berichten der sächs. Soc.* for 1858, page 173. I shall abstain here from a discussion of these corrections since they can almost always be neglected.

Formulas and rules that make possible the determination of the significance of average errors and sums of deviations according to the number of observations are of greater importance than these corrections, as are rules by which the separately observed results can be combined to form the most probable over-all results. Anything that is necessary in this respect can be derived from the theory of probability and put into usable form for practice. An adequate explanation would necessitate preliminary discussions, which would lead us too far astray for the present, however.

Insightful handling of the method of average error demands in any case a knowledge of the chief points of the mathematical theory of errors, which is a branch of probability theory. I trust that I can explain the essentials in this respect in "Methods of Measurement" in such a way as to make it comprehensible even for someone who does not wish to immerse himself in this theory. Obviously I cannot do so here.

f. Mathematical Relationships of the Three Methods

One may question the relationship the measurements made by the three methods bear to one another. Let us assume that the just noticeable difference, the average error, and the ratio r/n (and thereby $t = hD$) had been determined in a given sense domain, and that differential sensitivity stayed constant. The question is: how will they be related to one another? The answer must be based on the following considerations.

Strictly speaking, the just noticeable difference is that difference which, when found in an application of the method of right and wrong cases, would give no wrong cases, but could not be made any smaller without resulting in some, for the fact that the difference is just noticeable implies its presence and therefore excludes any wrong case, and the fact that it is only just noticeable implies that it cannot be felt if the difference is made the least bit smaller. In reality, however, if one wants to avoid wrong cases with a given difference, one must make this difference large enough so that chance factors do not lower it below threshold. The size of this difference, and the number of wrong cases, among an overwhelming number of right cases, that one might permit and still consider the difference to be just noticeable, depend both on the average size of the relevant chance factors and on subjective estimates.

The average error, on the other hand, is necessarily smaller than the just noticeable difference, if no wrong cases are allowed or only admitted exceptionally. For with the method of average error, if a difference (for example, the separations of two compasses) is still noticeable, then this distance is changed until the difference is no longer noticeable. In general, all errors, starting with zero, that are smaller than the just noticeable difference, contribute to the determination of the average error. For these reasons no strong relationship between the just noticeable difference and the average error can be adduced.

Such a mathematical relationship does exist, however, between the method of right and wrong cases and the method of average error, tied together by the major probability integral. One can express by it the ratio of right to wrong cases that will be found when the size of the simple or of the quadratic average error is used to make up the difference D in the method of right and wrong cases, under otherwise comparable circumstances. The ratio r/n, as I shall show in "Methods of Measurement," will then amount to about $\frac{2}{3}$, or more exactly 0.655032, if the simple average error is used as the weight differential (the additional weight in weight-lifting experiments).

This theoretical relationship must still be proven experimentally, a test which might entail some difficulties, as the circumstances must be made comparable in such a way that chance factors can play the same role in both cases.

2. METHODS OF MEASURING ABSOLUTE SENSITIVITY

With respect to intensive sensations these methods are almost completely untried. Apart from a determination by Schafhäutl of the just audible absolute loudness, and the determinations by E. H. Weber and by Kammler of just noticeable pressure (which will be covered in detail in Chapter XI), I would not know what to cite here. In the area of visual sensations a pure determination of absolute sensitivity is not even possible, as an inner source of light sensation, which I treat in Chapter IX, cannot be eliminated.

On the other hand, methods of measuring absolute sensitivity have found wide application in the area of extensive sensations. Various people have occupied themselves with the determination of just noticeable magnitudes or distances on retina or skin. With respect to the latter we have particularly the well-known pioneer work in psychophysics by E. H. Weber on just noticeable distances on the skin. This method lends its name to one of the procedures that can be employed to measure absolute sensitivity, a procedure analogous to the method of just noticeable differences in measuring differential sensitivity. The other two methods of making these measurements also find their parallel in analogous measures of absolute sensitivity.

Volkmann bases his conclusions on the easily noticed observation that the separation of compass points which yields a just noticeable distance is not absolutely fixed, but varies within certain limits. In successive trials the same compass setting can sometimes be felt as separate, while at other times the tips cannot be experienced separately, as long as an upper limit is not exceeded—above which a separation is always felt as a distance—or a lower one, below which a separation is never felt. These limits, however, cannot be determined with absolute exactness, but this fact does not prevent us, as we have learned by experience, from finding comparable distances in various experiments. We can determine the modal value according to the method outlined above, by touching the skin with the compass points at varied settings to find a distance falling close to the upper limit, or we can determine a distance falling between the upper and lower limits as a just noticeable average distance to use as a base for our measurement. Were this not the case, Weber's experiments and the results confirmed by others would be impossible. A modification of Weber's method can be based on these observations, whereby the method becomes an analogue to the method of right and wrong cases, and indeed this has been done by Volkmann. It consists in (1) repeatedly applying a given compass separation between the afore-mentioned upper and lower limits, noting the outcome of each single application, and counting the number of cases where the separation is noted and not noted; (2) repeating this procedure with different compass separations within these limits. The greater the extensive sensitivity of the specific part of the skin, the larger would be the number of cases, for a given separation of the compass points, that in this instance take the place of the right cases (that is, where a real separation is also perceived as noticeable), and the smaller would be the separation that would still give the same number of right cases. One could use any given ratio of right cases to the total number of cases as a basis for comparison of sensitivity, by seeking the compass separations for different parts of the skin that give the same ratio. However, it might perhaps be best to use the ratio, preferred by Volkmann for this purpose, where the separation is noted as often as it is not noticed. Since the proper separations of the compass points cannot be achieved with absolute exactness one will have to determine them with sufficient precision by interpolation with separations close to the ones that were used in the experiment. Volkmann's experiments using this method, on the effect of practice on tactual sensitivity, are contained in the *Berichten der sächs. Soc.* for 1858, pages 47 ff. Their interesting results have well demonstrated the utility of this method.

Another variety of Weber's method, which I call the method of equivalents, has been used and developed by me in the area of touch, in connection with the method of average error, to which it is analogous. In the meantime, E. H. Weber had used the same methods even earlier in experiments on absolute sensitivity to pressure of different parts of the skin.*

This method, as applied to touch, essentially consists in alternately placing two compasses, A and B, on two different points of the skin, A and B, for comparison of their extensive sensitivity in place of applying one compass to one point of the skin. Keeping the same separation A of compass A on point A, one changes the separation B of compass B at point B until to the sense of touch the separation appears equal at both points. Actually, of course, they may be quite different depending on different degrees of sensitivity of different parts of the skin. In this way one obtains equivalents in terms of separations that are estimated as equally far apart for each part of the skin. Their reciprocal, determined from the mean of a large number of trials, can serve as a measure of extensive sensitivity.

One may easily satisfy oneself that this method is very sensitive and exact, since it yields very constant results of vanishingly small unreliability, so long as the points on the skin maintain the same relative degree of sensitivity. Their constancy can be shown by the comparison of the different partial results, while their reliability can be demonstrated by the easily calculated probable error of the mean of the results. Should the ratio of the results vary, however, the method permits an examination of these variations in detail. In experiments I have continued for months on the same parts I have actually seen the ratio maintained, when only a few trials were made every day. Just as definitely, however, often when many trials were carried out every day, generating a considerable practice effect, I have seen a gradual change of the equality of results, consisting in general in the less sensitive part approaching the more sensitive part, since practice apparently favored the former more than the latter.

Another advantage of this method over the two previous ones is that it is not confined to making comparisons of skin sensitivity limited to just noticeable distances, but permits comparisons with any given distance. On the other hand, there is the disadvantage that only relative data for absolute sensitivity are found, whereas the value of a just noticeable case (or of an equal number of noticeable and not-noticeable cases) results in a distance which can be regarded as a datum characterizing the absolute sensitivity of a given part of the skin in an absolute way. One will there-

---

* *Progr. coll.*, p. 97.

fore have to allow each of these methods to function in its own particular manner.

It is easy to see that the procedure chosen for the method of equivalents is essentially the same as that chosen for the method of average error, only the adjustment of the distance of the compass points is not made on the same, but on different, points on the skin, and one observes not the difference but the ratio of the magnitudes being compared. There is nothing to prevent us, however, from taking into account also the ratio of the distances being compared—that is, the standard distance and the variable distance—with the method of average error, nor, with the method of equivalents, from paying attention to the deviations of each B distance from the average B distance as if they were corrected Δ errors. According to these considerations the method of equivalents is essentially only a generalization of the method of average error, and it, in turn, a special case of the method of equivalents, where out of all possible places one could use as B to compare with an A, one chooses A itself, transforming A into the standard distance and B into the variable distance. The same effect also shows itself in that the relationship of the constant error and the corrected variable error of the method of average error is found again in the method of equivalents, only in a more general way. Just as in the case of the method of average error, the method of equivalents, therefore, demands various considerations and precautions that relate to the former method.

Particularly essential is the reversal of every comparison. When one has, for example, established the equivalent of B (lips) to A (chin), one must determine by an equal number of trials the complementary equivalent of B (chin) to A (lips). Each result should be recorded separately but then averaged in order to avoid a one-sided result suffering from constant error. My "Methods of Measurement" will bring sufficient proof and explanation of how essential this precaution is. The magnitude of the constant error can in this case also be found by a simple calculation.

FUNDAMENTAL LAWS
AND FACTS

IX.
Weber's Law

The law that I call by Weber's name and characterized in Chapter VII, speaking in general, as a main foundation for psychological measurement, will now be discussed in detail—insofar as present investigations will allow—as to its purpose, its basis, and its limitations.

One may state this law in different ways, all of which turn out to be essentially the same. Depending on circumstances, one or the other may be more practical for purposes of reference.

The first statement is as follows: A difference between two stimuli (or an addition to or subtraction from one or the other stimulus) is always perceived as equal, or produces the same difference or increment of sensation, if its ratio to the stimuli (or in case the difference is expressed as an increment, its ratio to the stimulus to which it is added) remains the same, regardless of how the absolute size changes. For example, an addition of 1 unit to a stimulus expressed as having a magnitude of 100 units is perceived the same as an addition of 2 to a stimulus of 200 units, of 3 to a stimulus of 300 units, and so on.

Equivalent to the above are the following briefer expressions: The difference or increment in sensation remains the same as long as the relative stimulus difference or relative stimulus increment remains the same; and sensation differences or sensation increments remain the same, if the ratios of stimuli remain the same. One may recall (p. [41]), that with constancy of the relative stimulus difference or stimulus increment, constancy of stimulus ratios is automatically assured and vice versa. This fact allows us to substitute this last expression of the law for the first.

Finally, referring back to the discussion of the abstract concepts of differential sensitivity in Chapter VI, we may state the law as follows: Simple differential sensitivity is inversely proportional to the size of the components of the difference; relative differential sensitivity remains the same regardless of size.

One can investigate the law in the areas of intensive and of extensive sensations, and in the former with respect to intensity and pitch (insofar as pitch represents a quantitative aspect of the quality of tones), without considering oneself justified, as a matter of course, in generalizing from its confirmation in one special area to its validity in another. Each area, rather, demands its own special investigation.

As far as the question as to whether this law can be confirmed in the area of extensive sensations is concerned, one has to substitute size and difference of extent, which can be perceived by the eye or by touch, for stimulus and stimulus difference in the law's formulation. The law will be found to be valid, if, for example, the difference between lines of doubled length has to be twice as large for it to be just noticeable, or more generally, for it to appear to be equally large.

In investigating the pitch of tones, the frequency of vibrations has to stand for the stimulus magnitude.

Truth of the law automatically implies the truth of some deductions. Demonstration that these deductions are confirmed experimentally should be regarded as part of the verification of the law. However, instead of discussing this in the abstract I prefer to let special cases in the various areas lead to its verification and refer in this respect particularly to the area of visual sensations.

As far as history is concerned, I have already remarked that while E. H. Weber was not the first to have formulated and verified this law, he was nevertheless the first to have given it some generality, to have confirmed it, and to have demonstrated it as a matter of general interest. He relied on experiments on just noticeable differences of weights, lengths, and pitches, which are, as one may note, examples of the three main aspects of sensation: intensity, extent, and quality. Since these cover all the aspects with which we can possibly be concerned, we are all the more justified in calling the law by his name. While he did not undertake a very thorough study of this law, because of his casual interest in it, he nevertheless provided by his own work a mode of attack for all later experiments. I shall therefore quote his statements verbatim, before turning to further investigations of the law. The present investigations became necessary when the claim was made that the law forms the basis of psychological measurement. This foundation needs to be strengthened and broadened, to the extent that it must support more complex and varied observations. Because of the fundamental importance of this law for us in this connection, I shall relate as completely as possible all that is known to me of earlier and modern findings, whether by others or myself, that are relevant to the law's confirmation and limitations.

I must confess finding, after a preliminary survey, that we are far from achieving a thorough verification, not to say proof of this law. In this respect the most work has been done with reference to intensive visual sensations, sensations of loudness and pitch, sensations of weight, and judgments of visual distance. Certainly there the law exists everywhere within more or less broad limitations. With respect to temperature sensations its existence still must be considered problematical. In the area of extensive touch sensations the experiments tend to speak more against than for its validity. In other fields of sensation no experiments have been reported as yet.

WEBER'S OWN REPORTS

Weber speaks in general of the facts concerning this law in his treatise on touch and common sensibility, page 559, under the heading: "On the smallest difference in weight which we can distinguish by touch, the smallest difference in length of lines which we can distinguish by sight, and the smallest difference of tones which we can distinguish by ear." After some special determinations he goes on to say:

I have shown that success in the judgment of weight is the same, whether one takes ounces or half-ounces, as the number of grains of the added weight is immaterial. It only matters whether the added weight makes up the thirtieth or the fiftieth part of the weight which is compared with the second weight. The same holds in comparisons of the length of two lines or the pitch of two tones.* It is immaterial whether the lines to be compared are about 2 or 1 in. in length, if first one and then the other is observed and both cannot be seen simultaneously next to each other, so long as the piece by which one line exceeds the other is twice as large in the first case as in the last. It is true that if both lines are close together and parallel to each other one compares the end portions of the lines and observes merely the extent by which one line exceeds the other. The only thing that is important now is how long the extra piece of the line sticks out and how far both lines are apart.—Comparing the pitch of two tones, it also does not matter whether the tones are seven steps higher or lower, as long as they do not lie at the end of the series of tones, where the exact distinction of small tonal differences becomes more difficult. The number of vibrations by which one tone exceeds the other is also unimportant in this case; only the ratio of vibrations of the tones we are comparing matters. . . .

---

* Delazenne in *Recueil des travaux de la soc. des sc. de Lille* 1827 abstracted in *Bull. des sc. nat.* XI, p. 275, and in Fechner's *Repertor. der Experimentalphysik*. Leipzig, 1832, vol. I, p. 341.

The perception of ratios of whole amounts, without measuring the magnitudes on a small scale and without knowledge of their absolute difference, is a most interesting psychological phenomenon. In music we perceive the ratios of tones without knowing the numbers of vibrations, in architecture the ratios of spaces without being able to determine their measurements in inches, and in the same way we perceive magnitudes of sensitivity or force in comparison of weights.

As far as the experience on which Weber bases his law is concerned, we have only a general statement with respect to tonal and linear relationships. One may, however, give it the weight of observations, knowing the absolute reliability of this experimenter. With respect to weight relationships, his experiments are to be found in his *Progr. coll.*, pages 81, 86 ff.

Weber makes a distinction between two modes of experimentation, one that involves only the sense of touch through the pressure of heavier and lighter weights on the hand resting on a table, the other where at the same time muscular sensation plays a role in lifting of weights, as when hand and weight are both raised. Now, regardless of whether a weight of 32 oz or 32 dr [drams] is employed as the heavier weight, in both modes of experimentation the just noticeable difference relative to the lesser weight remains practically the same. It amounted on the average for four persons and for both types of weight to 10.1 (ounces or drams) for the first kind and 3.0 for the second kind of experimentation.

In more detail, the description of his experiments is as follows (*Progr. coll.*, p. 86):

Several people rested their hands on a table, and on their hands I placed a piece of paper and on that, weights amounting to 2 lb. Afterwards, without their knowledge, I lessened the amount of one of the two weights, and exchanged the weights on the hands by transferring the definitely lighter weight from one hand to the other. Frequently I removed the weights and then replaced them on the same hands in such a manner that the person could not guess, but could only perceive by touch, on which side the heavier weight had been placed. Then if, upon repetition of the tests and with frequent changing of the hands, the men correctly discerned the heavier weights from the lighter, I made a note of it.

Afterwards, I repeated the same experiments on the same people, this time having them lift up their hands and compare the weights in them. After this was done, when I discovered by how much the weights had to differ for their discrepancy to be recognized with certainty, again I made a note, and calculating the difference in weight, I compared the resulting numbers.

After mentioning different experimental series, which pertain to relationships other than his law, Weber proceeds (p. 91):

We must not omit other experiments by which it was proven that, in observing touch and muscle sense with much smaller weights, the ratio between them would be the same as when 2 lb or 32 oz had been placed in each hand. In the same persons' hands in which I had previously placed two weights of 32 oz I now placed 32 dr (that is, ⅛ of the former weight). Although I suspected that they would not perceive clearly the difference between the weights of the two bodies eight times smaller, the experiments nevertheless proved that the difference between the smaller weights was distinguished by touch not less clearly than the same difference between the heavier weights.

I shall present four experiments as proof for this. After four persons, whom I designated by number, had compared two equal and larger given weights of 32 oz with their hands at rest, I began to diminish one of the two weights little by little until the men themselves perceived the difference between them. When that difference had been noted, I repeated the experiment in the same manner while they lifted the weights in their hands, and thereby estimated at the same time the power of touch and the common muscle sense. This done, the difference in weight that escaped their observation was noted anew.

Now in place of the bigger weight, but in the same manner, I used a smaller given weight of 32 dr, and the differences of weight that were not perceived in the experiment, because they evidently escaped observation, I marked down.

Thus if you compare the differences for the heavier and lighter weights obtained in our observations, you would find them to be nearly in the same relation.

Number of the Person Used in the Experiment	The Smallest Perceived Difference in the Weights Put on the Hands, in Ounces or Drams				
1. touch	32 oz	17	oz	diff. 15	oz
touch and common sens.	32 "	30½	"	" 1½	"
touch	32 dr	24	dr	" 8	dr
touch and common sens.	32 "	30	"	" 2	"
2. touch	32 oz	22	oz	" 10	oz
touch and common sens.	32 "	30½	"	" 1½	"
touch	32 dr	22	dr	" 10	dr
touch and common sens.	32 "	30	"	" 2	"
3. touch	32 oz	20	oz	" 12	oz
touch and common sens.	32 "	26	"	" 6	"
touch and common sens.	32 dr	26	dr	" 6	dr
4. touch	32 oz	26	oz	" 6	oz
touch and common sens.	32 "	30	"	" 2	"
touch and common sens.	32 dr	29	dr	" 3	dr

1. LIGHT

A full account of the confirmation of our law in the case of intensive visual sensation has been given by me in the *Abhandlungen der sächs. Gesellschaft der Wissenschaften, math.-phys. Cl.*, Vol. IV, pp. 457 ff, under the title: "On a fundamental psychophysical law and its connection to estimation of stellar magnitudes" and a supplement in the *Berichte* of the same society, 1859, pages 58 ff. I shall recapitulate here the essentials of these investigations with some few additions.

The law as applied to vision had, in the past, been stated by Bouguer, Arago, Masson, and Steinheil in connection with other investigations, and later by myself and Volkmann, without, however, anyone's paying much attention to it.

All verifications of the law except Steinheil's have so far been based on the method of just noticeable differences (which relies on the principles of the method of average error) and indirectly on the methods of estimating stellar magnitudes.

Since my own results present the simplest, even if not the most rigorous, verification of the law, and the first empirical knowledge of the law is associated with them, I shall begin with them here and connect the general explanation of the law with them.

In a partly cloudy sky it is usually easy to find a few adjacent clouds differing by a few nuances of shading, or a small cloud that differs only just noticeably from the background of the sky. Fixating two such components of a just noticeable brightness difference in the sky, I placed some dark glasses, like those opticians now carry for use of persons with light-sensitive eyes, in front of my eyes. Each of these, taken singly, allowed somewhat more than $\frac{1}{3}$, both together at the most $\frac{1}{7}$ of the light to pass through, according to a photometric, although superficial, examination. If we assume that simply placing a glass before each eye reduces the light of each component to $\frac{1}{3}$, then the difference between these components would immediately be reduced to $\frac{1}{3}$. The assumption seemed likely that the difference, now so much less, which had been only just noticeable before, would now be weakened to the point of disappearance, or if the limit of perception had not been reached before the glasses were used, the difference would at least strike one as less apparent. It did not turn out to be so, however. The difference remained at least as noticeable as before, and others whom I asked to repeat the experiment expressed themselves the same way.

The same experiment was repeated combining both glasses in front of only one eye and closing the other, so that the components together with their difference became as small as $\frac{1}{7}$ at the most. The difference still remained at least just as noticeable.

Finally, diminishing the light with colored glasses, a method by which I achieved at times considerably more dimming, gave the same result. Naturally different nuances of color of the clouds or of clouds against a blue sky should not be considered, since colored glasses absorb different colors in relatively different amounts.

If we note now that reducing the absolute difference between the components in the previous experiments left their ratio and thereby their relative difference unaltered, we will have to admit that the undiminished noticeability of the difference constitutes a proof of our law.

At first glance it might indeed seem rather extraordinary and contrary to common experience that a photometric difference reduced by $\frac{1}{3}$, $\frac{1}{5}$ or even more should still be at least as noticeable as before it was diminished, since we daily do notice differences in brightness grow less and disappear as the light grows weaker. One should not overlook, however, the conditions under which alone the law holds true, namely that the difference in brightness, as it grows less, must keep an unchanged ratio of its components as they themselves are proportionally diminished. Let us call the case satisfying this condition the first principal case. The difference may be lessened in yet another way, by means of diminishing the stronger component by itself, or increasing the weaker one by itself, in the direction of the other. In this case, which I shall call the second principal case, the difference, as it grows less, diminishes relative to its components. In this case, indeed, as later experiments readily show and in agreement with general experience, the difference becomes more difficult to perceive and disappears entirely when the components become sufficiently alike.

Still a third principal case can be cited in addition, which adds an indirect proof to the direct verification of our law found in the first case. It consists in adding or subtracting equal amounts from both components instead of changing them in equal proportions. In this third case, in contrast to the first, the absolute difference remains the same while the relative difference changes. It becomes less if we add the same amount to the components and increases as we subtract equal amounts. Now, since the rule of equal noticeability depends on the equality, not of the absolute difference, but of the relative one, we must expect, assuming this rule to be correct, that in our third case the noticeability of the difference would not remain the same in spite of the fact that the difference in the absolute sense is unaltered. Rather, we must expect the difference to decrease or increase, depending on whether the same amounts are added or subtracted.

As proof that this is really so there is no need of a specially devised experiment, even though experimental verification would be simple. However, the same kind of observation of an everyday experience, which has served us so far, is sufficient for purposes of verification.

At night everyone sees the stars; at full daylight one does not even see stars such as Sirius and Jupiter. Yet the absolute brightness difference between the stars' locations in the sky and the surrounding areas is still as great as at night. All that has happened is that equal amounts have been added to the intensity of both by the daylight.

One might possibly have interpreted the success of our first experiments on the nuances of shading of clouds in the same way. Thus, by using the dark glasses the difference between the clouds would be lessened, rather sharply as a matter of fact, but still would be there in an absolute sense. It should, therefore, have been perceived in view of its existence in an absolute sense, without it becoming necessary to make their continued noticeability dependent on the preservation of the same relative magnitudes. One may note, however, from the experience just described, that the absolute existence of a brightness difference is by no means sufficient to make it perceptible—indeed, that quite large absolute differences escape the eye completely, if they are of very small relative magnitudes. No one would consider the difference in brightness between the constellations Sirius and Jupiter and their surroundings in the sky at night to be small, and no one would be able, even paying the strictest attention, to discover these constellations by day. Our assertion that the brightness difference compared to their surroundings is just as large by day as it is by night may therefore appear strange. Physically speaking it is indeed so, but as far as sensation is concerned it is zero or even smaller than zero to the extent that it may need a certain magnification before reaching the point where it becomes visible.

One should not, moreover, assume that this phenomenon is only confined to point sources of light. Experiments on shadows that will be cited later will give the most convenient opportunity to observe the identical phenomenon on lighted surfaces of any extent when absolute differences are considerable. Everyday experiences also might be cited in this connection.

It may be noted that the figures on varnished oil paintings, daguerreotypes, painted plates, lacquered tables, and so on, become quite unrecognizable through reflected lights. Now, as is well known, the intensity of reflected light does not depend on the color or darkness of the surface from which it is reflected, but, as long as the substance is the same, only on its smoothness and the angle of incidence. It adds, in other words, the same amounts to the darker and lighter parts of the figures and the background, and thereby makes the difference between them unrecognizable.

The many examples mentioned above should be sufficient to prove the law in general. But can it be considered truly precise?

I mentioned intentionally that the differences between the nuances of shading of the clouds appeared at least as noticeable on regarding them through darkened glasses as they did when seen with the naked eye. Some people, whom I asked to repeat the experiment, even found the difference somewhat stronger with the glasses than without them, and it seems often, but not always, the same way to me. One can therefore be sure that in any case a brightness difference does not, as one might have expected, become less perceptible when its absolute size is reduced so long as its relative size remains the same. An improvement in the ability to perceive it at this time, however, would still be a deviation from the law, which ties a constant degree of noticeability to the equality of the relative differences.

Although it is possible in this case that altered conditions of irradiation may come into play, one may also consider subjective mistakes of the kind where one is prone to consider an equally noticeable difference more apparent, when it must be compared with the lesser impression made by its components. For a result that is as free as possible from subjective error I combine the following experiment with the usual approach.

With the glasses on I search for the least possible difference in the sky, which is judged as just noticeable, and then remove the glasses. If perceptibility has been increased to any extent, then the difference which was just noticeable with the glasses on must vanish when they are taken off. In spite of many repetitions of this experiment, however, with one or more glasses, I have never been able to find a difference so slight that it was not also noticeable after the glasses were removed, as soon as the first impression of momentary glare, which is felt when the eye is suddenly exposed to strong light, had passed. When putting the glasses in front of the eyes I also experience a momentary blurring of the difference because of the sudden change of illumination, which in both cases, however, passes fast.

In all of the experiments cited the use of only very insignificant differences, which might be characterized as just noticeable, is essential. Even though this law, as will be shown, can be extended to larger differences, it is not easy to employ them directly for testing. The judgment of whether such differences with and without the use of glasses are equally distinct is very uncertain and changeable and depends undoubtedly on a number of other circumstances. Even when only just noticeable differences are employed, equality judgments may, as mentioned before, be subject to the same illusions, even though they cannot be as significant in an absolute sense as when greater differences were used. The main advantage of using very small differences lies in our ability to combine the experiment with its counterexperiment, thus freeing ourselves from dependence on judgments of equality or inequality and allowing us to form conclusions based only on the presence of the difference in sensation, where one is less likely to make mistakes than in judgments of equality. When the least possible difference that can still be perceived without glasses remains recognizable with heavily darkened glasses, and when, on the contrary, the least possible difference that is recognized with heavily darkened glasses is still perceived without them, it can be taken as a kind of objective proof that there is no significant gain or loss in the perceived difference due to the glasses.

In any case, the combination of experiment and counterexperiment limits the possibility of a breakdown of the validity of the law. The range of light intensities within which it has been found valid, while extending neither to the near approach of complete darkness nor to very brilliant lights, leaves but little room beyond its limits. In the meantime, this statement does not assert or demonstrate unlimited validity of the law. In point of fact, a breakdown, at least for purposes of experimentation, is certain, above as well as below these limits. Before entering upon a further discussion of validity it will be useful to examine the law's limitations, since validation itself can only take place and be understood with respect to these limits.

Certainly no one could recognize sunspots with bare eyes, even if they could be observed without danger (at least as long as the sun is high in the sky), whereas everyone can see them with darkened glasses. Should the law, however, extend to the highest light intensities, then the spots should be just as easy to differentiate from the surrounding blaze of light as with the addition of dark glasses. Doubtless deviations from the law occur even at much lower light intensities, probably whenever the eye is subject to dazzling light, although any specific experiments on this subject are still missing.

It may, therefore, even be possible that with very brightly lit clouds there is really a small gain attributable to the dark glasses in making the differences in the nuances of shading of the clouds more apparent. Judging by the results of the combination of experiment and counterexperiment, this gain can only be of a low order, which I have not been able to note objectively in experiments with moderately bright clouds. I must admit that I have not been able to carry out experiments with very glaring illumination without trouble, and that frequently enough I have been unable to say anything definite about it, because of the sensitivity of my eyes.[1]

Concerning the lower boundary, it is immediately apparent that nothing at all, and therefore, of course, no difference, will be seen if one

[1] Ed. Note: Twenty years before (the late 1830s), Fechner had injured his retina by gazing too long at the sun in order to obtain afterimages. See also Translator's Foreword.

carries the darkening of the glasses to an extreme, even if the difference without glasses might appear ever so large and as indeed it might be. The principle of continuity would demand a lessening of clearness when this limit is only approached, as is confirmed by experience. Indeed, however large the difference may be, one can always find the pair of glasses that are dark enough for the difference to appear less clear than without glasses. The same sunspots that grow more apparent with moderately dark glasses, again become less clear with very dark glasses, and eventually grow quite unrecognizable.

Instead of laying claim to unlimited validity of the law, we can then only state that, on the basis of the experimental evidence, it is confirmed to the extent that no deviation from the law can be demonstrated between the rather wide limits of intensity within which normal seeing conditions occur.

One could in a way already deduce the validity of the law in the middle range from the opposite tendencies of the deviations in the up and the down directions. With intense light, dimming improves clarity, and with very dim light, clarity improves in equal proportion with brightening of the components. There must therefore exist, on mathematical principles alone, a certain middle interval where it stays unchanged by increasing or dimming the light. Only the wide extent of such an interval was not predictable by purely mathematical considerations.

I began with these experiments, not only because they were the first by which I attempted to find experimental proof of this law, before I had become aware of what had been accomplished in this respect in the past, but also because they were especially convenient, easily accessible to everyone, and at the same time as good evidence for the general facts of the law as any. The only drawback is the fact that one has no control over the specification, the uniform maintenance, or the change, of the shadings of light, and one cannot, therefore, set up all three principal conditions at will. Because of this it is desirable to add some other procedures which facilitate experimental observations.

There are very many different ways to create shadings of different tones down to a just noticeable difference, so that the experiment can be carried out in various forms. One very simple way is to use India ink to create the least possible shadings on vellum paper. It is true that these do not guarantee a measurable difference any more than do the shadings of clouds, but they at least have the advantage of evenness, controlled gradients, and easy handling.

Lately I have actually repeated the experiment and counterexperiment by these means and have found results corresponding to my former work on cloud nuances. Even with darkened glasses combined so as to allow only $\frac{1}{100}$ of the light to pass, according to exact photometry, I recognize, after only a brief time, even the least degrees of shading that I had also found just noticeable with the bare eye. It is important to have good daylight available. When I experiment by the light of my studio lamp by which I usually do my writing, the shadings become quite unrecognizable at the same grade of dimming, whereas dimming the light only to $\frac{1}{12}$ or more lets them appear just as clearly as without darkening.

Another approach that is simple and convenient, yet permits definite measurement and variation of the three main conditions, is the employment of two shadows side by side, generated by means of two lamps or lights shining on the same object. Here the photometric ratio of the shadows is not only easily adjustable, but also simple to measure by employing two equally bright light sources and using the reciprocal relationship of the squares of the distances of both sources from their shadows. The photometric equality of the sources is shown easily by the equality of the brightness of the shadows at equal distances from the light sources. It can be varied by trimming the lights or adjusting the lamps. Actually it is on the whole much more practical to use a shadow and its surrounding ground rather than two shadows as components of the difference in testing the law, since the ratio of a shadow to its surround can be judged more easily. The following procedure spells out in more detail what has to be considered.

Let L and L' be two light sources and let L' be the light source for the shadow we wish to examine. This shadow is illuminated only by light L, the surround by both sources, L and L'. As one moves the light source L' back from the surface on which the shadow appears, while L remains stationary, the surround receives less and less additional illumination from L'. Eventually when this illumination is reduced to the point where it becomes unnoticeable to the eye, the shadow merges into the surround. Once this point is reached, a small movement of one of the lights or the adjustment of one of them in the right direction is sufficient to make it again just noticeable.

To start with, one might now repeat experiment and counterexperiment using the dark glasses. The law itself, as well as the lower limit of the law, can thus be substantiated.

Instead of dimming both components in equal proportion by means of the dark glasses, one can effect the same purpose by moving both sources, L, and L', away from the surface on which the shadow appears through greater and greater distances, while maintaining the same proportional distance between them. The following experiments used this method and also reversed the procedure. In the past it had been observed that the difference remained equally noticeable where the components were dimmed in equal proportions. Now, however, the effect of making the difference between the shadows equally noticeable was observed, as what follows will clearly show. In this manner the new experimental approach constitutes rather a supplement and check of the earlier series than a repetition.

Since my own very weak eyes would not be able to tolerate such experiments, which demand the most exacting attention and strictest fixation in order to follow the traces of the shadows as they disappear and reappear, Volkmann, with the aid of some other observers with good eyes, took over this task. The following describes the essentials of the procedure and its results.

A rod placed vertically in front of a white vertical panel cast two shadows on it under the influence of two light sources L and L'. One light source, L, a stearin candle, was placed at a given distance from the panel. The other, of equal intensity, as determined photometrically in two ways, was moved away from the panel by an assistant observer until the shadow it cast, on which the observer had fixated, became just no longer noticeable. For Volkmann's eyes this distance of candle L' from its shadow had to be ten times that of candle L, that is, the difference of illumination, where the shadow just ceased to be noticeable, amounted to $\frac{1}{100}$ of the absolute illumination. The same proportion of distances (and consequently of illumination), where this point was reached, could also be found with quite different absolute intensities of illumination. These, it should be noted, could be produced by changing the intensity of the lights themselves as well as by means of placing the light L at greater or lesser distances from the panel. In all cases the distance of the light L' from the panel had to be just ten times that of light L in order to bring the shadow to the vanishing point. Experiments were made with intensity of illumination of L equal to 0.36 and varying through 1, 2.25, 7.71 to 38.79 (where illumination of the white screen by a stearin candle at a distance of 3 dm [decimeters] counted as one), without resulting in noticeably or considerably different proportions of the distance of the other light source to the panel. Only at the lowest intensity (0.36) was there a small decrease worth mentioning, that is, the distance of light L' had to be somewhat less than ten times the distance of the light L (according to the tabulated results from six to nine times as far) in order for the shadow just to disappear. No doubt at this point the lower limit at which the law is valid in this experiment had just been passed.

For the sake of brevity I have referred only to the vanishing point in this description. Actually, light source L' was moved forward and backward around the point of disappearance, in order to locate the point where the shadow was just noticeable as accurately as possible, between the point where it just disappeared and that where it just reappeared. Since the moving of the light source L' by an assistant occurred only on command of the observer, while he was fixing his eyes and attention fully on the apperception of the shadow, the definitive fixation of the distance occurred without knowledge of the observer. It could, therefore, not be influenced by such knowledge, making the results of these experiments that much less doubtful.

These experiments were undertaken by Volkmann with the aid of Prof. Knoblauch, Dr. Heidenhain in Halle, and Dr. Jung of Berlin, and were partially repeated in my presence. Surprisingly, the same value, varying only a little around $\frac{1}{100}$, was found for all the observers as the just noticeable difference.

It is true that this procedure does not admit great precision of individual results, as one can always move the light L' within a certain distance (which according to Volkmann is of the order of $\frac{1}{10}$ of the total distance), without knowing exactly where the point where the shadow becomes just noticeable should be fixed. In general, therefore, the mean of several experiments was considered as the final result for each observer. However, the individual results vary only very little around the mean, and the uncertainty remaining after the means are calculated is quite insignificant.

This experimental procedure, using shadows, corresponds to the first condition; understandably it is easy, however, to make it correspond also to the second condition, by moving one light alone closer to or away from the panel, to make it brighter or dimmer. In order to make it correspond to the third case, one illuminates both shadows, or one shadow and the surround, by a third, sufficiently strong light. One is thus in a position to make a very vivid difference vanish to the eye.

So much for my own experiments and those inspired by me. Although they are essentially not new, as I mentioned at the start, their discussion can still be considered useful even after those earlier ones, insofar as they were carried out independently of them and with some modifications. Thus they may contribute to the validation and explanation of the law. Now, however, I shall add all that is essential of what became known to me in the course of time of the earlier confirmations. Bouguer was the first (according to his *Traité d'optique sur la gradation de la lumière par*

Lacaille, 1760, p. 51) who carried through the experiment with vanishing shadows in a way very similar to Volkmann's* and who describes it under the title: "Observations made to determine what strength one light must have to cause another weaker one to disappear."

I might add that he only cites the result of one experiment at a single distance of both the lights, according to which the shadow disappeared at about $\frac{1}{64}$ of the difference (instead of $\frac{1}{100}$ as with Volkmann). He does say further that this degree of sensitivity might differ, depending on the eye of the observer; as far as he was concerned, however, he believed that for his eye it was independent of the light intensity.

According to a verbal communication cited by Masson,† Arago repeated Bouguer's experiments and even employed colored lights. Arago himself takes a positive attitude about the correctness of the law in his popular astronomy‡ where he writes, after analyzing Bouguer's experimental method: "whatever the absolute brightness of M and L (the two lights of Bouguer's experiment), the experiment will always lead to the same results (the same just noticeable relative difference)."

In his *Memoires sur la photométrie* (p. 256) Arago does not refer back to the law, but taking the law for granted, it seems, cites experiments which prove the influence of movement on the visibility of a difference, and to which I shall refer below.

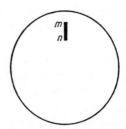

Fig. 1.   Masson's disk.

Masson§ arrived at his experiments supporting the law while conducting an extended investigation of electrical photometry. This procedure is to the point and simple and his account demonstrates a much more pre-

---

* I take these citations from Masson's literal rendering in *Ann. de Chim. et de Phys.* 1845. Vol. XIV, p. 148, since Bouguer's writings themselves were not accessible to me.
† *Ann. de Chim. et de Phys.* 1845. Vol. XIV, p. 150.
‡ Edited [W. G.] Hankel, Part I, p. 168. [Trans. Note: Fechner worked on this 16-volume translation of Arago's complete works, published by Otto Wiegand, Leipzig, 1854–1860.]
§ *Ann. de Chim. et de Phys.* 1845. Vol. XIV, p. 150.

cise and complete proof than do the descriptions of Bouguer and Arago. Essentially it consisted of the following: A white disk, approximately 6 cm [centimeters] in diameter, on which a sector, measuring, for example, $\frac{1}{60}$ of its area, was blackened in one part *mn* (as shown in the accompanying figure), was set in rapid spinning motion. Due to the persistence of the visual image, the black part would expand into a ring or wreath on the white disk, which, according to the known law of the brightness relationships of fast-moving bodies applicable here, was $\frac{1}{60}$ darker than the white background. An eye that still is capable of differentiating the ring from its background would, therefore, still be able to perceive a difference that does not amount to more than $\frac{1}{60}$ of the intensity. Masson had a whole series of such disks made up, in which the proportion of the angular size of the sector to the area of the disk amounted to $\frac{1}{50}$, $\frac{1}{60}$, $\frac{1}{70}$, and so on in progression to $\frac{1}{120}$. He was thus able to determine the limits between which the threshold of sensitivity fell. The following method, leading to corresponding results, is of interest at the same time, compared to the one just cited, since it shows that an instantaneous light is equal to a steady light as far as the law is concerned.

We know that when a disk, divided into alternating black and white sectors and illuminated by daylight or artificial light, is spun rapidly, it will appear a uniform gray. Substituting illumination by an instantaneous electric spark, each sector is seen separately. When both kinds of illumination are applied simultaneously, it will depend on the proportion of the intensities, whether a uniform gray is seen or the sectors are differentiated. The former occurs when the instantaneous electric light is weak, the latter when it is sufficiently intense. According to Masson the proportion of intensities at which a uniform gray starts to be seen varies for the eyes of different people, although it remains the same for the eye of each individual observer. The sectors disappear and seem uniformly gray when the instantaneous illumination of the white sectors by the electric light (the black ones do not reflect light appreciably) is not sufficiently higher than the uniform gray color which would be seen without the electric light, to be discriminated by the eye. Depending on the relative width of the black and white sectors, which effect the changing appearance of the gray color, different levels of electrical illumination under the identical fixed illumination are needed for this point to be reached. Where the eye still recognizes differences of $\frac{1}{100}$ in the last experiment, now, with white and black sectors equal, the illumination of the white sectors by the electric light must amount to $\frac{1}{200}$ of the illumination of the steady light, as the spinning of the disk has reduced its illumination to a gray of half the photometric brightness. The experiments using this method were undertaken by Masson in many variations for purposes different from those of validating our law, but we find their outcomes correspond with those using the previous method.

Masson cites details of his results, first with respect to the first method of observation, then with respect to the second as follows:*

Testing different people's vision, I found, that for those eyes that are considered weak, sensitivity has varied from $\frac{1}{50}$ to $\frac{1}{70}$. It was from $\frac{1}{80}$ to $\frac{1}{100}$ for ordinary sight, and for good vision from $\frac{1}{100}$ to $\frac{1}{120}$ and beyond. I have encountered two persons who perceived quite distinctly the ring produced on a disk giving $\frac{1}{120}$.

By causing the intensity of the lighting to vary, I found that, when it was sufficient so that one might easily read in an octavo size, the sensitivity did not vary for the same individual. Thus, as Bouguer had recognized, the sensitivity of the eye is independent of the intensity of the light. In several ways I varied the strength of the light reflected by the disk. I have taken the light of a Carcel lamp placed at various distances from the disk, the lighting effect of dark and overcast weather; I have worked in diffused light after sunset; I have used sunlight reflected by a heliostat, and sometimes I have produced a divergent beam by means of a lens. The distance from the eye to the disk is without influence on the sensitivity, provided that a certain limit determined by the angle subtended by the ring is not reached.

The results were not modified when I changed the relationship between the diameter of the disk and the width of the ring. I used disks on which the surface traversed by the black sector was a third or a quarter of that of the circle. I placed the black part at the edge of the disk, in the center, and between the center and the circumference. Finally I arranged on one circle several black portions belonging to sectors having different relationships with the circle, and I used disk number 5†. In every case the limit of sensitivity remained invariable.

By lighting the mobile disk with colored lights, I was able to determine whether the sensitivity of the eye varied with the nature of the luminous beams. With the exception of several restrictions of which I am going to speak, I found that the limit of sensitivity is independent of color. Thus, I see the ring as distinctly at $\frac{1}{100}$, whether I light the disk with natural light or use colored rays.

I have produced lights of various colors by causing sunlight or the rays of a Carcel lamp to pass through colored glasses. I have used the colors of a spectrum and finally the photometric apparatus of M. Arago.

The glasses, for which I am indebted to the kindness of M. Bontemps, were all tried with the spectrum. Except for the red glass, which allowed only the red extremity of the spectrum to pass, all the others let pass all the colors in variable quantities. Some, the red one for example, absorbed such a quantity of light than one had difficulty in seeing the ring.

In the preceding trials, the observer having fixed his eye on the disk for a variable length of time, we cannot affirm that the limits of sensitivity, thus

---

* The circumstance that, as far as I know, this work of Masson's never found its way into any German scientific journal justifies this somewhat long verbatim citation.

† This disk contains an interrupted black sector.

determined, will remain the same when the lighting is instantaneous. I assured myself by the following means that, in this last case, the limit of sensitivity underwent little variation.

After having lighted the sectors of the photometer* with a Carcel lamp, I placed an electric light at the farthest distance, then I varied either the distance of the spark or that of the lamp in such a manner as to make the sectors apparent. I worked with various intensities of lighting. By comparing thus the variation of distance necessary to produce the appearance of the sectors at the farthest distance of the lights, I found, and this results also from the experiments that I shall cite farther on, that one could take as a limit of sensitivity in my photometric experiments the numbers obtained for fixed lights.

By subjecting several individuals to my experiments, I noted a fact of the greatest importance for absolute photometry, I mean for the comparison of steady lights with an instantaneous light taken as a unit. I found that two persons who had the same sensitivity, gave, after having acquired sufficiently the habit of the experiments, the same numbers to the electric photometer.

I substituted for the white papers lighted by colored lights, colored papers lighted by natural light. The limit of sensitivity always appeared to me to be smaller in this latter case, and a bit variable with the color of the papers. However, I do not think that this fact must be considered as an exception to the rule which I have established. It is indeed just about impossible to obtain uniformly colored papers; the light which they reflect is always very weak, and the black which is put on their surface does not adhere well and itself reflects a quantity of white light which varies within rather wide limits in relation to the light reflected by the colored disks. However, in the case of the red and blue papers, I arrived very approximately at the limit obtained by the other means.

Having observed that at the extremity of the ring described by the black part of the sector, there was always a certain contrast which, making the ring more apparent on its edges, helped in seeing it, I ended the black part of the sector with a fringed edge (see figures 6 and 7 in the original).

There results also from some experiments that I performed on several individuals that, the sensitivity of their organ remaining the same for all colors, they experienced, while looking steadily at the disk lighted by the red, a fatigue, a discomfort, which indicated in them a kind of repugnance for this color. It would be interesting to investigate whether this effect is not produced on some eyes by a color other than red.

Finally, I come to Steinheil's experiments. In his famous treatise on the prism photometer† he had occasion to investigate whether the error committed in estimating equality of light intensities varies according to the level of intensity. He cites briefly (p. 14 of his treatise) the results of the relevant observations: "They show that one recognizes

---

* Masson refers here to a photometric arrangement, described in his original work. It consists of a rapidly spinning disk, divided into black and white sectors, illuminated by an electric spark. (Cf. p. 127.)

† *Elemente der Helligkeits-Messungen am Sternenhimmel*, by Steinheil, in *Abhandl. der mathemat. phys. Kl. der kön. bair. Akad.* 1837.

the point at which two surfaces are equally bright with great exactness. The uncertainty of each and every estimate of this kind does not amount to more than $\frac{1}{38}$ of the total brightness, whether it be at a high or low level."

This statement includes an expression of our law. For the uncertainty in estimating the equality of two light intensities understandably depends on the magnitude of the just noticeable difference. If at the different intensities equally large errors are committed on the average in the majority of experiments, then the limits of noticeability of a difference must lie at an equally large proportion of these intensities.

Thus Steinheil himself states, when he says (p. 71) with respect to the same observation: "In part B it will be shown . . . that each error in estimating equal brightness amounts to an aliquot part of the total illumination. From the latter fact it follows that, when one reduces the light on surfaces to that intensity where it can no longer be distinguished from the surrounding sky, then it is of an intensity proportional to the surrounding sky."

The ratio $\frac{1}{38}$ seems strange compared with the previous findings of $\frac{1}{64}$ to $\frac{1}{120}$. It is questionable whether this discrepancy depends on a difference of eyes or of methods, but this discrepancy does not affect the law with which we are concerned here. One should note, in this regard, that the fraction $\frac{1}{38}$, which, according to Steinheil, denotes the uncertainty, should be looked upon as proportional but not as necessarily identical with the just noticeable differences expressed by the findings of $\frac{1}{64}$ to $\frac{1}{200}$ of other observers. This remark does not, however, explain the size and direction of the difference between the results.

Steinheil's experiments (pp. 75 ff of his treatise), insofar as they can be looked upon as comparable for the purpose of validation of our law, concern only a scale of three intensities, which stand in a ratio of 1.000 to 1.672 to 2.887. They do not, therefore, cover a wide range. They are, however, very valuable and important, not only because they originate with an excellent observer well versed in the application of photometric measurements, but also because they depend on a principle of validation different from the one used so far, and thus show even better that the law can stand any kind of test.

Indeed, it is easy to overlook the fact that the underlying principle of Steinheil's validation is the method of average error, whereas the earlier validations were based on the method of just noticeable differences.

Since it would be too troublesome to give here an exposition and calculation of Steinheil's results, I refer the reader to the original or to page 477 of my own work,[2] where I make the fraction out to be $\frac{1}{40}$ instead of $\frac{1}{38}$, according to a somewhat modified computation and excluding one experimental series that is not quite comparable to the rest. Only a summary of the observed data and the simple average errors calculated under the supposition of the validity of the law and proportional to the square roots of the intensities follows herewith.

Observed Value	Calculated Value
2.517	2.426
1.712	1.846
1.471	1.428

Validations of the law, so far, have been concerned with very small differences, since, as shown in Chapter VII, this limitation is essential if a psychic measure is to be based on it. The direct validation for the case of more than just noticeable differences presents some difficulties, since it should be noted that equality judgments in that case are not very certain and in this case the combination of experiment and counterexperiment does not allow us to draw any conclusions, as was true by the mere presence of just noticeable differences. However, I do cite on page 489 of my work[3] the experience that on covering one eye a slight shadow passes over the visual field, which one is not inclined to consider as brighter or darker, whether one fixates a light or a wall. Under some circumstances this experience may be considered to fall under our law and be interpreted as a validation in the case of differences somewhat greater than just noticeable. A discussion of this experience may be consulted directly in my treatise.

There does exist, however, still another method of validating the law for greater than just noticeable differences, which is much less equivocal. It is at the same time the earliest method pertaining to the law, and refers again particularly to that distinguished field of observation in which I first cited evidence for the law's validity, namely the methods of estimating stellar magnitudes. One must presuppose here that the practiced eye of the astronomer has been able to overcome successfully the difficulties inherent in making estimates required for our law.

Estimation of stellar magnitudes, as is well known, has been carried out since antiquity (Hipparchus), not according to the photometric value of

[2] Trans. Note: These page references refer to Fechner's articles on the psychophysical law and its relation to the estimation of stellar magnitudes in *Abhandl. d. Kgl. sächs. Ges. d. Wiss.* 1859. Vol. IV pp. 457–532. and *Berichte d. Kgl. sächs. Ges. d. Wiss.* 1859. Vol. XI, pp. 58–86.

[3] Trans. Note: See previous note.

their light, but according to their appearance to the eye, so that astronomers could divide the stars into first, second, and third magnitudes, and so forth, according to their apparent differences in brightness. Thus, as the number of stellar magnitudes was said to decrease, apparent brightness increased. Now, according to our law the perceived difference in brightness in adjacent classes of magnitudes can be equal only insofar as the photometric relation between them stays the same; thus an arithmetic series of stellar magnitudes must fit to a geometric series of stellar intensities, in order to describe the photometric value of a star by stellar intensity.

We must take into account here, to be sure, the contradiction of a statement in v. Humboldt's *Kosmos*, based on J. Herschel's observations, that the series of stellar intensities of successive stellar magnitudes is a quadratic power series rather than a geometric series, thus

$$1, \tfrac{1}{4}, \tfrac{1}{9}, \tfrac{1}{16}. \ldots$$

In a geometric series each value should be obtainable from the immediately preceding number by multiplying by a constant, and one would find, keeping as close as possible to the previous series, rather

$$\tfrac{1}{2}, \tfrac{1}{4}, \tfrac{1}{8}, \tfrac{1}{16} \ldots .$$

At first glance this contradiction seems all the more important since the quadratic power series is preferred to the geometric series by Herschel himself, and his very careful revision of stellar magnitudes and their comparison with stellar intensities, according to his own photometric determinations, constitutes one of the most extended and important bases on which one may rely in this matter with any degree of certainty. In the meantime I have clearly demonstrated in my treatise, I believe, that this contradiction is only an apparent one, which on closer examination resolves itself in a full validation of our law. Here are the essential points.

Any considerable discrepancy between these series $1, \tfrac{1}{4}, \tfrac{1}{9}, \tfrac{1}{16} \ldots$ and $\tfrac{1}{2}, \tfrac{1}{4}, \tfrac{1}{8}, \tfrac{1}{16} \ldots$ is found only in magnitudes of the first class. But in these the intensity of individual stars may vary from 1 to about 16 times, so that, if one chooses the intensity of a star of this class at random as representative of the intensities of the whole class, one may make it correspond at will with one or the other of these series. Such an arbitrary choice has indeed been made by Herschel. He had a preference, as we know, for the quadratic power series of intensities, as under this hypothesis the proportions of the numbers denoting magnitudes would determine at the same time the relative distances at which the stars were located. Accordingly, he picked as his representative star of the first magnitude one which best fitted this hypothesis, but one which was by no means of average intensity, being one of the brightest, third in order of stars of the first magnitude. This star was α *Centauri*, yet Herschel himself expressly mentions at various times another star, α *Orionis* (Betelgeuze), as the average star among those of first magnitude—in his words a "typical specimen," a star "of an average first magnitude." Placement of this star is indeed confirmed by Herschel's own observational data, where among the other 14 stars which were ranked according to fractional magnitudes based on photometric determinations, 8 were found to have a lesser, 6 a higher intensity, and therefore 6 a lower and 8 a greater magnitude than α *Orionis*.

It is clear, accordingly, that if an average or typical value for stars of the first magnitude without arbitrary selection in the light of any preconceived notions is sought, α *Orionis* and not α *Centauri* must be chosen. Now, according to Herschel's own photometric determinations, α *Orionis* and α *Centauri* stand in a ratio of 0.484 to 1. Substituting 0.484 for 1 in the quadratic power series we can change it to

$$0.484; \; \tfrac{1}{4}; \; \tfrac{1}{9}; \; \tfrac{1}{16}. \ldots$$

But 0.484 differs so little from 0.5 or $\tfrac{1}{2}$, and $\tfrac{1}{9}$ differs so little from $\tfrac{1}{8}$, that, in light of the difficulty, pointed out by Herschel himself, in exact determination of magnitude and intensity, and further in view of the fact that he himself declares that the quadratic power series do not coincide precisely with the observed values, this difference may be regarded as small enough for us to substitute the geometric series

$$\tfrac{1}{2}, \; \tfrac{1}{4}, \; \tfrac{1}{8}, \; \tfrac{1}{16}. \ldots$$

for the quadratic series. We may grant that with higher orders of magnitude both series would diverge more widely, but Herschel's photometric determinations do not go beyond the fourth magnitude and do not provide a basis for further comparisons.

A thorough calculation, for which I must refer to my treatise, has further shown that the geometric series of stellar intensities not only fits Herschel's data, but represents them better than does the quadratic power series, provided it is brought suitably into relationship with them and exponents are correctly chosen. Accordingly, taking observations and computing according to Herschel we find that the sum of squared errors based on the hypothesis of a quadratic power series is 2.719 while only 2.2291 remains according to our formula based on the assumption of a geometric series.

Herschel's investigation, though one of the most important, is by no means the only one on which we can base ourselves in this respect. All doubt is removed about the fact that a geometrical series of stellar intensities is associated with an arithmetic series of stellar magnitudes by various other very thorough investigations, such as those by Steinheil, Stampfer, Johnson, and Pogson, which have all, completely independently, led to the same results. Summaries of these investigations may be found partly in the first-mentioned major treatise, partly in the addendum in the *Berichten der sächs. Societät.*[3a]

The exponent of the geometric series does not depart, according to the results of these various investigations, very significantly from 2.5 or 0.40, depending on whether one takes an ascending or descending series of intensities. Determinations were as follows:

			Ascending	Descending
according to J. Herschel's data			2.241	0.4427
"	" Steinheil *	(1)	2.831	0.3588
"	" "	(2)	2.702	0.3705
"	" Stampfer †	(1)	2.519	0.3970
"	" "	(2)	2.545	0.3929
"	" Johnson ‡	(1)	2.358	0.424
"	" "	(2)	2.427	0.412
"	" Pogson		2.400	0.417

* (1) According to Steinheil's own computations, (2) according to a somewhat different computation, see my own first *Abhandlung* pp. 518 ff.

† (1) Determined on fixed stars, (2) determined on planets.

‡ (1) According to my own revision of stellar magnitudes, (2) with the addition of further magnitude estimates.

The differences between these exponents are explained partly as deviations due to the estimates of magnitude, partly as due to the photometric determinations of the various observers. The absolute values of the determinations may also have been influenced to some extent by the fact that the intensity of the background sky was not taken sufficiently into consideration, as I show more thoroughly in my second *Abhandlung*. Here is not the place, however, to discuss this fact in more detail, since the general agreement of these investigations concerning those results essen-

[3a] Trans. Note: See note 2.

tial to us, that is, the validity of the geometric series of stellar intensities, is sufficient.

After all the previous discussion, we must be struck by an incidental disagreement with our law which may be found in J. Herschel's accounts. We cannot neglect this disagreement, since it originates with so reliable an observer, even if it contradicts the results stemming from another aspect of Herschel's data, as discussed above, and altohugh it cannot negate the result of all prior investigations.

Herschel remarks in a description of his Astrometer (Cape Journey,[4] p. 357), in a note, that it would be useful to employ reflecting power of an equal sided prism to make the line that joins two stars to be compared parallel to the horizon. He adds: "Occasionally, too, it may be used to enfeeble the light of nearly equal bright stars, by external reflexion in an equal ratio (by bringing the line joining their reflected images parallel to that joining their direct [observation].) In this enfeebled state, shades of inequality become apparent, which would otherwise escape detection. By increasing or diminishing (equally) the angles of incidence, the reflected images may be more or less enfeebled. A plain metallic mirror may be used for the same purpose." (A parallel can also be found in "Outlines," p. 522.)

Now, regardless of this contradiction, it seems impossible to me, after what has been said, to look upon this discrepancy found by Herschel as more than a deviation of negligible proportion, which occurs under certain conditions of observation. It appears that he observed this deviation only "occasionally," without making a specific investigation of this point. Since he himself speaks at other times of "innumerable reasons," which "play a role in determining our judgment in these experiments in a manner scarcely believable," one should not consider occasional observations sufficient to be the basis of a discrepancy, compared to the specific experiments which have already been presented. From a different point of view one may think that an observer as experienced and practiced as Herschel would eventually acquire a sensitivity for small differences, and thereby for small deviations from the law which represent only measurements of a very small magnitude at intensities where they are not yet noticeable to an unpracticed eye. In addition, it is not improbable that Herschel's statement primarily pertains to bright stars, where deviations due to the upper limit of the law are perhaps already noticeable, since he himself stresses the difficulty of a determination in the case of the brightest stars and, therefore, may have preferred to use here the above-mentioned aid. Unfortunately we cannot be sure on this point because of the lack of a definite statement. Nevertheless this contradiction, which surely has a factual basis, calls all the more for further investigation of the conditions under which the law is valid.

[4] Trans. Note: Sir John Frederick William Herschel's (1792–1871): *Results of astronomical observations made during the years 1834, 5, 6, 7, 8 at the Cape of Good Hope being the completion of a telescopic survey of the whole surface of the visible heavens commenced in 1825.* London: Smith, Elder and Co., 1847. The "Outlines" mentioned below refers to *Outlines of Astronomy*, first published in London in 1849 and reprinted as vols. 19 and 20 of *A Library of Universal Literature*, New York: P. F. Collier & Son Corp., 1901.

Our topic so far has dealt with the proof that, within certain limits, there exists a law at all, without fixing these limits exactly. Nothing of this kind has as yet been done. There needs, however, to be much discussion of the conditions and the nature of these limits and of the reasons for them. Such discussion will to some extent provide an occasion for bringing up certain factors, which influence the perception of intensive differences irrespective of the law's validity and must therefore be held constant or made comparable in experiments testing its validity. These matters will be treated here, when first brought up, in sufficient detail for later reference.

The upper limit of the law, when the eye is dazzled, undoubtedly is dependent upon the fact that the eye is thereby harmfully affected. In a way an upper limit of this kind is obvious. The inner activity, on which sensation depends, undoubtedly cannot be raised above a certain limit without damaging the organ and rendering any further increase impossible. Two stimuli of different strengths, each of which reaches or surpasses this limit of stimulation, will only bring about an identical maximum of sensation, and therefore could not cause a difference between sensations. In any case, even an approach to these limits brings with it a deviation from the law.

It might appear reasonable to ascribe the upper deviations from the law simply to the fact that the eye, by adapting to the light stimulus, becomes less sensitive to differences in the intensity of light. This observation seems to be conclusively confirmed when momentarily one cannot see any differences after passing suddenly from full daylight into a dim room. Gradually, however, one can learn to make better and better distinctions. Now, this same phenomenon also makes itself felt in the opposite direction. Whoever suddenly steps into the light after a long stay in a darkened room is at first just as incapable of distinguishing objects. He learns to see distinctly only gradually. If adaptation were the reason that one does not see differences well in a very strong light, then one should be able to distinguish them most clearly in the first moment on entering a bright room from the dark and then gradually less and less well. This twofold condition was already apparent in the experiment and counter-experiment on page [120] on the nuances of clouds.

One might be inclined, accordingly, to assign the cause for the inability to make out objects when entering the dark from a bright room rather to an after-effect of the light, as a blunting of the impression, and the corresponding inability when entering a bright room from the dark to the gradual way in which impressions make themselves felt. Thus, if the intrinsic light of the eye[5] were to

_____

[5] Ed. Note: In complete darkness the eye has some light sensation which may get lighter as time persists. Fechner called this light *Augenschwarz* (meaning the eye's black-

persist for a time when one goes from light to dark, then impressions that are weakly luminous could not be perceived at all, according to the principle of the vanishing of the stars in the daytime. If, conversely, when the change takes place in the opposite direction, the stronger impression were to appear to be felt more slowly than the weaker one, then even differences between strong lights would not be perceived initially. I have indeed tentatively tried this explanation in my treatise on "a fundamental psychophysical law,"[6] page 487. Yet after more careful consideration both aspects of this explanation seemed no longer tenable, for according to all experience so far the phenomenon of persistence dies down too quickly; besides there are other difficulties. Furthermore, the assumption that a strong light makes itself felt relatively more slowly than a weak one is contradicted by positive experiments by Swan.[*]

Unless I am wrong, the initial inability to see anything after entering the dark from a brightly lit place is governed essentially by principles that will be discussed in Chapter XII. However, these rules do not explain the similar disability when we are moving from the dark into brightness, and we should perhaps add as an explanation that, just as the previous effect of a strong light stimulus makes us more or less insensitive for a while to the effects of a weak light, so the previous effect of a strong light difference makes us more or less insensitive for a while to the subsequent perception of a weak difference. Now, whether we go from a very bright to a very dim light or vice versa, there is a great difference in light, which, although appreciated successively, could still more or less blunt our senses for a time against differences in light that afterwards can be appreciated simultaneously. Yet even this explanation remains very uncertain.

Be this as it may, it still appears overwhelmingly likely, according to the principles to be cited in Chapter XII, that when the eye adapts to both components equally the outcome is just the same as when both components are dimmed in equal proportion. The difference remains equally noticeable under these conditions, so that a disturbance of the law cannot take place on this account.

---

ness) and Helmholtz *Eigenlicht* (self-light of the eye), and the translation is usually *self-light* or *intrinsic light* of the eye or of the retina. Ewald Hering, making the point that black is a positive sensation and that adaptation of the retina proceeds toward gray, called this *constant gray*, which G. E. Müller named *cortical gray* on the assumption that it was an addition by the visual area of the cerebral cortex, an addition that remained when the retina by adaptation went entirely out of function. A more modern term is *idioretinal light* or sometimes the *noise level* of visual excitation. In general, see H. L. F. v. Helmholtz, *Physiological Optics*, Eng. trans. Amer. Optical Soc., 1924, II, p. 12 ff, 16. For a modern treatment see Barlow's findings that dark adaptation limited by intrinsic light (= noise) of retina. *Science*, 1964, *144*, 1309–1314.

[6] Trans. Note: *Ueber ein psychophysisches Gundgesetz und dessen Beziehung zur Schätzung der Sterngrössen. Abhandl. d. Kgl. sächs. Ges. d. Wiss.* 1859. *Vol.* IV, pp. 457–532.

[*] *Sillim. J.* 1850. IX, *p.* 443.

In respect of the lower limit of our law we note that it cannot, on closer examination, be considered as a true limit. What appeared to be, so far, a deviation from the law, is strictly speaking a consequence of it. In order to show this to be true some preliminary discussion is necessary, which subsequently will become important in many other respects.

Under abnormal conditions, sensations can originate in all sense modalities through internal causes (inner stimuli) independently of external stimulation, and these sensations are, as we know, called hallucinations, which offer proof that such a possibility exists. There is in itself nothing remarkable when such a sensation expresses itself in a given area in a constant and normal manner. A factual example is found in sight, where we have to admit the existence of more or less normal hallucinations. The blackness that we see in the dark and with eyes shut is just such a visual sensation that has no external stimulus. It should not be confused with seeing nothing, like seeing with the finger or the back of the head, nor should it be compared with hearing nothing in the absence of an external sound. The blackness that is present when the eyes are closed is rather just the same impression of light as we get when viewing a black surface, one which can change through all gradations to the most intense visual sensation. Indeed, this intrinsic blackness of the eye changes occasionally through purely internal causes into bright light and contains, so to speak, a sprinkling of light phenomena.

By paying strict attention, one discovers in the blackness that is seen when the eyes are closed a kind of fine dust composed of light, which is present in different people and under different conditions of the eye in various states of abundance, and in certain diseases may increase to a lively phenomenon of light. In my own eyes there exists, since the time when I had a lengthy disease of the eye, a strong continuing flickering of light, which increases according to the stimulation of my eyes and is subject to great fluctuations. Such active subjective light phenomena may, moreover, take very different forms in various individuals. I shall not cite further details here, but refer to writings on diseases of the eye and chapters on subjective light phenomena in physiological tests. See, for example, *Rüte's Ophthalmol.* 2d ed., p. 192.

The intrinsic ocular blackness can also increase and decrease in depth. Proof of this fact is easily found. If one has fixated a white disk on black paper sharply and persistently, a deep black afterimage of the disk will appear subsequently against a relatively light ground, even with the eyes closed and with hands held in front of them (in order to exclude light seeping in through the eyelids). At the same time the retina appears insensitive to external light at the place of the afterimage. For if the open eye, with the afterimage, is directed toward a white surface, one notices there a dark spot against a white ground. The intrinsic light thus becomes dimmer when the eye is fatigued and becomes relatively brighter when it is rested.

The same effect as that of fatigue is also found in cases of sensory paralysis, whether partial or total, transitory or persistent, or affecting only the retina or also the central part of the visual apparatus. Not infrequently only some places on the retina are affected. Dependent upon the degree of loss of sensitivity to different colored rays, the patient in this case sees gray, black, or colored spots on objects corresponding to the affected location.* In some patients these effects are transitory. Even the whole visual field may darken either permanently or temporarily because of internal causes. Rüte† "observed a woman whose eyes were often enveloped by sudden complete darkness under conditions of constant illumination. Visible objects would now and then break through the darkness like phantoms and promptly disappear when the patient attempted to fixate them."

Should not only the retina, but also the central parts of the visual sense be impaired completely, one might expect the blackness of the visual field not only to darken, but itself to disappear (as it does at the boundaries of the visual field with closed eyes), and one would expect no more seeing with the eyes than with the finger or a dead nerve fibre. I have not been able to find anything on this matter and have not been able to get a final opinion from famous ophthalmologists on whether such an effect has been observed to be total and permanent; it would appear not to be the case. But transient and partial conditions do seem to occur, according to the information provided by Rute:‡ "It happens occasionally in subjects with nervous disorders, during momentary deterioration of isolated parts of the retina, that the part of the external world which corresponds to the impaired places does not appear to exist at all." § The central conditions of visual sensations in the brain are most likely tied up so essentially with the conditions of life, that a complete and lasting cessation of one without the other cannot take place.

Under assumptions of unlimited validity of the law downwards, even the photometric intensity of the intrinsic light can be determined by experiments analogous to those that have so far been used for validation of Weber's Law. One merely has to move a single light away from a shadow-producing body, in the dark of night, until the shadow, which is filled only by intrinsic light, is just no longer distinguished from the surrounding ground, which is simultaneously illuminated by both the intrinsic light and external illumination. Applying the fraction $\frac{1}{100}$, as determined

---

* *Rüte's Ophthalmol.* II, p. 458.
† *Ophthalmol.* I, p. 156.
‡ *Ophthalmol.* I. p. 154.
§ A treatise of Gräfe's "On the Interruption of the Visual Field by Amblyopic Affections" in *Gräfe's Arch. f. Ophthalmol.* II. Abth. 2, p. 258, appears to pertain only to cases where parts of the visual field did not really drop out, but were only darkened.

by Volkmann, the illumination which this light adds to the intrinsic light at this distance amounts to $\frac{1}{100}$ of the intensity of the intrinsic light.

This experiment has actually been carried out, even though as yet very casually. The shadow on a background of black velvet disappeared for Volkmann's eyes when the light, a common stearin candle in a long dark passageway lengthened by some rooms, had been moved back a distance of 87 ft. If at this distance the illumination which this light added to the intrinsic light amounted to $\frac{1}{100}$ of the intrinsic light, it would have been equal to it at $\frac{1}{10}$ of that distance, that is, at 8.7 ft. The experiment tells us therefore that a black board receives an illumination from a common stearin candle burning at about a distance of 9 ft, which is equal to that of the intrinsic light alone without external illumination. Therefore the photometric intensity of the latter illumination is equal to the former.

Perhaps one may find such a degree of brightness of the intrinsic light remarkable and much too large, in that it is supposed to be equivalent to the illumination of a surface by a common candle at practically 9 ft distance, but one must not overlook the fact that it is the illumination of a black surface which forms the basis of this assertion, grounded, as it is, on experimental proof. An absolutely black surface would not be illuminated even by a flame of any intensity standing right next to it, as it absorbs all light. Only the circumstance that no absolutely black body exists permits us to speak of the low degree of luminance of a black ground at all. The black ground therefore still reflects some, but only very little, light in the vicinity of the shadow, with which the intensity of the intrinsic light might very well be commensurable, as indeed it turned out to be in the experiment.

I have cited at this point only results for Volkmann's eyes in the most careful experiment that he has carried out so far. Two others whom he called in for this experiment still recognized the shadow at that distance of 87 ft, beyond which the experiment could not be pushed because of the nature of the situation. This finding proves that either their intrinsic light or their sensitivity was not the same. Volkmann intends to follow up these experiments with further and more precise determinations. In the meantime his results suffice to show that the photometric intensity of the intrinsic light is neither an indeterminable quantity nor an immeasurably small amount. That point is all that matters for us now.

Since, according to what has just been said, the blackness of the visual field under complete exclusion of external light must still be looked upon as a true visual sensation, it may not be neglected in checking Weber's Law. If we observe with the unaided eye the nuances of shading of two

clouds or shadows that are closely alike, then the brightness of the intrinsic light should be added to both. If we now reduce the light from both
of these clouds or shadows by placing a gray filter in front of them, the
brightness of the intrinsic light stays unchanged. It therefore adds its own
constant intensity each time to the clouds or shadows, which then do not
really remain at the same ratio and do not show, at the same time, the
same relative difference as before, but rather are found to have a lesser
one, which according to the law must be accompanied by a decline in the
differences of the sensations. Indeed, if we keep on using darker filters the
intrinsic light alone remains eventually in place of the nuances of shading,
and all differences disappear. The intrinsic light of the eyes acts in fact,
strange as it may seem, quite like the bright luminance of the sky in
which the stars disappear. Weber's Law with respect to external light
stimuli can, therefore, be proven only to the degree that the intrinsic
light is vanishingly small compared to the extrinsic light. Even Masson
claims the validity of the law only above the point where one is able
to read regular printing. On the other hand, if one carries the experiments down to the point where the light is too dim, the differences of
shading become less clear. Corresponding rules apply to all modifications
of the experiment and have many times been proven by experience.

An illustration of what I have just said is furnished by the observation
that one can make a light that differs only very little from the intrinsic
light disappear by a means which appears to be quite the opposite but
actually obeys the same principle.

In the evening, if one fixates a star that one can just differentiate from
the black background of the sky, one can make it vanish either by putting
a darkened glass in front of the eyes or by bringing a lamp up to the eye
from the side. A beautiful example of a corresponding experience could
be found at the time of the splendid comet of the beginning of October in
the year 1858. Gray or tinted filters, as well as bringing up a bright lamp
from the side, shortened the tail perceptibly, and a dark red filter, through
which I was able to recognize the finest details of the clouds by day, even
caused the whole comet to disappear. The first experience is explained by
the fact that the light of the star or comet, but not the intrinsic light of the
eye, was considerably cut down by the filter. The second is due to the fact
that not only the place on the retina on which the image falls, but to a
certain extent the whole background of the eye is illuminated by the light.
Various factors contribute to this phenomenon, as different observers
note.

First, the light shines through sclera and choroid with a reddish color. Some
remarkable instances of objective and subjective coloration of the images depend

on this fact, as has been studied with special care by Brücke in *Pogg. Ann.* LXXXIV, page 418. Secondly, from the image a direct scattering reflection extends to other parts of the retina, as also back to the cornea, from which it is in part reflected again to the retina. (This fact and also the following one have been stressed by Helmholtz in *Pogg. Ann.* LXXXVI, pp. 501 ff.) In the third place, because of the microscopic make-up of the ocular media of cells, fibres and membranes, an irregular scattering, apparently a consequence of refraction, is found. The colored halos seen around light sources that Meyer has made subject to a special study in *Pogg. Ann.* XCVI, page 235, are dependent on this factor. Because of this last reason, and because of the direct scattering reflection from the image of the light source on the remaining retina, the illumination of the retina is strongest in the vicinity of the image. It extends, however, in a diminishing manner over the whole visual field.

The very weak light of a star or of the tail of a comet, like the light of the stars in the daytime, is more likely to be overwhelmed by the combined action of these causes, the closer it falls to the image of the light source in the eye, since the illumination of the optical field is strongest in that vicinity.

Brewster* states therefore:

"When the light of a candle held close to the right eye acts on a part of the retina, it desensitizes all the remaining parts of the retina to a greater or lesser degree with respect to all other light stimuli. The lack of sensitivity reaches its maximum close to the illuminated spot and decreases with increasing distance from it. Moderately illuminated objects disappear completely in the vicinity of strongly stimulated parts; and bodies with vivid colors not only are robbed of their shine, but also are changed chromatically."

For the same reasons one can, by Helmholtz's method,† perceive the so-called ultraviolet rays of the sun's spectrum, which cannot be seen by the usual methods, even without the use of fluorescent substances. One only has to arrange matters so that these rays can be perceived isolated from the remaining parts of the spectrum, which tend to overwhelm them by stray light.

A further general conclusion may be drawn from the foregoing comment. In spite of the fact that under stronger illumination the amount of light reflected from black and white surfaces increases in equal proportion, the difference between the black and the white appears greater under increased illumination, because the brightness of the intrinsic light will always constitute a greater part of the brightness of the black. This fact is, for example, the simple reason why one can read better in the light than in the dark.

Except for the limits of the law, which are related to the degree of in-

* *Pogg. Ann.* XXVII, p. 494.
† *Pogg. Ann.* LXXXVI, p. 513.

tensity of the light, one should not forget that its validation by observation can be expected only to the extent that, apart from intensity, the remaining conditions, which could exert an influence on the perception of the difference in illumination, remain equal. The investigations of the conditions with which we could be concerned in this respect are still largely incomplete. However, we shall make mention of some matters, which deserve special notice according to our experiences up to the present.

As mentioned on page [126], Arago noticed an influence of the movement of components on the perception of their difference. Volkmann also noticed this effect. In order to appreciate the faintest traces of the appearance or disappearance of a shadow, the light that throws the shadow had to be moved, setting the shadow in motion at the same time. The just noticeable difference of $\frac{1}{100}$ could then be fixed under the influence of this motion.

In the experiments of Arago with which we are here concerned the components did not consist of two shadows but were obtained in the following way. A telescope, with a Rochon prism inside that doubled the image and a Nicol prism in front of its objective lens, was aimed at a hole in a black cardboard screen, through which the covered sky could be projected.[7] By turning the Nicol prism one of the double images could be darkened at will by an amount measurable as compared with the other. The relative position of the main portions of the Nicol and the Rochon prisms allowed the relative intensity of the two images produced by the latter to be determined. By a straight-line motion of the Rochon prism inside the telescope in the direction from the eyepiece toward the objective lens the weaker image could be set in motion, in such a way that it could shift in due course from a position where its edge crossed the middle of the stronger image to a position where the edges of the two images just touched each other.

In three series of experiments, conducted in this manner with the aid of several observers, the weaker image, which was superimposed over the stronger, disappeared when moved at a speed of 12 angular minutes per second of time, and when the intensity of the weaker image amounted to the following fractions of the stronger one:

[7] Ed. Note: A Nicol prism is a split rhomb of calcite. Light passing through it is divided into two beams, of which the ordinary one is reflected to one side and largely absorbed and the extraordinary one transmitted directly as polarized light. It is used to obtain polarized light. A Rochon prism consists of two apposed wedges of calcite; it divides the light into ordinary and extraordinary beams and was used by Arago to give a double image. See A. C. Hardy and F. H. Perrin, *The Principles of Optics*. New York and London: McGraw-Hill, 1932, pp. 597–602.

	At Rest	In Motion
I	1/39	1/58
II	1/51	1/87
III	1/71	1/131

Concerning the great differences shown by the absolute values of these three series of experiments Arago merely remarks: "I shall not attempt here to explain how the sensitivity of the eye in a state of rest was so different in these three series of experiments. This is a physiological phenomenon to which we shall have to return." The difference cannot have been due to the differences between the observers, since Arago remarks: The above were "results in approximate agreement, obtained by M. Laugier, by M. Goujon and by M. Charles Mathieu"; nor could it depend on the difference between the absolute intensities. That would contradict both the express acknowledgment of our law in popular astronomy and in part the general findings which he adds as the result of all experiments: "Let us add, as information calculated to enable us to judge the degree of darkness of the field, that the weak image, when it was projected outside the strong image, disappeared when its intensity was $\frac{1}{2100}$."

The following remarks by Förster* are also of interest with respect to the influence of movement. He says with respect to use of his photometer:

In very weak illumination and with very small objects it is observed that the latter, when looked at quietly for some moments, suddenly disappear, instead of becoming clearer, only to reappear shortly afterwards. I believe that this change does not depend on fluctuations of energy, which are a property of the retina, but on the fact that in the moment where the object again reappears in view the eyes have carried out tiny movements so that the images now fall on new parts of the retina which had so far been excited in other ways. I had on the occasion of experiments on the spatial sense of the retina carried on in collaboration with Aubert (see *v. Gräfe'sches Arch.* III) the opportunity to observe this fact with the greatest certainty. We were then looking, in a darkened room, at large sheets of paper at a distance of some feet, on which were written large numbers, isolated by large spaces in between, and it was important to keep the eyes very quiet. The room was so dark that the numbers appeared to us merely as black specks. When I fixated one of them, it was not long—at a certain weak illumination— until the fixated number as well as all others completely disappeared in the grayness of the sheet of paper, which became darker and darker. When this moment occurred, further fixation became impossible, there was an unpleasant feeling in the orbits, the eyes made a small movement and the whole sheet, with its specks of numbers, immediately became visible again. The eye movement

* *Ueber Hemeralopie*, p. 13.

either was noticed as such or else it was made consciously, or, finally, it could be inferred from the fact that now a number at a different place appeared at the fixated point.

It is still not clear on what influence this movement depends. It has been sought in the fact that the difference would now fall on a new spot, which had not yet been fatigued, but since components of the difference themselves are not changed by the movement, which only serves to displace the location of the very small difference, it does not appear that the state of fatigue could be lessened to any extent by the movement.[8]

Another possibility would be that the improvement of difference perception in movement would be determined by the multiple perception of the difference by a number of elements rather than the freshness of the elements themselves. Perhaps a summation of the impressions takes place as successive points are stimulated within certain time limits. Finally, the following situation (which is admittedly not explained so far) might still, in its generality, serve as an explanation. Any comparison of two different magnitudes stands a better chance of success when done successively with the same organs than when done simultaneously with different ones, as E. H. Weber has pointed out and documented with experimental evidence, and as we have also seen on page [73]. We apprehend a small difference between two weights more easily by successively weighing them with the same hand than by lifting them simultaneously with both hands. By moving the components in our experiments with lights, however, a simultaneous difference is changed into a successive one for various points on the retina. The same points which were subject to a stronger light are now stimulated by a weaker one and vice versa, and the quicker the movement, the more points are reached successively in a given time. As yet, however, this explanation also is only speculative.

A further condition that influences the perceptibility of a difference is the size of the components, a variable which does not change the law with regard to intensity, however, if the extents always remain comparable. This statement follows directly from the fact that it has been shown to be valid for stars as well as for extended shadows. However, a point source of light is not as easily discriminated from the ground as is a surface when intensities are equal. Since this matter will be treated more thoroughly in Chapter XI, I shall not take it up further here.

---

[8] Ed. Note: It has long been noted that moving objects in vision or on the skin or changes in pitch in music are determiners of attention, and that movement may even lower the intensive threshold so as to make perceptible what was imperceptible before. See W. B. Pillsbury, *Attention.* New York: Macmillan, 1908, pp. 48–50.

Thirdly, it has been shown that a given relative difference in brightness is easier to discriminate when its components are darker against a lighter ground than when they are lighter against a darker ground. On this matter we have not only a specific statement by Arago based on his experience regarding the choice of one or the other of these conditions in a photometric apparatus, which he describes,* but also the fact that Hankel has found the same to be true on the occasion of other photometric experiments (which are so far unpublished).

Finally the following remarks: In the analogy of pitch and color, which is usually considered valid in other respects, the fact that Weber's Law does not exist in the field of color is a remarkable exception. As will be shown immediately, this means that in contrast to pitch, equally noticeable differences in vibration are by no means proportional to the frequency of oscillation of colors. Indeed, the eye is hardly capable, at the limits of the spectrum, of seeing changes of color at intervals of a minor— or even a major—third, whereas in the region of yellow or green the noticeable changes in color follow each other so quickly that all intermediate steps between yellow and green are bunched in the interval of a small half tone†). There are, by the way, also other points not discussed here, where the analogy between tones and colors does not hold.

2. SOUND

In the field of sound we must distinguish mere noise, which has no specific pitch and where only intensity can be measured, from tones, where we must consider both intensity (which depends on the amplitude of vibrations and is proportional to their square) and pitch (which both depends on and is measured physically by the frequency of vibrations). Intensity can be investigated for one as well as the other, pitch only for the latter. Let us first examine intensity.

Under Vierordt's direction, Renz and Wolf‡ have carried out experiments, using the method of right and wrong cases, on the differences in loudness in the ticking of a clock, which was placed at various distances from the ear under suitable circumstances. These are the chief results of their experiments:

"If two sounds of relatively weak absolute intensities are perceived one immediately after the other, then the judgments become more certain with increasing differences of intensity in such a way that sound intensities in the ratio of 100 : 72 can be quite clearly distinguished under all cir-

---

*Arago's Works, edited by Hankel.
† Helmholtz in the Berichten der Berl. Akad. 1855, pp. 757 ff.
‡ Vierordt's Arch. 1856, H. 2, p. 185. Pogg. Ann. XCVIII.

cumstances. When the ratio is 100 : 92 the number of correct choices surpasses the number of false or indeterminate ones by only a small amount."

These carefully conducted experiments deserve attention as examples of the use of the method of right and wrong cases and because they point to the relatively poor ability to recognize differences in loudness, a fact important in view of what will follow. The experiments are not suitable, however, for deciding the validity of our law, since they had not been aimed at judgments of equality of difference sensations at various absolute levels of intensity. The following experiments refer to this matter.

After Volkmann had carried out his photometric experiments, I spoke to him about the great importance of a general validation of Weber's Law. He improvised on the spot the following apparatus for a preliminary proof of the law applied to loudness, which was built the same day at a cost hardly worth mentioning.

It consists simply of a free-swinging hammer, which knocks against a plate made of some substance that either does or does not give off a tone. A strong knitting needle served as the axis of this pendulum. It was fastened in two brass holes in a crosspiece held between two uprights, supported by a plank. The sound produced is understandably stronger or weaker, physically speaking, if the hammer is made heavier or lighter, if it is allowed to drop from a greater or lesser height against the plate, or if one stands closer or further away from the apparatus. Since the initially improvised apparatus did not have any circular divisions for determining the elevation of the hammer, a quadrant with a few markings at different heights was placed next to the apparatus and the elevation of the hammer determined each time with its help. The hammer was made of wood and fell against a square glass bottle. Two elevations of the hammer were chosen, which yielded sounds sufficiently different so that an observer standing next to the apparatus could not be mistaken when guessing which sound was the louder, without knowing the elevation. Still, the sounds differed little enough so that when the difference was reduced by about a half, judgment became unsure and yielded partly right and partly wrong cases. Subsequently the observer moved away successively by 6, 12, and 18 paces, so that his initial distance from the apparatus was multiplied at least 12 times. At each of these distances the same experiment was repeated a number of times at both of these heights, which had previously presented to the observer a difference that, while still recognizable with certainty, was only very small. Since the twelvefold increase in distance reduced the physical intensity of the sound for the observer by $\frac{1}{144}$,* the

* Strictly speaking this would be true only if the experiments were carried out in free space. These were undertaken in a closed room.

difference, which was not much more than just noticeable close up, should have disappeared, if it depended on the absolute intensity of the sound. At all three distances, however, the observer's judgment remained just as sure and correct as near by.

While apparatus and experiment were crude in certain respects, the essential aspects seemed to be sufficiently covered and the results were so conclusive that it could be foreseen that a more exact execution with a carefully constructed apparatus would not lead to any other results. This expectation has indeed been fulfilled in later experiments by Volkmann, specifically in large-scale experiments with sound intensities varying from unity by more than a hundredfold. These were not carried out, however, with a falling pendulum, but with steel balls dropping freely on a steel plate with suitable precautions. In some of them I took part myself. In these experiments height of drop, weight of the falling balls, and distance of the observer were varied within wide limits. The height from which the balls were dropped and their variations were exactly determined by a vertical scale placed along the path of the fall. In other respects the method and outcome of the experiments agreed with those already described. With the most varied absolute sound intensities, a ratio of 3 : 4 of the heights from which the balls were dropped (corresponding, as we shall show, to the same ratios of sound intensities), was just sufficient to effect a sure discrimination by two observers with good powers of discrimination. This value agrees well with the results found by Renz and Wolf.

Herewith follows a more detailed description of the experiments, extracted from Volkmann's journal:

A prismatic rod has a scale marked on it and stands vertically on a board. It can be adjusted to an exact vertical by three screws. Sliding on this rod are two horizontal arms α and β. A ball is dropped onto the board from the height indicated by the two arms. The ball was grasped between thumb and forefinger, the tip of the finger touched arm α or β and the fingers were then carefully pulled apart in order to drop the ball. I had two balls which were equally heavy. One was grasped with the left and the other with the right hand, so as not to have to lift, or worse, to search for the ball at the second trial after it had been dropped the first time.

The closest distance of the listening observer from the instrument amounted to 1m [meter], the greatest was 6 m.

The absolute heights which were compared differed in the ratio 3 : 11.

The weights of the falling balls differed in the ratio of 1.35 gm : 14.85 gm. . . .

Numerous trials within the range of these differences of sound showed that Heidenhain and I were able to discriminate with certainty differences in sound intensities which stood in the ratio of 3 : 4. When this difference is lessened to a ratio of 6 : 7 some errors and more often indecision in judgment occurred.

On the other hand, Fechner committed errors very frequently at a ratio of 3 : 4. Apparently, however, practice influenced his ability to make discriminations, for at the end of a very long series of observations he distinguished correctly sound intensities in the ratio of 3 : 4 every time, whereas in the beginning he heard more often wrong than right and after lengthy trials was still making ⅓ false statements to ⅔ right ones.

The earlier experiments had been based on the method of just noticeable differences. For reasons I have already mentioned we cannot reach the same grade of precision by this method as by the methods of right and wrong cases and average error. Unquestionably, therefore, experiments using those methods are needed. However, considering the extraordinarily wide variation of absolute intensities used in the experiments that were carried out, the results are decisive enough to validate the law in general. At most, only deviations of a low order are possible within the limits of the existing experiments, without these giving any reasons for such a probability.

It might be useful to add something on the theoretical and practical aspects of the apparatus to be used in this kind of experiment.

Schafhäutl* has described an instrument with falling balls for measuring sensitivity to sound, but has used it only to measure absolute sensitivity.

The sound pendulum also has been of service in this respect. Itard† has made use of such an instrument (called an acoumeter) for examining the sensitivity of hearing in cases of hearing disorders. It consisted of a hammered copper ring suspended freely from a rod fastened to a post standing on a pedestal. The ring was struck by a pendulum, whose elevation was measured by a graduated arc.

I myself have made up a double sound pendulum with graduations which had two pendulums, constructed alike, striking both sides of a thick piece of slate;‡ but I have not had time to carry out experiments with it.

The following remarks concern the theory of these instruments:

It is plain that when a body is in free fall or as a pendulum strikes another body, the intensity of the sound originated is proportional to both the height of the drop and the weight of the falling body,§ as long as the

---

* *Abhandl. d. baier. Akad.* VII. Part 2.
† *Gehler's Wört. Art. Gehör.*, p. 1217.
‡ I was unable to achieve the same sound with both pendulums when using wood.
§ Schafhäutl makes the intensity of the sound proportional to the square root of the distance of the drop (*München. Abhandl.* VII, p. 517), a rule which I do not find correct according to the proportion given above.

influence of the resistance of the air and some other possibly disturbing influences can be neglected.

Actually, the intensity of the sound is proportional to the square of the amplitude of the vibrations of the sounding body; the amplitude of these vibrations is (according to well-known formulas) proportional to the velocity with which the particles pass their position of equilibrium, which is the same as the speed with which they move away from it. This velocity in turn depends both on the speed at which the falling body lands and its weight. How fast a falling body hits (the terminal velocity of its fall), is, according to the laws of falling bodies, proportional to the square root of the height from which it was dropped. Therefore, since the square of this terminal velocity is proportional to the height from which the body was dropped, the square of the velocity with which the particles move away from their resting position (and so forth) is also proportional to this height. Since we know that it makes no difference with regard to this terminal velocity whether a body falls freely or by a devious pathway through a given distance, the same considerations apply to the head of a falling pendulum (assuming the friction of the axle to be negligible) as to a freely falling body. One must only be careful in both instances not to impart a velocity to the falling body at the start, if the given dependence of sound intensity on the height of the drop is to remain valid. Resistance of the air should be negligible at the small distances involved and at the velocities at which one will operate in general, especially if lead is used for the falling body.

The preceding argument demonstrates that the sound intensity of the sound pendulum is not proportional to the angle of elevation φ of the pendulum, but to the vertical height to which the hammer is lifted above its lowest position; in other words, it is proportional to $1 - \cos \varphi = 2 \sin \varphi^2/2$. The instrument can be calibrated accordingly. Since, for example, $\cos 45°$ is equal to $\sqrt{\tfrac{1}{2}} = 0.707$ and $\cos 90°$ is equal to zero, the proportion of sound intensities at these two elevations is $1 - 0.707 (= 0.293)$ to 1, or practically 3 to 10. The angles of elevation of $60°$, $90°$, and $180°$ correspond to sound intensities of $\tfrac{1}{2} : 1 : 2$. As long as the elevations do not exceed $60°$, one can assume the sound intensities to be approximately equal to the square of the elevation, so that double the elevation almost corresponds to fourfold and triple the elevation to ninefold sound intensity.*

* This follows from the well-known formula

$$\cos \varphi = 1 - \frac{\varphi^2}{1 \cdot 2} + \frac{\varphi^4}{1 \cdot 2 \cdot 3 \cdot 4} - \cdots$$

There follow two brief tables giving the sound intensities corresponding to elevations of a sound pendulum from 0° to 90° and vice versa, when 90° is taken to produce an intensity of 1.0000 (Table I) or 10 (Table II). At 180° it would then be twice that at 90° and all intensities for elevations between 90° and 180° fall in between. One is not very likely, however, to use a pendulum at elevations above 90°.

RELATIONSHIP BETWEEN SOUND INTENSITY AND HEIGHT OF SOUND PENDULUM

I				II			
Height	Intensity	Height	Intensity	Intensity	Height	Intensity	Height
90°	1.0000	45°	0.2929	10	90.00°	3	45.57°
85°	0.9128	40°	0.2340	9	84.26°	2	36.87°
80°	0.8264	35°	0.1808	8	78.46°	1	25.84°
75°	0.7412	30°	0.1340	7	72.54°	1/2	17.19°
70°	0.6580	25°	0.0937	6	66.42°	1/4	12.97°
65°	0.5774	20°	0.0603	5	60.00°	1/8	9.07°
60°	0.5000	15°	0.0341	4	53.13°	1/16	6.41°
55°	0.4264	10°	0.0152				
50°	0.3572	5°	0.0038				

With regard to pitch, where the number of vibrations takes the place of the stimulus intensity, we have, besides Weber's general statements, Delezenne's, also cited by Weber. Delezenne's observations, however, as I was able to convince myself from his original works, concern themselves mainly with what deviations from the purity of this or that kind of interval (single notes, octaves, fifths, and so forth) could still be distinguished, rather than with the question of whether deviations from the equality of two tones appeared equally large at equal ratios of the number of vibrations (at different heights on the scale), which is actually the question raised by Weber's Law. Meanwhile there is no necessity for special experiments to validate the law in this respect. After all, it is the simple —even the notorious—testimony of a musical ear, that equal ratios of vibrations correspond to equally large differences between tones at different octaves, so that one can consider the law proved here more directly than anywhere else and this even for large differences. Euler, Herbart, and Drobisch have also based their conclusions on this fact in their mathematical consideration of tonal relationships.

I have on occasion asked several people with a good musical ear when carrying on experiments with a wooden pendulum striking a piece of wood, whether they were able to compare sound intensities at 45° and 90° with comparable ratios of pitch. Some declared they were not able to do this. Remarkably enough, most of those who could be persuaded to make a comparison (independently of one another and not knowing anything about the judgment of the others) agreed that this ratio could be compared to a fourth. However, I shall not attach much weight to these experiments in their present crude and provisional execution, especially since this agreement was not unanimous. Personally, I still consider it very questionable whether a direct comparison of ratios of intensity and pitch of a sensation can be made. In any case, the outcome of these experiments confirms the results obtained by Renz and Wolf, as well as those by Volkmann. According to them one is not likely to consider rather extensive differences in sound intensities (3 : 10) as very great.

In connection with the same problem I found it very interesting to hear the statement made by a musician (the violin virtuoso von Wasilewski) about the Rhine choral festival, that a choir of 400 males voices did not cause a significantly stronger impression than one of 200.

3. WEIGHTS

Weber's results, obtained by means of the method of just noticeable differences, which offered the first confirmation of our law in the area of weight judgment, have already been cited on page [115]. His experiments had the special merit that in part of them the pressure sensitivity of the skin was isolated from the muscle sense and the results obtained in this way were compared with those based on the joint expression of these sensations. My own experiments, on the other hand, carried out by means of the method of right and wrong cases, will be concerned with the natural combination of both these sensations found in comparisons of lifted weights, and will be discussed in detail presently. An exact separation of the two could not be carried out with my mode of procedure. However, a common proof of the law for each seemed useful in view of the degree of precision the method promised. In addition, these experiments were designed as much to study method as they were to check the law.

In order to understand the following account, reference will often have to be made to what has been said on pages [77–100] in the chapter on methods. I do not, however, feel it necessary to return to this matter in detail. On the other hand, one will find in the following discussion many proofs and examples of what has been said there.

There are two major series of experiments on the topic under discussion, one a two-handed the other a single-handed series (carried out separately with the right and the left hands). Both of these were comparable, completed on a series of six standard weights of 300, 500, 1000,

1500, 2000, and 3000 gm, and led to results which agreed very well with one another. The single-handed series was completed in October and November 1856, the two-handed series during December 1856 and January 1857. The conditions of the experiment were essentially the same as the normal conditions described on page [80]. The following facts should specially be noted in this respect:

Each series consisted of 32 experimental days, each having 12 sessions involving lifting the weight 64 times, so that there were in all $32 \times 12 \times 64 = 24,576$ simple liftings or cases. With each standard weight P (and periodically interchanged with it) two specific proportional increments, namely $0.04P$ and $0.08P$, were used as additional weights. The latter comparison weight may appear large, but still yields enough wrong cases, as one may convince himself from the table that follows. The reason for this finding lies in the procedure as described on pages [78–79] where each comparison is based on a simple pair of weight lifts instead of on repeatedly lifting the weight back and forth, when a $D = 0.08P$ hardly would bring out any wrong cases. On every day of experimentation $12 \times 64 = 768$ weights were lifted, and all six of the standards, each in two sessions of 64 liftings, were tested with the same relative D, which changed only after days or weeks, as mentioned below. In addition, the procedure provided for ascending (↑) and descending (↓) series of standards, to be changed daily. Each of the two experimental series added up to a total of $32 \times 128 = 4096$ liftings or cases for each of the standards. There were 2048 with $D = 0.04P$ and as many with $D = 0.08P$, with 1024 of these ↑ and as many ↓ . In the two-handed series the daily 128 liftings of the weights were continuous. In the one-handed series 64 trials with the left hand were followed by 64 with the right, where the left hand or the right started off alternately. $D = 0.04P$ and $D = 0.08P$ were interchanged in the two-handed series after two days and in the one-handed series only after eight days. This procedure made a difference in that in the two-handed series the values of sensitivity for the two D's are quite comparable. This series can therefore serve to substantiate our law, according to which the ratio of right cases to total cases r/n depends on the magnitude of D, provided the sensitivity h is constant.* This is not the case with the one-handed series, when the weeks with $0.08P$ yield comparatively smaller values for sensitivity than those of $0.04P$, as noted in my remarks on page [70]. However, the influence of the magnitude of

---

* This law can be expressed, as discussed in Chapter VII, by the relationship of the values of r/n to the magnitude of $t = hD$ in our fundamental table on page (90). Accordingly, doubling D yields twice the t, when the influence of p and q is eliminated.

the standard weight on the values found, which is all we are concerned with here, can be compared just as well with the one-handed procedure as with the two-handed procedure.

I shall begin by giving the total number of right cases r for the several standards P, in order to start with the simplest, even if not the most exact, use of this series of observations. The values are subdivided according to their major conditions, but are not separated into the four major cases nor referred back to the exact measurements (that is, the values of $t = hD$ that can be computed from them). However, even without this calculation the main results with which we are concerned can be determined from the relationship of the right cases r summed over all major cases. Even a more precise treatment of the series would not accomplish more than a somewhat more exact demonstration of the same results.

The unit of weight used here is always the gram.

So that the meaning of the numbers in the tables which follow immediately cannot be misinterpreted I shall mention them specially for the first number in the first table. The number 612 for $P = 300$, $D = 0.04P$, $n = 1024$, (↑) means that with a standard of 300 and an added weight equal to 0.04 of the standard (that is, 12 gm) the number of right cases over all days when the standard was used in ascending series (↑) was 612, while the total number of cases, both right and wrong, was 1024 under the same circumstances. The number of wrong cases accordingly would be $1024 - 612 = 412$. The meaning of the other numbers will now be obvious. Naturally, the sum r in the final column is based on an n four times that in the separate columns, that is, 4096, as shown in the parentheses, since the r's of the four separate columns have been added across rows. On the other hand, the r in the final row is based on an n six times that of the individual numbers, that is, 6144, since r's belonging to the six P's of each column have been added to yield the final sum.

I. NUMBER OF RIGHT CASES r OF THE TWO-HANDED SERIES

P	n = 1024				Sum (n = 4096)
	D = 0.04P		D = 0.08P		
	↑	↓	↑	↓	
300	612	614	714	720	2660
500	586	649	701	707	2643
1000	629	667	747	753	2796
1500	638	683	811	781	2913
2000	661	682	828	798	2969
3000	685	650	839	818	2992
Sum (n = 6144)	3811	3945	4640	4577	16,973

II. NUMBER OF RIGHT CASES r OF THE ONE-HANDED SERIES

P	$n = 512$								Sum $(n = 4096)$
	$D = 0.04P$				$D = 0.08P$				
	Left		Right		Left		Right		
	↑	↓	↑	↓	↑	↓	↑	↓	
300	352	337	344	318	387	372	386	342	2838
500	339	332	348	335	383	402	413	366	2918
1000	325	343	382	388	383	412	389	422	3044
1500	353	358	371	383	406	416	435	430	3152
2000	378	353	369	382	413	418	414	421	3148
3000	367	343	364	386	426	433	429	438	3186
Sum $(n = 3072)$	2114	2066	2178	2192	2398	2453	2466	2419	18,286

I shall omit as not proper here any discussion of differences between the tabulated results according to different conditions (such as different magnitudes of D, the use of left and right hands, ↑ and ↓) which one may easily note for oneself. These matters will be discussed in detail in "Methods of Measurement." The breakdown of results according to these differences was here made mainly in order to show that the number of right cases under these conditions follows mainly the same course, that is, it rises slowly as the standard is increased and changes only little with the highest standards of 2000 and 3000 gm. Once the agreement of the various experimental conditions is recognized, one needs to regard only the last column, which in both tables shows the number of cases right for each standard with an n of 4096.

Should these experiments prove the law to hold directly and precisely, all r's for the different standards should be not only approximately but exactly alike, when the same ratio of additional weight to standard weight holds everywhere. This is not the case. The deviation of the experimental values from those predicted by the law should, nevertheless, be given no more importance as a true deviation than the one we found at the lower limits in the field of photoreception, but rather should be regarded in the same way as an analogous consequence of the law. Just as we had to take into account in the case of light sensations the inner stimulation which exists, even if no external light is admitted, so we have to consider here the weight of the arm and of possible covering pieces of clothing (in my own experiments only light shirt sleeves*) which are

---

* In addition there is the question to what extent air pressure on the skin would have to be considered at a specific value, but this seems to be, so to speak, included in the organism.

present even without the external weight P and are lifted when it is lifted. Now, just as the law can be proven experimentally in the former area only to the extent that the intrinsic light of the eye could be neglected as compared to the external light, so it can be shown to hold in this other area only to the extent that the weight of the arm, which in the process of lifting has to lift itself as well, can be neglected compared to the lifted weight.

We see actually only a very insignificant deviation at our highest standard weights from the values called for by the law, and generally the course of the deviations lies in the direction which is to be expected in line with the previous concept; that is, the number right increases somewhat with P. If we consider the same absolute addition A, due to the weight of the arm, added to the standard weights P as they increase (whereas D increases only proportionately to P), then naturally $D/(P + A)$, on which the number right depends, will increase as A tends to vanish compared to P in the divisor, that is, as P itself becomes larger. It will stay practically constant from the point where P has become so large that A does not have to be considered as compared to it. This is just as the experiment demonstrates.

Since the weight of the arm is not inconsiderable, it might strike us as odd that the increment which it represents to the standard weights of 300 to 3000 gm does not reveal itself as a greater increase of the number right as P is made larger. It is particularly striking that this increment is not more apparent in going from the lowest standards of 300 to 500 gm, where in the two-handed series there is even a small decrease. Apart from this latter anomaly, to which I shall return later, it is by no means certain, in the first place, that the stress imposed on the arm by its own weight should count the same as an external weight added to it. In the second place, one must remember that the weight P, when lifted, acts at the end of a lever formed by the arm doing the lifting, whereas the weight of the arm (residing in its center of gravity) acts on a shorter lever, with a comparably smaller moment. Thirdly, adding this moment to the moment of P concerns only the muscular and not the pressure sense, since only the weight P, but not the weight of the arm, can act to put pressure on the skin. In the fourth place and finally, we must consider that the number right found in the tables does not furnish us with an exact yardstick of sensitivity, but merely demonstrates the changes of sensitivity as the standard weights are increased. What we noted on pages [97–98] is particularly valid here; and we must take into account especially the circumstance, mentioned on pages [96–97], that the effect of the sequence of lifting p increases as the standard is made heavier, and because of this fact, according to the remarks on page [96], the sum of the number right turns out to be somewhat smaller than it would have been without these disturbing influences. Indeed, without this source of error, the number right would have turned out to be somewhat higher with the largest standards, and would therefore have been found to be somewhat more differentiated compared with the smallest standards. This consideration is particularly applicable with the smaller additional weight of 0.04P, whereas compared to the larger addition of 0.08P the influence of p more or less disappears. Thus one finds in the two-handed series the sums of 1321 and 1335 as the number right for standards of 1500 and 3000 with 0.04P, whereas with 0.08P the sums are 1592 and 1657. In the one-handed series, similarly, the numbers 1465 and 1460 are found with 0.04P, while with 0.08P the numbers are 1687 and 1726. The difference between the two series is then much larger with 0.08P than with 0.04P.

One may do away completely with the disturbing influence of secondary effects by means of the procedure of complete compensation already described on pages [93–96], which depends on the separation and separate calculation of the four main cases. Here follows, to begin with, the specification of r values according to the four main cases in the next table (III). A second table (IV) follows with the t values derived (without subgroups) from it by means of the fundamental table. In "Methods of Measurement" I shall give the corresponding specifications for a one-handed series. At this point I have no wish to amass too many figures. The definitive results with which the following discussion is concerned are found in columns 4hD and 8hD in Table IV. The remaining columns of this table and all of Table III are to be considered for the present only as a basis of these definitive results. They may also be incidentally useful to illuminate the manner of derivation and in general to demonstrate details of the method and are therefore included parenthetically.

III. VALUES OF r ACCORDING TO THE FOUR MAIN CONDITIONS OF THE TWO-HANDED SERIES

P	$n = 512$								Sum $(n = 4096)$
	$D = 0.04P$				$D = 0.08P$				
	r_1	r_2	r_3	r_4	r_1	r_2	r_3	r_4	
300	328	304	328	266	404	358	372	300	2660
500	352	274	321	288	399	339	364	306	2643
1000	334	318	335	309	377	365	410	338	2796
1500	346	323	308	344	408	402	399	383	2913
2000	296	365	309	373	404	385	439	398	2969
3000	244	393	265	433	392	447	390	428	2992
Sum	1900	1977	1866	2013	2384	2296	2374	2153	16,973

IV. VALUES OF t DERIVED FROM THE PREVIOUS TABLE FOR THE
TWO-HANDED SERIES

$n = 512, \nu = 1$

P	$D = 0.04P$					$D = 0.08P$					Total 8hD
	t_1	t_2	t_3	t_4	Sum 4bD	t_1	t_2	t_3	t_4	Sum 4bD	
300	2547	1677	2547	346	7117	5679	3692	4260	1535	15,166	22,283
500	3456	624	2290	1112	7482	5444	2958	3932	1749	14,083	21,565
1000	2769	2181	2807	1856	9613	4469	3973	5971	2920	17,333	26,946
1500	3224	2363	1820	3147	10,554	5873	5584	5444	4726	21,627	32,181
2000	1394	3973	1856	4301	11,524	5679	4813	7558	5397	23,447	34,971
3000	−416	5168	312	7200	12,264	5123	8067	5034	6915	25,139	37,403
Sum	12,974	15,986	11,632	17,962	58,554	32,267	29,087	32,199	23,242	116,795	175,349

To make my point clear I would like to give again the meaning of the first numbers in the two following tables:

The number $r_1 = 328$, when $P = 300$, $D = 0.04P$, and $n = 512$ in Table III means that when $P = 300$ gm and $D = 12$ gm, 512 trials under the first main condition (that is, where D lies in the left container and this is the first one lifted) give 328 right cases.

The corresponding number $t_1 = 2547$ in Table IV is taken from the fundamental table since $r/n = {}^{328}/_{512} = 0.6406$ and the number given represents the corresponding value of t. The statement $n = 512$ and $\nu = 1$ at the top of the table means that each t value is derived from 512 cases at once (that is without subgroups).

One may observe how much r changes under the four main conditions, and the extent to which these variations are influenced by the weight of the standard. When $P = 3000$, the number right is $r = 244$ and thus smaller than the number wrong, 268 (derived by subtracting the number right from the total number of 512), resulting coincidentally in a negative value of t (as shown in Table IV). Such cases, incidentally, appear quite often in my other tables of observations.

One could also use Table III, employing the rules given on pages [93–96], for completely balancing and determining the effects of p and q for oneself, although we are at the moment not interested in such a determination.

Further, one may convince oneself by comparing the sums appearing in the table of t's under $D = 0.04P$ and $D = 0.08P$ that the values of these sums are proportional to a noteworthy extent; in other words, that the sums obtained under 0.08 P are double those under 0.04P. This fact justifies the correctness of carrying out the calculation according to the remarks made on page [85].*
All this will not, however, be taken up here in detail.

The important point is that we observe to what extent the values of the sums 4hD and 8hD, which arise by adding t_1, t_2, t_3 and t_4, are constant at the various P's. They would have to be constant, like the sums of the r's from which they are derived, if our law were valid and if the weight of the arm would not be added to P.

* There are, incidentally, other trial series available to me on this topic.

The numbers in the two columns 4hD, and those in the column 8hD represent the actual numerical measurements that are our concern here, the first two with respect to each of the comparison weights by themselves, the last for both of them together. They are the same as would have been found independently of the effects of the temporal or spatial arrangements of the containers p and q, that is to say, would have been found as products of the measure of differential sensitivity h multiplied by the additional weight D four or eight times, so that the differential sensitivity measure h for the different standard weights could be found by dividing by $4D$ or $8D$.* According to our law, this term should be inversely proportional, except for the weight of the arm, to the weights P and simultaneously to the added weights D that are proportional to them. It follows that the products $4hD$ and $8hD$ should be found to be equal for the various standard weights. Now, since deviations from equality can be judged more easily than from proportionality, we leave the products $4hD$ and $8hD$, rather than finding h itself.

For the sake of greater clarity we summarize the values found in the three main columns, reduced by division by four or eight respectively, to their simple value hD, in the following table. The designations $\nu = 4$ and $\nu = 8$ on top of the columns mean, according to the nomenclature adopted on page [78], that each number in the column was derived from four or eight times n observations; and n is equal to 512.

V. VALUES OF hD FOR TWO-HANDED SERIES
$n = 512$

P	$D = 0.04P$ ($\nu = 4$)	$D = 0.08P$ ($\nu = 4$)	Mean ($\nu = 8$)
300	1779	3792	2785
500	1871	3521	2696
1000	2403	4333	3368
1500	2639	5407	4023
2000	2881	5862	4371
3000	3066	6285	4675
Sum	14,639	29,200	21,918

If we want to make the abstract concept of hD, which was used here only to substantiate our law, meaningful with respect to the experiment, we can put the matter in the following way: if for each of the standard weights, one used, instead of the same relative additional weight, as we did, that value divided by hD or a given multiple or fraction of hD, the same fraction r/n would always

---

* The D for column $8hD$ is $0.06P$ on the average. More precisely, the calculation of h for $D = 0.04P$ and $D = 0.08P$ should be done separately for the columns under $4hD$ and the most probable average of h determined from them.

have been obtained. For example, in the two-handed series that follows, one would have to divide the weights added to the standards of 2000 and 3000 gm, which are themselves proportional to these weights, by numbers proportional to 4500 and 4909,[9] in order to have them give rise to equally strong sensations.

Although these are not the definitive results of our calculation—those we will come to later—I list them here, because, since they do not deviate significantly from the final ones, one could still rely on them, and also because their basis can be demonstrated without going too far afield. One could recalculate them according to the rules given in Chapter VIII. One takes the number right for each condition, the same P and the same D for a whole month of observations, and uses them, without division into subgroups, to find the values of t in the fundamental table. As pointed out on page [99], I preferred in all my own experimental series to calculate the values of t separately for each condition from groups with $n = 64$ and to combine these in sums and averages, in order to be sure of eliminating the variability due to the effects of p and q. That was the procedure then for both the two-handed and the one-handed series. It would take too much space to reproduce here all the number right of these groups of 64 and each t value derived from them. I shall limit myself, therefore, to giving here the final result for both series, divided by the number ν of each part-series as my last figures.

VI. VALUES OF bD FOR TWO-HANDED SERIES
$n = 64$

P	$D = 0.04P$ ($\nu = 32$)	$D = 0.08P$ ($\nu = 32$)	Mean ($\nu = 64$)
300	2023	3918	2971
500	1965	3705	2835
1000	2530	4637	3584
1500	2774	5910	4342
2000	2966	6034	4500
3000	3296	6520	4908
Sum	15,554	30,724	23,140

I take the opportunity here to refer again to a methodological point, which can be demonstrated by a comparison of Table VI with Table V. Both of these tables are for a two-handed series and are based on the same data. They differ only in that the values of hD in Table V are derived without breaking the total n of 512 into subgroups, while Table VI is based on subgroups of 64. This difference is responsible for the fact that all values in the second table are somewhat larger than those in the first (see p. [100]). This difference would be of no

[9] Trans. Note: A misprint for 4908 judging from Table VI.

VII. VALUES OF hD FOR ONE-HANDED SERIES
$$n = 64$$

P	Left			Right			Left and Right
	$D = 0.04P$ ($\nu = 16$)	$D = 0.08P$ ($\nu = 16$)	Mean ($\nu = 32$)	$D = 0.04P$ ($\nu = 16$)	$D = 0.08P$ ($\nu = 16$)	Mean ($\nu = 32$)	Grand Mean ($\nu = 64$)
300	3916	4845	4381	3658	5360	4509	4445
500	2876	5246	4061	3349	5584	4467	4264
1000	2906	5649	4278	5103	6230	5667	4973
1500	4016	6426	5221	4638	7647	6143	5682
2000	4700	6515	5608	4517	6821	5669	5639
3000	4455	8084	6220	4551	7616	6084	6152
Sum	22,869	36,765	29,769	25,816	39,258	32,539	31,155

concern, if it were relatively the same for all values, since we are only looking for proportional changes. However, some numbers are proportionally larger than others. Responsibility for this difference rests on the fact, demonstrable by separate examination of each series of experiments, that p and q did not remain completely constant during the month that it took to carry out one series of trials, but varied irregularly. By breaking the series into so many subgroups that for each of them variability can be neglected, one does away with a disadvantage by eliminating this variability of p and q. For this reason the values of Table VI are to be preferred to those of Table V. In the meantime, however, since there does not appear to be any essential difference in the course of these tabulated values, one might well have stopped at the first, which is much briefer in its derivation. A comparison of these tables can in any case give us an idea of the approximate changes of the absolute measurements as they depend on the fineness of the subgroups.

Comparing means of the one-handed and two-handed series one finds

P	One-handed: Two-handed
300	1.496
500	1.504
1000	1.325
1500	1.309
2000	1.253
3000	1.254

It is clear that the ratios of these two figures diminish gradually as the standards increase, but they seem to approach constancy.

A glance at the course of the values of hD in the previous Tables VI and VII shows us that the outcome is essentially one and the same as the course of the figures of r in the earlier tables, with the exception that the growth of hD as P increases is somewhat more noticeable at the highest values of P than that of the r's, for the reason already stated. In any case, the increasing approach to equality as P increases shows up clearly enough.

Thus we find average hD's of 4342, 4500, and 4908 for the three highest P's of 1500, 2000, and 3000 gm in the two-handed series and of 5682, 5639, and 6152 in the one-handed series. Whereas P is doubled as it increases from 1500 to 3000, hD increases relatively little—by 1.13 or 1.08 times, respectively.

It seemed to me to be of interest to confirm again the approximate equality of hD for the higher weights at the two heaviest standards of 2000 and 3000 gm in particular, since they are so important for the validation of the law. I took this opportunity in an experimental series which at the same time was designed to compare the one-handed and the two-handed procedure in alternation. The two previous series, since they were presented as a whole, one after the other, did not afford any assurance for such a comparison (see p. [152]). In addition I wanted further to extend the test for proportionality of the t values and the D's employed.

This series, also lasting 32 days, was carried out in December 1858 and January 1859, under the standard conditions described on page [80]. It was, therefore, quite comparable to the earlier series, though obtained much later. Each experimental session comprised 8 subgroups of 64 weight lifts each. The whole series therefore involved $32 \times 8 \times 64 = 16,384$ lifts of the weights. The standards were changed each day. The one-handed procedure was alternated with the two-handed procedure every two days. In addition, on each day the added weight D was alternated between $0.04P$ and $0.08P$ after every two subseries, corresponding therefore to 80 and 160 gm when P equaled 2000, and 120 and 240 gm when P was equal to 3000. In addition, as I always do, I interchanged the left and right hands after each subgroup of 64 weight lifts in the one-handed procedure.

To differentiate it from the previous series I call this one the two-and-one-handed series. I present, to begin with, in Table VIII the sums of r for the four main conditions for preliminary inspection. Table IX presents the values of hD calculated from subgroups of 64, each with parts keeping the four main conditions distinct. This procedure is comparable with the one used in Tables VI and VII, although, because of their bulk, I cannot give here the basis of these calculations in detail.

If the external circumstances and methods of calculation of this series were strictly comparable with the previous one, the figures in Table IX should be identical with those in Tables VI and VII for P's of 2000 and 3000. However, we

VIII. NUMBER RIGHT r OF TWO- AND ONE-HANDED SERIES

	Two-handed		One-handed			
	n = 2048		Left n = 1024		Right n = 1024	
P	D = 0.04P	D = 0.08P	D = 0.04P	D = 0.08P	D = 0.04P	D = 0.08P
2000	1280	1503	708	840	681	863
3000	1297	1536	737	882	703	847
Sum	2577	3039	1445	1722	1384	1710

The sum r when P = 2000 is 5875.
" " " " " = 3000 " 6002.

find that they are considerably smaller in the two-handed series. It is true, they come close insofar as the one-handed series is concerned in the case of the results with 0.08P, but they are noticeably smaller with 0.04P. We should remember, also, that the results of the one-handed series at D's of 0.04P and 0.08P

IX. VALUES OF bD OF TWO- AND ONE-HANDED SERIES
n = 64

	Two-handed (ν = 32)		One-handed (ν = 16)			
			Left		Right	
P	D = 0.04P	D = 0.08P	D = 0.04P	D = 0.08P	D = 0.04P	D = 0.08P
2000	2461	5018	3456	7078	3709	9464
3000	2702	5326	4270	8310	4212	8028
Sum	5163	10,344	7726	15,388	7921	17,492

The sum of bD when P = 2000 is 31,186.
" " " " " " = 3000 " 32,938.

are not comparable among themselves, as it is apparent that the latter are not twice the former, a finding that comes, as pointed out on page [153], from the fact that they were obtained during different weeks. This fact may serve to support the statement on page [69], that one cannot count on comparability of measures obtained at different times, even when the external circumstances are the same. In the meantime, this argument will not diminish the comparability within each series in respect of the conditions with which we are concerned here.

The finding that in our present series, where D's were changed on the same day, the values of hD calculated from the r's are in the ratios of the given D's, is one of the validations of our method of calculation.

Looking at our final results, we see then that hD only increased in the ratio of 31,186 to 32,938 as P changed from 2000 to 3000. The deviation from equality represents the difference from the exact conformation with Weber's Law, explained by us as due to the added weight of the arm. The figure 9464 in the table is undoubtedly too large, due to chance, as can be seen by comparison with the other figures. Because of it, the difference has turned out to be somewhat smaller than it would have been. Otherwise the essential result of this series completely confirms the results of the previous series.

Since the proportion which the moment of the arm contributes to the weight being lifted cannot be determined beforehand, partly because the moment cannot be measured exactly on the living arm, partly because the extent to which the effect of the muscle sense enters into the total is not sufficiently known, one might consider determining the value that should be added to P from our figures for hD, under the assumption that our law is valid. However, on second thought it is apparent that these factors would probably not be enough.

According to the statistical theory applicable to the combination of independent estimates of error the following relations hold. If the effect of the muscle sense by itself is expressed as $t' = h'D$ and the effect of pressure alone as $t'' = h''D$ for a given weight D, we can expect a value of

$$t = \sqrt{t'^2 + t''^2} = \sqrt{h'^2 + h''^2}\, D$$

We could use this relationship as the basis of our attempt. Our law states that t' is inversely proportional to $P + A$, where A is to be understood as stated earlier, and that t'' is inversely proportional to P. One can write, therefore,

$$t^2 = (hD)^2 = \frac{c'}{(P + A)^2} + \frac{c''}{P^2}$$

where c' and c'' [misprinted c in original] are constants. The three unknowns c', c'', and A would have to be determined from our figures of hD obtained for different P's. However, even if we could overcome the difficulties in making these calculations, the anomalies for small P's, of which we will speak now, would be an obstacle to exact calculation.

The anomalous finding that when P is changed from 300 to 500 gm, t becomes somewhat smaller rather than showing an increase, cannot be explained by what has been said so far. I can scarcely believe that this is a chance result due to an insufficient number of observations (although this possibility exists, since the difference is small and many data are necessary to make sure that small differences are significant). Yet, aside from the agreement of both series of experiments, each consisting of a large number of trials, there should be, relatively speaking, the largest increase of t as a function of P at the smallest P's, because the increase of the moment of P by the moment of the arm is here relatively the largest. And, unless special disturbing conditions exist at the smallest weights, which are masked by greater weights, this effect on the measurements should, in my opinion, have made itself felt.

Nevertheless, although I cannot give any definite explanation of this anomaly, and although it would undoubtedly be desirable to confirm this finding by new experiments, the following argument appears to offer some likelihood that the phenomenon actually exists in nature.

One might assume that rising pressure exerts a diminished influence on sensitivity because of mechanical compression of nerve endings or of the associated structures related to the perception of pressure (apart from the reduction in sensitivity, which according to our law is proportional to the increase of the stimulus). This effect vanishes for heavier weights, compared to the influence of our law, which must have a more general and fundamental cause, but may prevail at the lesser weights. This reasoning would explain the diminishing t at the lowest values of P. I am not averse to connecting this effect with the circumstance, which also has always seemed puzzling to me, that a slight tickling is felt more strongly and can bring about a stronger reflex movement than a somewhat stronger touch, although the greater sensations are always associated with very heavy pressure. However, I will be glad to admit that these are only thoughts which demand further proof and perhaps will serve to inspire further work.

It seems very probable that, by analogy to the fact that the law has a lower limit in common both in the field of the judgments of weight and in the experimentation with light, the same relation would be true with respect to an upper limit. However, my experiments were not continued by myself as far as this limit, where the weight would begin to become detrimental. Of course, the method of right and wrong cases, with its tremendous number of cases, could not be extended far enough to secure valid data without permanent damage. Perhaps we could gain enough experience in this respect with the method of just noticeable differences without having to worry about damage, since the maximum degree of precision which this method can achieve is tied less firmly to the number of trials.

Reviewing what we have said, we see that the investigation of the validity and the limits of our law in the area of experimentation with weights is still far from being finished. My own experiments can only be the second step, following Weber's, in attempting to solve this problem, which many must follow using new modifications of method. One can say only, from what has so far been done, that in general the observations agree quite well with the law, so that one cannot doubt its approximate or exact validity within certain limits. However, the anomaly at the lower limit, the question of an upper limit, the exact determination of the effect of the weight of the arm, and a complete and exact differentiation between the sense of touch and the muscle sense are aspects that await clarification in future experiments. Weber's experiments were the first to prove the law in general, but his method was not suitable for making statements about its fit. My experiments have allowed us to recognize deviations but are not sufficient to eliminate them by taking into exact account the circumstances on which they depend.

There can be no doubt that the isolation of the sense of pressure was achieved in Weber's method where the weight was placed on the last digit of the finger while the hand rested on a table. It appears less certain to me that the muscle sense was isolated just as surely by means of the other procedure, described in his treatise on touch and common sensibility on page 546, in which the observer grasps with one hand the joined corners of a piece of cloth in which the weight has been placed. There the weight necessarily would tend to make the ends of the cloth slip through the fingers to a greater extent the heavier it is, unless this tendency is counteracted by a stronger grasp, and, therefore, a greater pressure. Should the pressure also be held constant, then it would merely serve to complicate matters further.

In fact I cannot imagine an experimental method to isolate the muscle sense precisely. Perhaps the use of balls or hammers dropping on the skin from a fixed height might be more suitable to separate out the sense of pressure by use of our method than the use of resting weights. A comparison of results obtained in such a way with those of lifted weights would be of considerable interest.

Quite apart from the question of our law's validity one might frame the direct results of the experiments we have just described as follows:

If a given weight is lifted in comparison with another which has been increased by a given additional weight, then as the standard is made heavier, so must the added absolute weight be, in order for the two weights to create an impression of equally noticeable difference.

If one allows the weight to increase proportionally to the standard, so that its relative, but not its absolute, magnitude remains constant, then the relative increment of weight is somewhat more noticeable as the standard is increased. The tendency is, however, toward equality, so that the difference in the capacity to note equal increments of relative weight with standards of 1500 and 3000 gm becomes quite small, corresponding to a ratio of perhaps 11 : 10. That means that the relative increments for the 1500 and 3000 gm standards must be in a ratio of approximately 11 : 10 in order to be equally noticeable, instead of their being the same;

that is, instead of their bringing about an equal ratio of right to wrong cases in the method of that name.

There is one exception to this positive growth of equally noticeable weight increments with magnitudes of the standard, at very low standard weights. With an increase from 300 to 500 gm, just noticeable differences become somewhat smaller rather than showing an increase. On the other hand, above 500 gm positive growth is continuous.

The cause for the exceptional behavior at low standard weights is unknown and could only be guessed at in passing (p. [165]). The reason why we do not find relatively equal increments of weight as standard weights increase may possibly lie in the fact that the weight of the arm that is doing the lifting and is itself lifted in the process of raising the weight may come into play as an addition to the standard weight, and should be included in considering the relative equality of the weight increment, which should really be related to a standard weight including the extra weight of the arm.

If we add various additional weights to one and the same standard weight they become more easily noticed as the amounts of these extra weights increase. Because they are more perceptible, it follows that there occurs a greater proportion of right to wrong cases, as well as to total cases, when one uses the method of right and wrong cases for comparing the weights. The number of right cases does not grow, however, in proportion to the magnitude of the added weight, but in a lesser ratio.

The rule given on page [93], for finding by means of the fundamental table how the number right varies with the extra weight, is confirmed by experience.

These results were found in experiments with standard weights of 300, 500, 1000, 1500, 2000, and 3000 gm, to which weights of 0.04 and 0.08 times the standard had been added. The results are in agreement when the weights were lifted with one hand and with both hands, provided constant errors depending on the temporal and spatial order of the weights are eliminated.

4. TEMPERATURE

Much is still obscure when we take up the question of the extent to which our law applies to temperature sensations. E. H. Weber* is inclined to assume "that we tend to feel the rising and falling of skin temperature rather than the degree to which the temperature has been raised

---

* Der Tasts. und das Gemeing., p. 549.

or to which it has fallen. One is not aware, for example, of whether his forehead or hands are warmer until he places his hand on his forehead, when he can often perceive a large difference and sometimes find his hand and at other times his forehead to be a warmer temperature." Other experiences, also cited by Weber as pointing in the same direction, can be added. Nevertheless it appears to be true that we are able to feel continuous warmth as warmth and continuous cold as cold, if they are sufficiently different from the common or average temperature.

However that may be, there can be no question that, when one wishes to take up Weber's Law with respect to differences in temperature, the stimulus can by no means be a difference from an absolute zero but must be the difference from a temperature at which we feel neither warmth nor cold, for the magnitude of the corresponding sensations depends only on this point. Now, this difference may increase or decrease, and it will be a question of Weber's Law, whether an equally large relative increase, not of the absolute temperature but of this difference in temperature, would bring about an equally noticeable or, in general, equally large increase in temperature sensation.

According to some, but very inadequate, experiments which I carried out with regard to this question, this rule appears to hold within certain limits in the middle range of temperatures but is definitely not the case with very cold or very hot temperatures.

My relevant experiments were carried out during six days (in December 1855) with the method of just noticeable differences. I employed Weber's procedure of dipping two fingers of the same hand to a constant depth alternately into two vessels filled with water at unequal temperatures. A pair of very accurate and exactly compared Greiner's thermometers from the Leipzig department of physics, reading to one half of a degree on Reaumur's scale, were used for observations. On them $\frac{1}{10}$ of each half-degree interval, or $\frac{1}{20}$ of a whole degree, could easily be estimated. As one of the thermometers read $0.05°$ or $\frac{1}{20}$ of a degree higher than the other according to Hankel, who was kind enough to let me have them for the experiments, and because this difference was substantiated by myself, each observation was corrected for this constant error. As for the rest of the conditions of the experimental series, I shall mention whatever is necessary after I have given the results.[10]

Within the temperature range from approximately 10° to 20°R I found the sensitivity to differences in temperature so large, that just noticeable differences could not be determined precisely. In any case a maximum of sensitivity, where vanishingly small or almost vanishingly small differ-

[10] Trans. Note: $1°C = 5/4°R$.

ences are perceived, seems to lie within these limits, without allowing an exact direct determination. Above 20° and up to body temperature, beyond which my experiments did not go to any extent, I found my results quite well in agreement with Weber's Law, when I took (quite empirically) the excess of temperature over the mid-point between freezing and body temperature (= 14.77°R*) as the measure of the thermal stimulus, since the just noticeable temperature difference appeared to be proportional to this rise above the mean temperature. There follow the temperature differences D and the temperatures t at which they were taken, which were recorded as just noticeable before any calculations were made. These are given as the mean of the two temperatures between which the difference D had been observed. The calculated values of D were based on the assumption that the just noticeable differences are proportional to the excess of temperature above 14.77°. The first part of this table (I) cannot be taken seriously since the observed differences are much too small and may merely serve to prove the unimportance of the just noticeable differences between the limits of the temperatures in this part of the table. On the other hand one should examine the second part (II), beginning at 19.13°, with regard to the correspondence between observation and calculation.

TEMPERATURE SENSITIVITY 15.03° R TO 31.35° R

Date of Experiment	$t°$ R	$D°$ R		Date of Experiment	$t°$ R	$D°$ R	
		Observed	Calculated			Observed	Calculated
Dec.				Dec.			
2	15.03	0.19	0.009	26	19.13	0.15	0.16
26	15.40	0.10	0.023	26	20.45	0.20	0.21
26	15.55	0.09	0.028	26	20.63	0.15	0.21
26	16.18	0.15	0.051	26	21.20	0.20	0.23
21	16.70	0.20**	0.070	26	21.73	0.25	0.25
26	16.71	0.09	0.070	21	23.30	0.30	0.31
21	16.75	0.10**	0.072	21	25.35	0.40	0.39
21	16.88	0.25*	0.076	21, 26	26.30	0.40	0.42
21	17.00	0.00**	0.081	21, 26	28.80	0.60	0.51
26	17.20	0.20	0.088	26	30.50	0.60	0.57
21	17.30	0.10**	0.092	26	31.35	0.60	0.60
26	17.69	0.23	0.106				
26	18.78	0.15	0.145				

One arrives at the calculated values of this table by multiplying the amount the temperature exceeds 14.77° (that is, $t - 14.77°$) by 0.03623. This constant is derived from the observations of $t = 19.13°$ to 31.35°

---

* This temperature is based on the temperature of the human body as determined by Lichtenfels and Fröhlich in *Abhandl. der Wien. Akad.*

only. However, both the observed D's and the values of D calculated by means of this constant above 14.77° and below 19.13° (which, as mentioned previously, are minute) have been added in the first part of this table. The observations on which the table is based pertain to only three of the six days on which experiments were conducted, since the observations on the other three days concern only temperatures below the mean temperature, which I shall give separately below.

The starred values of D in the first part of the table are those that were marked not only as just noticeable, but as noticeable (one star) or clearly noticeable (two stars) in the record of observations and thus were counted as more than just perceptible. One of these differences that was clearly noticeable as far as sensation was concerned (at 17°) was not large enough to be read on the thermometer (when the necessary correction of 0.05° was made). In general, one might be inclined to assume the average temperature of greatest sensitivity to be between 16° and 17° rather than at 14.77°, according to these values, and it is possible that it does lie there. One cannot, however, be sure of anything at these almost vanishingly small values of D in the vicinity of the average temperature when one remembers that, apart from variations in sensitivity (the yardstick of what is noticeable), errors in reading or very small differences between water temperature and thermometer are sufficient to bring such differences about or to hide them, even though every care is taken to reduce these sources of error as much as possible. The use of 14.77° as the starting point for the calculations does on the whole correspond better with the observations.

Moreover, even were these traces of D below $t = 20°$ almost of the order of errors of observation, still they cannot be considered only as such, since the test was generally carried out without my knowing which water had the higher temperature. Only after repeated alternate dipping, when I believed myself to be quite sure of the result did I make my decision, and this I did to the degree that I made only one mistake near the average temperature in a very large number of trials, a region where the just noticeable differences become almost vanishingly small. In this case a later check revealed that the difference I had judged as just noticeable was in the opposite direction to the one in which I had assumed it to be, whereas very frequently cases occurred, in which I could find no difference between both containers of water, and later found by means of the thermometer that there was indeed none or one that was below the limits for this part of the thermal scale. This finding serves simultaneously as a mutual check that the thermometer readings and the evidence of the senses were in general reliable.

Inspection of the table reveals that no symmetry seemed to exist below the average temperature compared to the course of the just noticeable differences above this point. The latter followed Weber's Law well enough, as far as can be judged, considering the minuteness of the differences. Down to about 10° the just noticeable differences were still too small to reveal anything of their relationships, but, continuing below that point, they increased much more rapidly than would be compatible with their course above the average temperature or with Weber's Law. Empirically one might represent them fairly accurately as proportional to the third power of $T - t$, where $T = 14.77°$, t is the temperature where the just noticeable difference had been observed, and 0.002734 is a constant by which $(T - t)^3$ has to be multiplied, to get the just noticeable difference in terms of the thermometer reading. Undoubtedly this finding depends on the great loss of sensitivity with cold. One would probably find similar deviations by going above body temperature to approach the point where burning sensations commence. Yet it still is remarkable that the deviations above the average temperature start only at higher degrees, whereas below it they start immediately.

There follow the values calculated according to the formula

$$D = (14.77 - t)^3 \times 0.002734$$

in conjunction with the observed values between the limits of $+ 10.5°$ and $+4.5°R$. Lower than that, the values obtained in a couple of days were too variable for one to make anything of them.

Considering the manifold difficulties presented by these detailed experiments (and particularly the fact that values from quite different days are combined), one might well be satisfied with the way these results show a correspondence between calculated and observed values and the way in which we get now positive and now negative differences between observation and calculation. One can after all never be quite sure of day-to-day levels of sensitivity or whether the same subjective yardstick of what is just noticeable is retained from one day to another. Naturally we could have increased this correspondence still more, if I would have omitted some values which did not quite fit, but I have given everything I marked as just noticeable before the calculation was started. I am far from asserting that the equation I have just given should be looked upon as anything more than an empirical formula, valid only between certain limits. For the sake of completeness I finally append the values of D above 10.5° and up to 14.20°, if for no other purpose than to make sure that it can be observed that they are very small. In spite of this, they are still somewhat

TEMPERATURE SENSITIVITY 4.6° R TO 10.5° R

Date of Experiment	$t°$ R	$14.77° - t°$	D		Diff.
			Observed	Calculated	
Dec.					
5	4.60	10.17	2.80	2.88	+ 0.08
23	5.32	9.45	2.54	2.31	− 0.21
23	5.43	9.34	2.40	2.23	− 0.17
21	5.65	9.12	2.00	2.07	+ 0.07
23	5.69	9.08	2.54	2.05	− 0.49
5	5.73	9.04	2.22	2.02	− 0.20
2	5.81	8.96	1.62	1.97	+ 0.35
5	5.85	8.92	1.80	1.94	+ 0.14
2	5.88	8.89	1.75	1.92	+ 0.17
2	6.11	8.66	1.55	1.78	+ 0.23
1,25	6.98	7.79	1.06	1.29	+ 0.23
25	7.15	7.62	1.40	1.21	− 0.19
23,25	7.18	7.59	1.49	1.20	− 0.29
25	7.20	7.57	1.30	1.19	− 0.11
2	7.21	7.56	0.91	1.18	+ 0.27
23	7.64	7.13	0.93	0.99	+ 0.06
26	8.18	6.59	0.75	0.78	+ 0.03
5	8.20	6.57	0.80	0.78	− 0.02
23	8.43	6.34	0.65	0.70	+ 0.05
23	8.56	6.21	0.61	0.66	+ 0.05
23,26	8.71	6.06	0.53	0.61	+ 0.08
23	8.73	6.04	0.45	0.60	+ 0.15
2,15	9.15	5.62	0.48	0.49	+ 0.01
2,25	9.77	5.00	0.40	0.34	− 0.06
5	10.5	4.27	0.40	0.21	− 0.19
			33.38	33.40	

larger than they should be according to the calculations, if we make use of the foregoing equation, as the compilation of the calculated and the observed values show.

In spite of the careful execution of these studies, their repetition would be desirable, especially by using only an ascending series below the average temperature and a descending series above this point, so as to reduce somewhat the comparability of the results. A much larger number of observations than I could present here also would be necessary to confirm Weber's Law above the average temperature, so that finally I can only consider the result of this experiment as a preliminary one, which might possibly still be open to revision. I want to label it expressly as such, and consider Weber's Law within the stated limits as quite probable, but by no means proven. It was my intention to complete my experiments in this connection or to do them anew. However, I was interrupted and have found no time since to come back to them.

TEMPERATURE SENSITIVITY 10.88° R TO 14.2° R

Date of Experiment	$t°$ R	D	
		Observed	Calculated
Dec.			
25	10.88	0.15	0.161
23	11.36	0.13*	0.108
5	11.45	0.30	0.100
5	12.15	0.30	0.049
5	12.40	0.20	0.036
25	12.50	0.15	0.032
21	13.30	0.20	0.009
21	13.40	0.25	0.007
5	13.50	0.15	0.006
5	13.90	0.25	0.002
5, 21	14.20	0.15	0.001

* Clearly perceived as opposed to just noticeable.

Let me add the following about the way in which the experiment was carried out.

The two vessels that contained the water at different temperatures were large clay pots employed so as to slow up changes in temperature as much as possible. They were filled with water up to a point where the joint between the first and second phalanges of the forefinger (counted from the palm) was just covered as the forefinger and middle finger of the right hand reached bottom. Thus the area exposed to the water always remained the same. The thermometers, fastened to a suitable stand, were inserted so that their bulbs were submerged to the center of the water, which had been well stirred before each observation. The temperature of the water was changed by stirring it either with ice or with metal or clay implements that had been standing in a hot oven. The two fingers that were used in the experiment were first left in one of the vessels, submerged to the bottom, until they reached a constant temperature. Then they were alternately dipped into one or the other container until a judgment could be made. If the temperature sensation was above the level which I denote as just noticeable, the temperature was changed in the opposite direction, so that I could not tell whether the excess temperature had changed to the opposite container, and the observation was repeated until a just noticeable difference was found, which was often after several repetitions of these changes. (I have to admit that this procedure tended to be quite tedious.) The temperature was read as soon as the judgment was formed.

Although I counted only the degree of sensation that I call just noticeable, I recorded the values of sensation in my register of observations, trying to keep them as constant as possible. In order of increasing magnitude these values were as follows:

Not noticeable, scarcely noticeable, just noticeable, noticeable, clearly noticeable, definite, strong, and very strong. Naturally one cannot depend on a sharp separation of these readings. The values called "scarcely noticeable" were those in which I could not be quite sure of freedom from error, and although this point could be checked after the observation, there still existed the possibility of an agreement by chance. These values therefore were used only to the extent "scarcely noticeable," "noticeable," or "clearly noticeable" closely coincided on the same and also on different days on which observations were made. In this case I used the mean of these determinations as just noticeable, and I had to follow this course several times.

Undoubtedly it would be desirable if experiments using methods other than the method of just noticeable differences could be added in this area. Volkmann has had Mr. Lindemann, a student of medicine, carry out experiments by the method of average error and write his doctoral dissertation on this topic, which he then defended under the title, *De sensu caloris. Halis* 1857. We cannot deduce much from this experiment, however, since, although the range of temperature covered extended from 7° and 14.6°C respectively, to 45.55°C, twice in ascending and twice in descending order, only a few experiments fell in each temperature interval, so that the use of the method of average error is precluded. The right hand was submerged to the wrist in this series, always into the initially warmer water in the ascending series, and into the initially colder water in the descending series. Colder or warmer water was then poured in to equalize the temperatures as judged by the sensations.

In the two ascending series (that is, when Lindemann equalized the temperatures of both bodies of water at successively higher temperatures), positive errors were present at all times, whereas negative errors marked the two descending orders. One might ask whether this error was caused by the fact that in the ascending and descending series the temperature range was covered in opposite directions, or by the fact that in each single trial the transition from the initially warmer or initially colder water was made in opposite directions. We might deduce the latter from the circumstance that these conditions occurred from the first trial of each of the four series. Exact details, in these and in some other respects, are lacking here.

We have results, then, that are subject to constant errors in essential respects. Judging by the regularity with which single errors in each series vary with ascending or descending temperature, almost all the errors seem to be constant, since variable errors must necessarily show more irregularities in detail. Their insignificant size is especially remarkable.

Between 26.4° and 38.8°C inclusive,* 23 trials of the first ascending series regularly yielded errors of +0.05°, with the exception of five trials. At higher or

* I always cite here the lower of the two temperatures between which the difference existed.

lower temperatures the error increased, but only a little and somewhat irregularly in an upward direction, so that in the interval from 39.4° to 45.5° only errors of 0.5°, 0.6°, 0.7°, and 0.8° occur, and somewhat more in the downward direction (+0.5° at 14.6°, the value where the ascending series began, +0.4° at 16° and 18.2°, and so on). In the second ascending series, errors of +0.05 were found without exception in 14 ascending trials in the range from 31.35° to 42.9°. The error increased at higher levels to 0.1° at 44.8° and 45.1°, and lower down to +0.25° at 7.9° and 8.4°. In the first descending series an error of −0.05° was noted in 22 descending trials between 41.5° and 19.5° with three exceptions; it increased to −0.1° at 44.7° and to 0.29° at 7°. In the second descending series an error of −0.05° was observed in 21 trials from 41.65° to 19.35° without exception; it increased to −0.1° at 44.9° and to −0.25 at 7.55°.

The experiments are in agreement with my own in that, starting at an interval where the errors almost vanish, they increase at a greater rate or to a larger extent in the direction of cold than in the direction of warm. Errors are much smaller than the just noticeable differences found by myself and previously by Weber. There is no contradiction here, since, as I remarked on page [107], the average errors must always be smaller than the just noticeable differences. Partially it may also depend on the fact that only two digits of two fingers were submerged by myself, as compared to the whole hand by Lindemann. A substantial difference exists in the fact that Lindemann found the interval containing the smallest error in the vicinity of the body temperature, whereas in my work the interval containing the least noticeable differences lies in the vicinity of the average temperature. In the meantime there is no way to judge whether there is a real contradiction, since Lindemann's errors appear to be mainly constant. In any case new experiments on this topic are necessary. We can at least conclude that the smallness of the differences which can still be recognized, as well as of the errors which are committed on the average, presents great difficulty in exact measurement.

Perhaps an analogous use of the method of right and wrong cases, as employed in my weight experiments, might be most suitable for experiments on this topic. It is true that one might not easily be able to obtain such constant temperatures and temperature differences as can be obtained for weights and weight differences. It seems likely, nevertheless, that by reducing the causes of changes of temperature as much as possible and, for example, recording the temperature anew after each ten observations and regulating it, if necessary, it may be possible to achieve useful results, particularly in the light of the reductions which the fundamental table makes possible.

5. EXTENSIVE MAGNITUDES (VISUAL AND TACTUAL MEASURES OF SIZE)

In addition to Weber's general statements (p. [114]), F. Hegelmayer,* a medical student at Tübingen, has given us an approximate confirmation of Weber's Law for estimates of visual size according to the method of right and wrong cases. However, his work leaves much to be desired, due both to his inadequate number of trials and to the fact that the several trials from which averages were drawn were not comparable. It cannot, therefore, be given much weight. Essentially, the experiments consisted in comparing lines of a given length, some horizontal, some vertical, with other lines had been observed before. These lines would differ by specified larger or smaller fractions. The observer's main purpose was to investigate the effect of different intervals of time between the observation of the standard and comparison lines and to count how often the estimate was of larger or smaller, how often it was correct, incorrect, or undecided. As far as could be told from his observations the ratio of right to wrong cases essentially did not depend on the absolute, but only on the relative size of the fractions, a conclusion to which Hegelmayer himself also came. In general his results are quite irregular, and I shall therefore omit any special discussion of them here.

My own and Volkmann's experiments, employing the method of average error, where distances between two small points or between parallel threads were observed, resulted in a definite confirmation of the law for any considerable distances, that is, from 10 to 240 mm [millimeters] at a distance from the eyes of 1 ft to 800 mm, since the sum of errors or the average error which was found turned out to be as closely proportional to the distances as one might reasonably expect. On the other hand, Volkmann's experiments—as well as those he inspired Appel (a student with especially sharp eyesight) to undertake—on micrometric distances of 0.2 to 3.6 mm at about normal ocular distances did not reveal this proportionality. The resulting error sums or average errors (after eliminating constant errors) can be split into two components. One, which I call Volkmann's constant† remains constant at different standards; the

---

* *Vierordt's Arch.* XI, pp. 844, 853.

† This error should not be confused with the constant error in the sense given on p. (101). Rather, it originates in variable errors, just as does the other error component, and is called constant only because, when determined in the above manner, it remains constant when standard distances vary and does not change as a function of them as does Weber's variable error.

other, which I call Weber's variable, remains proportional to the distances in the sense of Weber's Law. Probably the former also becomes effective in experiments dealing with larger distances, but it is so small that it vanishes compared with the other component, the one which is proportional to distance, and is submerged in the uncertainty of their determination, whereas at very small distances it forms the greater part of the sum of the variable error. At the very smallest distances of 0.2 and 0.3 mm the error seemed also, as far as Volkmann was concerned, to be abnormally enlarged by the spread of the excitation.

One can see that we are dealing here also with the lower limit of the law. Perhaps one could also find an upper limit for very large distances.

The main results appear in what follows. They all pertain to the pure variable error Δ, used in the sense cited before (p. [101]), and always yield the pure sum of errors $\Sigma\Delta$; often also (when I calculated them) the pure sum of squared errors $\Sigma\Delta^2$, derived separately for each distance from subgroups of m observations each. The total number of errors contributing to each sum was therefore μm. The values of μ and m are given separately for each experimental series. The value of μ should be doubled for the horizontal rows of sums, since these sums were always combinations of two special sums, for L and R or O and U, respectively. Results are specified for equal numbers of observations taken to the right and left of the standard distance (L or R), when the distances were horizontal, or at the upper or lower position, when they were vertical and the placing is over or under (O or U).

Only the micrometric series V was carried out with vertical distances, that is, between horizontal threads; all others were with horizontal distances, between vertical threads (when threads were used).

The proportionality to the distances can be shown directly by means of the simple sums $\Sigma\Delta$, without first deriving the average error $\epsilon = \Sigma\Delta/\mu m$ from them. The sum of the squared errors can serve, if one wants, for the calculation of the quadratic average error

$$\epsilon_q = \sqrt{\frac{\Sigma\Delta^2}{\mu m}}$$

by which one can convince himself of the constancy and the occurrence of the normal relationship

$$\frac{\epsilon_q}{\epsilon} = \sqrt{\frac{\pi}{2}}$$

within the limits of chance, but I shall omit, at this time, an examination of this relationship. One might also use it to prove, as can easily be

deduced from the previous relationships and is examined more thoroughly in another place, that the sum of squared errors $\Sigma\Delta^2$, divided by the
square of the sum of the errors, multiplied by twice the number of observations (here $2\mu m$), is approximately equal to Ludolf's number π. Unfortunately the observations of series I and II at the smallest distances do
not lend themselves to this proof because of a circumstance which does
not demand attention now. In any case we are not particularly concerned
here with these relationships.

All series cited here were subject to more or less constant errors. To
cite them at this time would have no purpose, but will be taken care of in
my "Methods of Measurement."

Series I. Fechner (December 9, 1856 to January 17, 1857)

Five horizontal distances were used. They were determined on the tips
of two pairs of compasses, which were lying next to each other on the
table in front of me. They were covered except for their fine needle tips.
Viewing distance was approximately 1 Paris ft. Distances were measured
on a ruler with transverse lines, reading in tenths of half a Paris decimal
line (itself equal to 0.72 of a duodecimal line) as the basic unit. The compasses were covered to eliminate the influence of the angle between the
legs when estimating. Still, the procedure had the minor fault that the tips
of the compass which protruded from the covering were more inclined
when distances were large than when they were small. This fault was
avoided in later series by the use of parallel threads. In any case this fault
seems to have influenced essentially only the constant errors, rather than
the pure variable errors, which, as shown in the following table, behaved
in a manner exactly proportional to the distances.

So as to leave no room for error in interpreting the numbers in this
table I shall describe those of the first one separately; one should then be
able to understand all the others easily.

When the distance $D = 10$, which as mentioned previously represented
10 half Paris decimal lines, a pure error sum $\Sigma\Delta = 20.27$ was found
when the standard distance was to the left; that is to say, if one adds the
absolute values of all positive and negative absolute errors we obtain a
total of 20.27 half Paris decimal lines. The statement $m = 60$, $\mu = 2$ in
the head of the table means that this sum of errors, just as the others in
the rows L and R are composed of $2 \times 60 = 120$ single errors. Each such
sum of errors was, however, not just derived from the 120 observations,
but from two subtotals of 60 observations. The average error of distance
and the absolute error were then determined from each separately.

DISTANCE THRESHOLDS, FECHNER SERIES I
$m = 60$, $\mu = 2$ Unit: ½ Paris Decimal Line

D	10	20	30	40	50	Sum
$\Sigma\Delta$ {L	20.27	35.98	60.42	85.29	85.85	287.81
{R	18.37	40.87	60.49	69.19	99.55	288.47
Sum	38.64	76.85	120.91	154.48	185.40	576.28
$\Sigma\Delta^2$ {L	4.621	17.36	50.56	88.41	105.99	266.94
{R	4.056	23.06	47.11	57.74	122.47	254.44
Sum	8.677	40.42	97.67	146.15	228.46	521.38

Series II. Volkmann (March 22 to April 1, 1857)

Eight horizontal distances, determined on three parallel white threads, 220 mm in length, held tight by weights and viewed against a black background at a distance from the eye of 800 mm. They could be moved with respect to a horizontal ruler placed at right angles and reading directly in millimeters.

I report the sums $\Sigma\Delta$ in two versions, for $m = 48$, $\mu = 1$, and for $m = 16, \mu = 3$, giving us an opportunity to check the differences to which this procedure gives rise (see p. [103]).

DISTANCE THRESHOLDS, VOLKMANN SERIES II
(1) $m = 48$, $\mu = 1$ Unit: 1 mm

D	10	20	40	80	120	160	200	240	Sum
$\Sigma\Delta$ {L	7.552	7.914	26.95	39.90	75.05	102.30	87.11	117.96	464.7
{R	5.050	10.800	24.50	42.89	58.70	93.82	96.63	145.82	478.2
Sum	12.602	18.714	51.45	82.79	133.75	196.12	183.74	263.78	942.9
$\Sigma\Delta^2$ {L	1.657	2.558	22.66	48.67	199.96	371.83	229.63	394.45	1271.41
{R	1.021	3.406	18.11	60.47	117.37	314.56	331.57	612.95	1459.46
Sum	2.678	5.964	40.77	109.14	317.33	686.39	561.20	1007.40	2730.87

(2) $m = 16$, $\mu = 3$ Unit: 1 mm

D	10	20	40	80	120	160	200	240	Sum
$\Sigma\Delta$ {L	7.13	7.59	20.08	39.79	75.45	103.65	86.40	108.92	449.01
{R	4.86	11.06	23.58	42.10	58.45	77.23	96.20	140.20	453.68
Sum	11.99	18.65	43.66	81.89	133.90	180.88	182.60	249.12	902.69

One may note that the difference between the two methods of calculation is very small at most values, except that it is quite important at $D = 40$ R and $D = 160$ R. This fact is connected with the large variation of constant errors seen when the series is examined in detail.* Since this variability is better controlled by dividing the data into subgroups, the second method of calculation is preferable to the first.

Series III. Volkmann (December 6 and 17, 1857)

A repetition of the previous series under the same conditions, except that the two smallest distances are omitted.

DISTANCE THRESHOLDS, VOLKMANN SERIES III

$m = 16$, $\mu = 3$ Unit: 1 mm

D	40	80	120	160	200	240	Sum
$\Sigma\Delta\{^L_R$	21.1	42.4	57.0	90.0	81.4	98.2	390.1
	8.4	32.1	63.5	63.2	106.3	117.9	391.4
Sum	29.5	74.5	120.5	153.2	187.7	216.1	781.5

The close correspondence of L and R in the last column will be noted with interest. It is proof that the absolute variable errors are independent of the position of the threads, both left or right, whereas the constant errors, which are not listed here, showed themselves quite dependent on position, introducing great differences in the raw error sums of L and R.

The three series are in complete agreement in showing the proportionality of $\Sigma\Delta$ to distance. One can see this best by dividing the sums by distances, where each series demonstrates the constant nature of the quotients. One finds in this way (in the second series for $m = 16$, $\nu = 3$) the following values of $\Sigma\Delta/D$.

RATIO OF $\Sigma\Delta$ TO D IN DISTANCE JUDGMENT

$\Sigma\Delta/D$ in

I	II	III
3.864	1.2600	0.738
3.843	0.936	0.932
4.030	1.286	1.004
3.862	1.035	0.958
3.708	1.114	0.939
	1.226	0.900
	0.919	
	1.099	

* The particular distribution of errors causes a few values of Table 1 to be somewhat smaller than in Table 2.

If the mean error at unit distance or the average fractional error distance is wanted, one can divide the mean of the above numbers of each series by the number of observations that have contributed to each value. One must double the product m and μ, written above the table, since μ there applies to L and R separately, while now both are combined. However, since larger sums of errors promise to give more precise values at the greater distances than at shorter ones, one would obtain more exact results* if one added all sums of errors, an addition that is shown in the last row of the table. This sum is then divided by the sum of all distances, thus resulting in the sum of errors per unit distance, and this value is then divided by $2\mu m$.

So one arrives at

$$\text{I. } \frac{576.28}{150 \times 240} = 0.016008 = \frac{1}{62.5}$$

$$\text{II. (1) } \frac{942.9}{870 \times 96} = 0.011287 = \frac{1}{88.6}$$

$$\text{(2) } \frac{902.69}{870 \times 96} = 0.010808 = \frac{1}{92.5}$$

$$\text{III. } \frac{781.5}{840 \times 96} = 0.0096913 = \frac{1}{103.1}$$

Thus, my distance estimates had an error of about $\frac{1}{60}$ on the average, Volkmann made an error of about $\frac{1}{90}$ in his earlier trials (II), and of about $\frac{1}{100}$ in his later experiments (III). This proportion remained constant for each of the different distances. If one wishes, one can derive the probable error from this average error simply by multiplying by 0.845347, yielding the error that is exceeded as often as it is not reached. It must be smaller than the average error, because small errors are made more often than large ones in a normal distribution. More on that will be found in my "Methods of Measurement."

One can see that the precision of Volkmann's estimates was considerably greater than mine. This may be due either to the fact that distances between three parallel threads are easier to compare than the tips of two

---

* The method of least squares is somewhat more exact in principle, but more complex to carry out. Its results depart so little from those of the preceding method that its adoption is unnecessary.

adjacent compass points, or to the fact that his visual acuity is better than mine (as indeed seems to be the case) or to both these facts. Further experiments would be necessary to decide this point. There is no doubt that extensive experiments regarding the extremes and mean values of acuity for a number of individuals and under different conditions of observation would be of interest. The results might depend, for example, on whether the lateral thread is moved, as in Volkmann's experiments, whether the middle one is adjusted, whether observations are monocular or binocular, and whether vertical, horizontal, or angular distances between points, lines, or circular or square surfaces are made. Whatever the conditions, one must carefully take into account the magnitude and kind of constant errors. However, we will interest ourselves only in the law with which we are here concerned.

Volkmann's second series gave a considerably smaller average error, and therefore more precision, than the first one. This difference can be attributed to practice effects, since a good number of distance judgments were made between the first and the second series (including all the micrometric ones), although when the first series was split into subseries such progressive improvement was not apparent, as shown by a special examination of the partial series.

It is, perhaps, interesting to find that Volkmann's average error for visual extent agrees well with the just noticeable difference on visual intensity for him. However, such agreement cannot in general be found.

I have cited rough values such as $\frac{1}{60}$, $\frac{1}{90}$, and $\frac{1}{100}$ since more exact-appearing values such as $1/62.5$, given before, cannot be looked upon as precise and comparable since they were based on different m's, and this m always is finite. If we refer to my remarks on page [103], we can see that as the error sums and therefore the average errors become less, the smaller one takes the m during their derivation. Proof of this fact is found in series II, when 0.011287 ($= 1/88.6$) or 0.010808 ($= 1/92.5$) is found as the average error of the unit distance. Both values are determined from the same observations, but the first was subdivided by an $m = 48$ whereas the second was based on subgroups of $m = 16$ observations. One can see that the difference in results was not very significant, but nevertheless it was there and should be taken into account.

If we want to reduce all values to the normality, for which the number of observations would be infinite, one has to apply a correction. The formula, which I briefly mentioned on page [105] and which I derive theoretically in my "Methods of Measurement," demands that each value be multiplied by $(3m + 1)/3m$. Since m is, respectively, 60, 48, 16, and 16, applying the correction results in the following values:

$$\text{I. } 0.016970 = \frac{1}{62.1}$$

$$\text{II. (1) } 0.011366 = \frac{1}{88.0}$$

$$\text{(2) } 0.011634 = \frac{1}{89.7}$$

$$\text{III. } 0.0098933 = \frac{1}{101.1}$$

If this correction were to provide complete compensation, the first and second results in series II should be brought into complete agreement. One notices, indeed, that they approach each other to the extent that the difference becomes almost negligible. One might be inclined to ascribe the remaining difference to the fact that this correction is not based on absolute and certain measurements, but only on probability theory, which always can leave small differences due to chance fluctuations. This difference is, however, not a chance result, as I have learned from detailed examination of analogous cases. I can prove that it is always found to extend in one direction as mentioned briefly in Chapter VIII.* The reason for this behavior can be found in the fact that our correction does not allow for the variability of the constant errors, which contaminates the variable error when m is large. In this respect the corrected value of $1/89.7$ when $m = 16$ is preferable to $1/88.0$ when $m = 48$.

Since the constant error in my own observations of series I was negligible its possible variations could not have influenced the result very much, so that the corrected value of $\frac{1}{62.1}$ can be considered as accurate enough. I therefore did not engage in any special investigation of its validity.

I shall now turn to an account of the results of the micrometric series. These series were all carried out with a micrometer, reading to 0.01 mm, which could be further subdivided into ten parts by estimation. In the tables which follow, the unit to be used is therefore 0.001 mm and, for example, a distance of 300 represents a true distance of 0.300 mm, or a sum of errors of 265 equals one of 0.265 mm. When fractions are given— actually they are really superfluous—they originated in the correction of raw errors.

---

* Should one mistrust the above correction for the same reason, I would like to mention that the correction of the mean square error, given on page (105), which is accepted by all mathematicians and astronomers, is subject to the same faults for the very same reasons. I can and will support this statement by my own experience.

Distances in this apparatus* are determined by means of three fine parallel silver threads 0.445 mm thick and 11 mm long. These threads were observed at different distances, always given in whole millimeters, against the milk-glass shade of a lamp or against the bright sky.

In Volkmann's series the values at the smallest distances are given in parentheses because they did not fit into the series and were neglected in the following calculations. The reason for this deviation may be found in the glare, which made itself felt in this situation and almost made the threads invisible. Volkmann found estimations under these conditions very difficult compared to the other distances. Appel, whose eyesight is very sharp and who has little trouble with glare, did not find it necessary to make such an omission.

Apart from the micrometric series which I am communicating here, there are two other series, which I shall omit, because they were based on distances that were too few and too close together, and because they contain values that are too much out of line.

Series IV. Volkmann (March 22 to April 1, 1857)

Seven horizontal distances at 333 mm from the eye.

DISTANCE THRESHOLDS, VOLKMANN SERIES IV
$m = 30$, $\mu = 4$

D	200	400	600	800	1000	1200	1400	Sum
$\Sigma\Delta$ { L	(694.5)	534.0	630.6	740.5	824.2	1023.2	1057.6	5504.6
R	(630.5)	611.3	672.3	801.0	952.8	1097.6	1218.1	5983.6
Sum	(1325.0)	1145.3	1302.9	1541.5	1777.0	2120.8	2275.7	11,488.2
$\Sigma\Delta^2$ { L	(13,439)	8327	11,721	14,344	16,561	29,964	31,144	125,500
R	(11,134)	10,968	12,504	17,655	22,564	32,419	38,835	146,079
Sum	(24,573)	19,295	24,225	31,999	39,125	62,383	69,979	271,579

Series V. Volkmann (April to sometime in June 1857)

Six vertical distances 333 mm from the eye.

The experiments on vertical distances were carried out while the observer was wearing glasses since his vision was not clear enough for the difficult judgments involved here, whereas all experiments on horizontal distances were carried out without glasses.

* For details see *Berichte der sächs. Soc.* 1858, p. 140.

DISTANCE THRESHOLDS, VOLKMANN SERIES V
$m = 96, \mu = 1$

D		(400)	600	800	1000	1200	1400	Sum
$\Sigma\Delta$ {	O	(1429.2)	1645.3	1618.9	2417.4	2388.2	2993.6	12,492.6
	U	(1563.0)	1335.0	1998.7	2070.0	2810.3	3150.0	12,843.3
Sum		(2998.2)	2980.3	3617.0	4487.4	5198.5	6143.6	25,335.9
$\Sigma\Delta^2$ {	O	(28,170)	42,981	45,016	97,527	89,314	155,248	458,256
	U	(50,708)	27,011	72,011	73,199	128,531	176,638	528,098
Sum		(78,878)	69,992	117,027	170,726	217,845	331,886	986,354

Series VI. Appel (May and June 1857)

Seven horizontal distances at 370 mm.

DISTANCE THRESHOLDS, APPEL SERIES VI
$m = 48, \mu = 2$

D		200	300	400	500	600	700	800	Sum
$\Sigma\Delta$ {	L	592.44	508.00	653.02	643.90	726.64	739.12	716.00	4579.12
	R	594.20	679.00	681.00	575.50	719.52	649.00	778.61	4676.83
Sum		1186.64	1187.00	1334.02	1219.40	1446.16	1388.12	1494.61	9255.95

Series VII. Appel (October 1857)

Six horizontal distances at 300 mm.

Calculations of $\Sigma\Delta$ were made twice, once for $\mu = 2$ and once for $\mu = 6$.

DISTANCE THRESHOLDS, APPEL SERIES VII
$m = 33, \mu = 2$

D		200	400	600	800	1000	1200	Sum
$\Sigma\Delta$ {	L	442.6	647.8	661.9	929.2	941.9	1070.8	4694.2
	R	450.6	623.9	715.8	720.5	838.8	1027.0	4376.6
Sum		893.2	1271.7	1377.7	1654.9	1780.7	2097.8	9070.8
$\Sigma\Delta^2$ {	L	4773	10,046	9805	18,422	19,899	23,595	86,540
	R	4585	8620	11,895	13,149	15,810	22,901	76,960
Sum		9358	18,666	21,700	31,571	35,709	46,496	163,500

$m = 11, \mu = 6$

D		200	400	600	800	1000	1200	Sum
$\Sigma\Delta$ {	L	422.8	646.7	661.9	848.4	901.3	1049.1	4530.2
	R	455.2	620.4	688.8	691.2	812.0	976.0	4243.6
Sum		878.0	1267.1	1350.7	1539.6	1713.3	2025.1	8773.8

Viewing the results as a whole (with the exception of those in parentheses which have been omitted for the reasons cited) one may note the agreement not only between the various series by the same observer but also between the two different observers. There is a common increase of the sums of errors with distance, but at a lesser rate than would be expected if they were proportional to distance. Even the two extra series that were omitted were in complete agreement with this general result. As already mentioned, one may consider the sum of errors to be made up of two components, of which one is constant for the different distances and is known by the name of Volkmann's constant. It will be designated by the letter V. The other is proportional to distance, and under the name of Weber's variable, will be designated for unit distance by W. W must accordingly be multiplied by the distance D in order to give the same proportional value of WD for each distance.

According to the theory of combination for sources of error, the composition of the sum of errors $\Sigma\Delta$ for each distance is made up of the components V and WD, which cannot be represented merely by the simple addition of the two factors. We cannot therefore write

$$\Sigma\Delta = V + WD$$

but the sum of the squares of both components must be set equal to the square of $\Sigma\Delta$, so that we have

$$(\Sigma\Delta)^2 = V^2 + (WD)^2$$

and hence

$$\Sigma\Delta = \sqrt{V^2 + W^2D^2}$$

Since the square of a sum of errors $(\Sigma\Delta)^2$, has an a priori relation to the sum of squares $\Sigma\Delta^2$, according to the theory of error, one can substitute the sum of squared errors for the square of the sum of errors in the above equation. However, the physiological factors, to which I shall refer below, probably pertain more closely to the first form, which I consequently have used as my basis in what follows.

It is very easy to show theoretically and in terms of our direct experience that two given independent sources of error, one generating a sum of errors A, the other a sum of errors B, when combined, cannot add up to a sum as large as $A + B$, but will have a sum which is smaller. On the average, errors of opposing sign are committed as often as errors of the same sign, but the resultant error is equal to their sum only in the last instance, whereas in the first case the resultant error equals their difference. Theoretically, the sum of the individual squares of the errors of the component parts is normally (strictly speaking, for an infinite number of errors observed under comparable circumstances) equal to the sum of the resulting squared errors. Also, the sum of squares of the error sums is normally equal to the squares of the resulting combined sum of errors. These theoretical results may be easily checked by taking any two series of errors that are independent, and using them as components; by algebraic addition one then calculates the equivalent of the combination of two independent sources of error. Indeed, this is the way I have convinced myself of the correctness of the theoretical results with respect to the sum of squared errors as well as to the square of the sum of errors. I have made a number of tests, but shall cite the results elsewhere.

Inasmuch as there exists for the eye one error source that is independent of the distance and one that depends upon it in a specified manner, the preceding reasoning will apply to the relevant components, and the equations will be applicable. The question of the validity of all the assumptions can be answered by the observations themselves, since if they are valid, one would be able to calculate in reverse such values of V and W to show that the originally observed values can be represented according to these formulas.

Observations at two distances are sufficient to calculate V and W. Taking the sum of errors in series IV at $D = 800$ and $D = 1400$ as 1541.5 and 2275.7, respectively, and combining L and R, we can start by writing

$$V^2 + 800^2 W^2 = 1541.5^2$$

$$V^2 + 1400^2 W^2 = 2275.7^2$$

V^2 and W^2 are easily found by solving for two unknowns. After that, taking the roots will give V and W themselves.

As long as more than two distances are available, V and W can be calculated from a number of such combinations. One more assumption should be tested before calculating back to the sum of errors for V and W. The values of V and W of the various combinations should agree well enough so that the remaining deviations can be ascribed to the uncompensated chance variations of the observations. By taking the average of a number of such values, V and W can then be more precisely determined.

This procedure has one drawback only: the choice between the observed values that are to be combined is arbitrary, and each of the ways of making the combinations could lead to a different final average; although, if the observations satisfy the assumptions exactly, the differences between the definitive results will be so small that one could be used as well as another. In the meantime, calculation by the method of least squares remains preferable, since it excludes any arbitrariness and allows us to arrive at the most nearly exact result that can be found. The following table shows the results by this method, when the sums of L and R were combined and no allowance was made for equal m's or viewing distances (as was done later).* The probable error is shown with $\pm$, and μ is the one valid for a combination of L and R—in other words, twice that of the μ at the head of tabulated observations. If we want to make a decision on whether our assumptions regarding Volkmann's constant

VALUES OF V AND W FOR THE SUMS OF RAW ERROR ACCORDING TO THE EQUATION $V^2 + D^2W^2 = (\Sigma\Delta)^2$

Series	m	μ	Distance	V	W
IV. Volkmann	30	4	333 mm	974.36 ± 34.34	1.5008 ± 0.02628
V. Volkmann (vert.)	96	2	333 "	1398.2 ± 49.35	4.2411 ± 0.01332
VI. Appel	48	4	370 "	1169.9 ± 33.76	1.1603 ± 0.10008
VII. Appel	33	4	300 "	1008.6 ± 121.97	1.5668 ± 0.051576

and Weber's variable are justified, we might first regard the probable errors, which are found to be relatively very small compared to the sizes of V and W. In the second place, we might calculate $(\Sigma\Delta)^2$ or $\Sigma\Delta$ from the values of V and W tabulated for various D's, using $V^2 + D^2W^2 = (\Sigma\Delta)^2$ for the former and

$$\sqrt{V^2 + D^2W^2} = \Sigma\Delta$$

for the latter. We can then compare the results of our calculations and the observations, where satisfactory agreement is found. I shall show the compilation for $(\Sigma\Delta)^2$, omitting the listing of distances for brevity's sake. These were taken from the tabulated observations, leaving out the values in parentheses.

Agreement of calculation and observation is very satisfactory with the

* The procedure was to put the equations in the form $V^2 + D^2W^2 = (\Sigma\Delta)^2$, which is linear when V^2 and W^2 are the unknowns. The values of V and W were then obtained by taking the square roots of V^2 and W^2. The probable errors of V and W were calculated from the deviations of the calculated values as obtained from the observed $(\Sigma\Delta)^2$ for V^2 and W^2 and were then reduced to V and W, according to the principles of statistics, by division by $2V$ and $2W$, respectively.

COMPILATION OF THE OBSERVED AND THE CALCULATED VALUES OF
$(\Sigma\Delta)^2$ **TAKEN FROM THE PREVIOUS TABULATION OF** V **AND** W

IV		V		VI		VII	
Observed	Calculated	Observed	Calculated	Observed	Calculated	Observed	Calculated
1,311,700	1,309,780	8,882,200	8,430,000	1,408,000	1,422,444	797,820	1,210,970
1,697,600	1,760,270	13,087,000	13,466,000	1,409,000	1,489,750	1,617,300	1,392,280
2,376,300	2,390,980	20,137,000	19,940,000	1,779,600	1,583,980	1,898,100	1,861,120
3,157,700	3,201,880	27,023,000	27,855,000	1,486,900	1,705,130	2,738,700	2,517,500
4,497,800	4,192,980	37,744,000	37,208,000	2,091,500	1,853,200	3,170,900	3,361,400
5,178,800	5,364,280			1,926,800	2,028,200	4,400,700	4,392,900
				2,233,900	2,230,110		

exception of a few somewhat more deviant values in series VII. One may say, accordingly, that Weber's Law in the area of the judgment of visual distance is confirmed up to the smallest distances, except that it is subject to a complication which must be resolved before this fact can be seen.

It seemed of interest to me to undertake the evaluation of the data in a number of additional ways. Although they do not lead to essentially different results, they will serve to demonstrate the outcome of the possible choices between various approaches. These different approaches were applied to the data of series IV.

1. Instead of combining the L and R calculations as above, I determined the results separately, but otherwise according to the same procedure. The results obtained were as follows:

	V	W
Left	436.82	0.7540
Right	500.23	0.8005
	937.05	1.5545

2. One might perhaps consider setting up the equation in the form

$$\sqrt{V^2 + D^2W^2} = \Sigma\Delta$$

as a more suitable base for calculations by the method of least squares, since $\Sigma\Delta$ and not $(\Sigma\Delta)^2$ had been directly observed. But the equation has now lost its linearity and one has to apply corrections that, as the expert will easily discern, lead to a much longer computation. I have carried out these calculations on series IV separately for L and for R with the following results

	V	W
Left	444.1	0.7517
Right	502.0	0.7970
	946.1	1.5487

These values differ only very slightly from those found in the previous calculation. It will not be worthwhile, therefore, to continue in this complex manner.

3. I based my calculations on the sum of the squared deviations instead of on the square of the sums of errors, in order to derive constants V' and W' from the equation $V'^2 + D^2 W'^2 = \Sigma\Delta^2$. Thus I find for L and R:

	V'^2	W'^2
Left	6084	0.013591
Right	7429	0.016234
	13513	0.029825

Statistical theory shows the relationship between $\Sigma\Delta^2$ and $(\Sigma\Delta)^2$ to be

$$\Sigma\Delta^2 = \frac{\pi(\Sigma\Delta)^2}{2m}$$

where π equals Ludolf's number. Applying this formula leads us back to approximately the former values of V and W.

I have also carried out separate calculations for the series VI and VII by the method listed under number 1 for L and R separately. I found for VI:

	V	W
Left	507.88	0.69166
Right	609.47	0.41611
	1117.35	1.10777

and for VII:

	V	W
Left	515.66	0.81175
Right	447.48	0.75605
	963.14	1.56780

The table of V and W, given before, is taken from the sums of errors in each series and is therefore proportional to each of these sums. However, since the different series were based on a different number of errors at each distance, given by the product μm found in the table, the values of the various series must be divided by the number of errors: 120, 192, 192, and 132, respectively. The values of V and W obtained in this way will then represent the average values. One should further consider that a correction for finite m by multiplication by $(3m + 1)/3m$ is in order, since each set of observations was based on a different m. This correction is very small. Finally we have to take into account that the viewing distance at which the estimates were made was not the same at all times. While this fact can have no influence on W, since W will still show the same proportionate error (although the distances to be judged will look smaller from further away), it will affect V, which has an absolute magnitude that stays the same at all distances. To make this error comparable for different viewing distances we must reduce it to the same viewing distance by taking its reciprocal. First, however, we have to add to each viewing distance 7 mm to correct the distances which had been measured to the cornea by an amount equal to the distance from the cornea to the point of intersection of the rays of light,[11] so that, for example, we get for a viewing distance of 333 mm in series IV a value of 340 mm, which we use for the correction.

If we now undertake these three reductions or corrections, by reducing all values to an average of an infinite number of observations at a distance of $333 + 7$ mm, we find the following values, instead of those of the previous table.

CORRECTED AND REDUCED VALUES OF V AND W FOR AN ERROR AT 340 MM FROM THE NODAL POINT OF THE EYE

Series	V	W
IV. Volkmann	8.210	0.01265 = 1/79.1
V. Volkmann (vert.)	7.319	0.02220 = 1/45.045
VI. Appel	5.5331	0.00608 = 1/164.5
VII. Appel	8.5476	0.01172 = 1/85.3

There is much that is interesting and remarkable in this table. Volkmann's W in series IV, which was 1/79.1 when horizontal distances were measured by micrometer, does not turn out to be very different from his value of 1/89.7 obtained only shortly before in his series II for much larger distances. This value appears to be nothing but a W determined from a series in which the complications due to V vanish. Whatever difference still exists can probably be attributed to the very different methods of experimentation.

On the other hand, the differences in W between the micrometric series IV for horizontal distances (with vertical threads) and series V on vertical distances (with horizontal threads) strike the eye. Although both were taken not too much separated in time, W is almost twice as large for vertical distances as for horizontal distances. Estimates of the former were, therefore, much less exact than those for the latter. This fact agrees with what was directly believed to be true during the experiment. Constant

---

[11] Trans. Note: The nodal point of the eye. See Southall, J. P. C. *Introduction to physiological Optics.* New York: Oxford University Press, 1937.

errors, not shown here, were also much larger for vertical distances than for horizontal ones. Appel's values of W in his two series of observations, VI and VII, for horizontal distances disagree with each other by so much, and the value for series VI is so small, that they awaken distrust. There is nothing in the observations themselves that could confirm our doubts or explain the difference. The value of $1/85.3$ in series VII agrees well with Volkmann's of $1/79.1$, without there having been any knowledge of Volkmann's results, which otherwise might have acted to bring the agreement about. Special interest attaches to constant V. Apart from Appel's somewhat deviant series VI, which is also suspect regarding W, the three other values of V for two entirely different observers, with vertical and horizontal distances, agree so well, that one might surmise that we were dealing here with a natural absolute constant. After all, the difference between 7.319 and 8.210 between the V's for horizontal and for vertical extent is so small that it could not possibly be due to chance, considering the uncertainty of observation and taking into account the constant error of the magnitude of V for constant errors and of W for the uncorrected errors.* Appel's value of 8.546 agrees surprisingly well with Volkmann's value of 8.210. To make sure that we are dealing here with a constant would demand a wider extension and replication of the experiments than we have at present, in order to check for individual variation and test the reliability under different circumstances.

We might ask what the meaning of this constant might be. In anticipation of Volkmann's own planned publication, I will only briefly mention here the thinking which led him to surmise from the start the existence of such a constant, and which guided him in carrying out his tedious work. For its existence had indeed been suspected, although the question remains whether the value found is really the one that he had anticipated.

Fig. 2.   Schematic diagram of sense elements on retina.

If Weber's opinion is correct that the apparent size of an object depends on the number of retinal elements on which its image falls, then a line or distance would appear equally large whether its ends terminate on the nearest or most distant points of two retinal elements. In some

---

* The uncorrected error δ is made up of two components: the variable error Δ and the constant error c. V and W in turn are components of the variable error Δ.

cases a short line could therefore appear to be of the same length as a longer line. As an example I give the schematic case in Fig. 2 in which the circles must be considered to represent the sense elements of the retina. One can easily see that two distances which are longer or shorter by almost two diameters of a retinal element can, in some cases, appear to be equal. While this error can be neglected for longer lines or distances, which cover many retinal elements, it cannot be overlooked at the micrometric distances. A noticeable mistake in judging equality must depend on it in micrometric experiments, using the method of average error. Consequently the magnitude of average error must be related to the diameter of the retinal elements. Volkmann's constant represents perhaps this average error and might allow us to estimate the dimensions of these retinal elements, if we knew how one depended on the other.

In undertaking a closer examination of the question whether this average error can be represented by Volkmann's constant, three problems had to be solved: (1) The relationship between the size of this average error and the diameter of a retinal element had to be determined; (2) the error had to be investigated to see if it really remained sufficiently (or at least approximately) the same at various standard distances, so as to allow it to be identified with such a constant as V appeared to be; (3) it remained to be seen whether the magnitude of the constant agreed sufficiently well with the anatomically determined dimensions of retinal elements.

The first and second questions are matters that depend on the theory of probability. The principle of their solution can be stated, but its execution is too difficult even for a practiced mathematician.* However, one can take an experimental approach that duplicates the conditions supposedly found in the eye, an approach tried by Volkmann. The third question runs into the difficulty that the ultimate perceiving elements of the retina are perhaps not yet precisely known. I shall not enter into further discussion in this matter in order not to anticipate Volkmann's own communication, for this investigation belongs to him. The previous discussion should be sufficient to draw attention to the constant concerned.

In conclusion of this discussion of Volkmann's constant I would like to mention the calculations by means of which its observed magnitude can be reduced to the size it represents on the retina. This reduction is, of course, necessary if one wants to examine the question of its relationship to the retinal elements.

According to the table on page [191] Volkmann's constant, at a viewing distance of 340 mm, amounted to 8.210 as calculated from the nodal

---

* Apart from my own judgment I can cite the opinion of Professor Möbius in this matter.

point (that is, 0.008210 mm, using a unit of 0.001 mm, as in all these experiments with micrometers). If one assumes the intersection of the rays to be 15 mm (in round numbers) from the retina, the ratio of V on the retina to the observed V is 15 : 340, or in other words, the given constant V represents a distance of 0.0003621 mm on the retina. This estimate depends on the assumption that the linear extent of an image of a line on the retina is given by the limits of a ray drawn from each end through the intersecting point and allowed to fall on the retina. That, at least, is the usual calculation.

There is, however, the question—I have to thank E. H. Weber for raising it—whether the intersection of the rays is really the determining factor. Generally distances are measured with the aid of eye movements, by fixing the optical axis first on one end point and then on the other. Accordingly it appears that the pivot of the eye[12] would be a better point through which to draw the rays from the ends of the line to find the distance that its image occupies on the retina. This point, however, lies 5.6 Paris lines or 14.224 mm behind the front surface of the cornea.* This distance would correspond to a point 7.778 mm in front of the retina, whereby the previous calculation of the image size would be reduced by about one half. I must leave this question open at this time.

One might think that Volkmann's constant might depend on an error made in estimating the divisions on the micrometer. Naturally this kind of error would not depend on the size of the observed distance and thus cause a constant average error at every distance. But our V is much too large, for the micrometer scale could be read directly to 0.01 or ten units of a thousandth of a millimeter; V on the average amounted to 0.008 or eight thousandths of a millimeter. So large an error on the average would be very unlikely. Undoubtedly, however, Volkmann's constant was subject to a small addition from this source.

Should this constant really have a well-founded organic origin in the eye, it would represent a striking analogy in the area of extensive light sensations to what we had found in the area of intensive sensations. In other words, we would find that Weber's Law is confirmed here also only insofar as we take into account a constant which must be added to the external variable effect due to internal organic reasons.

Prior to applying the method of average error, I carried out a few experiments on visual estimates of distance by the method of just noticeable differences. I shall cite them here, although they are superseded by the

---

[12] Trans. Note: Center of rotation of the eye. See Southall, *op. cit.*
* According to Volkmann in *Wagner's Wörterb. Art. Sehen.*, p. 234.

more precise later measurements, because there is nothing else definite and available by this method.

Following a few preliminary experiments on the acuity of my visual estimates of distance, I took two pairs of compasses and set one of them with a span of 1 Paris duodecimal in. and the other to 1 plus $\frac{1}{40}$ in. I then mixed up the compasses so that I did not know which one was which. After that I attempted to discover by eye which one had the wider span. I made the right decision every time, but only after lengthy examination. The two pairs of compasses were held up next to each other, at the clearest viewing distance, so that their tips were horizontal. I made the same difficult but correct decisions when the distances were doubled or quadrupled, so that in the last case the span of one pair of compasses amounted to 4.0, and that of the other to 4.1 in. This small series of three experiments was repeated three times by myself, twice on one day and once on the following day. It seemed to me that it made no difference whether the compasses were held at a greater or lesser distance from the eye, as long as the limits of accommodation were not exceeded. It seems probable that I would have correctly distinguished an even smaller difference than $\frac{1}{40}$. But as I have already remarked, if one does not take the limit of what is just noticeable a little high, one gets into the tedious method of right and wrong cases, which is admittedly more exact, if many observations are available, but not very certain with only a few experiments. The difference was small enough, in any case, so that if I cut it in half, the judgments no longer were reliable. The task demanded the utmost effort of my eye, which was not yet very practiced in those days.

Even though Weber's Law was confirmed in the case of the visual judgment of distance, the question of what this confirmation actually means in the case of perceptions of extent remains open. In the sense of Weber's approach to the mediation of the magnitude of extensive sensations, the basic question which we would need to answer with reference to the meaning of Weber's Law in this area would have to be as follows. Do differences between spatial distances appear equally large or equally noticeable, when the values of the sensation centers involved differ by relatively the same amounts, and therefore does the number of active sensation centers in sensations of extent take the place of the magnitude of the stimulus in intensive sensations? However, none of the experiments on visual extent clarify this issue, since they were all carried out, as is natural for our eyes, under the influence of eye movements. Under these conditions the various distances were not compared according to the number of sensation centers which were covered by them, but as a function of the fact that the same point of clearest vision moved through a larger or smaller distance. Indeed, with the density of the neural distribution diminishing from the center of the retina to the periphery, one would not have been able to expect a direct confirmation of the law in our experiments, even if eye movements had not taken place.

One might suspect, accordingly, that our confirmation might be related to the muscular sense, as activated by the movement, to the extent that it had served to mediate the estimates of distance, rather than by the number of sensation centers involved in the estimation. Nevertheless, even if this explanation were to be confirmed, the verification of the law would still remain important. In any case, it would leave our basic question unanswered. Even the relationship to the muscular sense presents difficulties which I shall not discuss in detail here.

There is another avenue of approach, which might suggest itself as a way to answer this question. That is to try to use the skin, whose analogy to the organ of vision with respect to the appreciation of distance has been pointed out so well by E. H. Weber, and where one does not have to worry about the effect of movement. The only problem here is the fact that one cannot count on an even distribution of nerve fibres. It seemed useful to test how successful one might be on different parts of the skin in this respect. Accordingly I carried out some experiments on myself using the forehead, where a large flat surface with a hard base seemed to offer the most favorable experimental field. Volkmann, too, made some observations on the tip of his left middle finger and the back of his hand using the method of average error. All results agreed that there is not even an approximate proportionality between the corrected error and perceived distance. In general the average error increases more slowly, and not at all beyond certain limits or at larger intervals. So it is out of the question that they could be represented by a combination of two components, one proportional to distance and another constant with respect to it, this in analogy to what was revealed by the visual distance estimates with the micrometer. These experiments accordingly do not indicate the least probability that Weber's Law exists in this area—when approached in the way indicated—even though they cannot be counted on too heavily with respect to the investigation of our question, because of the irregularity of nerve distribution.

Meanwhile a new question arises: Do we really have to proceed in this way in the area of extensive sensations? At first glance it may seem to be obvious, if one wants to show the corresponding validities of the law in extensive and intensive sensations, since the latter were found in this manner. We should not overlook, however, the fact that the distances estimated by eye or by touch are limited to the given visual or tactual field. The extent of these fields is not affected, whereas the intensive light stimulus both sets the limits for the preceding intensity, and also is responsible for an intensity of the subsequent stimulation. Naturally this creates a different situation. I shall come back to this point in a chapter in the following part of this book. The series of experiments on which the preceding negative result is based will be communicated in my "Methods of Measurement."

6. PHYSICAL AND MENTAL WEALTH

One can pursue Weber's Law into a still more general field. Our physical possessions (*fortune physique*) have no value or meaning to us as inert material, but constitute only a means for arousing within us a sum of psychic values (*fortune morale*). In this respect they take the place of stimuli. A dollar has, in this connection, much less value to a rich man than to a poor man. It can make a beggar happy for a whole day, but it is not even noticed when added to the fortune of a millionaire. Weber's Law can handle this kind of situation. If the same amount is to be added to what Laplace called the *fortune morale*, the addition to the *fortune physique* must be in proportion to the physical possessions already there.

This principle was first mentioned in a treatise by Daniel Bernoulli entitled *Specimen theoriae novae de mensura sortis* published in *Comment. Acad. scient. imp. Petropolit. T.V.* 1738. It was later referred to by Laplace in his *Théorie analytique des probabilités*, pages 187 and 432, and developed further in his deductions. Finally it was mentioned and accepted by Poisson in his *Recherches sur la probabilité*.

The expressions *fortune physique* and *fortune morale* were first used not by Bernoulli, but by Laplace. Bernoulli says, after a few introductory remarks:

Certainly the value must not be estimated from the price of the thing, but from the advantage acquired therefrom. The price is estimated by the thing itself; the advantage, by the state of the persons involved. Thus, without doubt, the gain of 1000 ducats is far more important for poor persons than for rich persons, although the amount is the same for both.

And further (p. 177):

Thus, it is indeed exceedingly probable that any small advantage adds to the ultimate good in reciprocal proportion to the status of the people involved.

He bases his differential formula (p. 181) and his logarithmic formula

(p. 182) on these considerations. We later base the same on Weber's Law in a more general way.

Laplace writes (p. 187):

We must distinguish in the hoped-for wealth, its relative value from its absolute value: the latter is independent of the motives that make it desirable, whereas the former increases with these motives. No general rule can be given to appraise this relative value: yet it is natural to assume the relative value of an infinitely small sum to be in direct ratio with its absolute value, and in inverse ratio with the total wealth of the person concerned. Indeed it is clear that a franc has but little value for him who possesses a great number of them, and that the most natural way of estimating its relative value is to suppose it to be in inverse ratio with this number.

And on p. 432:

According to this principle, x being the physical fortune of an individual, the increase dx which it receives, produces for the individual a moral wealth reciprocal to that fortune; the increase in his moral fortune may then be expressed by kdx/x, k being a constant. Thus, designating by y the moral fortune corresponding to the physical fortune x, we shall get

$$y = k \log x + \log h$$

h being an arbitrary constant, which will be determined by means of a value of y corresponding to a given value of x. Concerning this, we shall observe that we can never suppose x and y to be null or negative, in the natural order of things; for the man who possesses nothing looks upon his existence as moral wealth, which may be compared to the advantage that a physical fortune would procure, the value of which is very difficult to assign, but which cannot be set below what would be strictly necessary in order to exist; for we can imagine that he would not consent to receive a modest sum, such as 100 francs, on condition that he would make no further claim when he had spent it.

Poisson says (p. 72):

Inasmuch as the advantage that gain procures for someone depends upon the state of his fortune, we have distinguished this relative advantage of mathematical hope and we have named it moral expectation. When it is an infinitely small quantity we take its relationship to the present fortune of the person as the measure of moral expectation, which may be positive or negative, according to whether it represents an eventual increase or diminution of that fortune. By integral calculus we then deduce consequences from this measure, consequences which are in accord with the rules which prudence indicates concerning the manner in which each one must direct his speculations.

X.
Thresholds

In general, a sensation or a difference between sensations increases with the magnitude of the stimulus or stimulus difference which gives rise to it. At first glance one might assume naturally that the point from which sensations or differences between sensations begin to be noticed would coincide with the zero value of the stimulus or the stimulus difference. However, the facts do not support this assumption. It can be shown that every stimulus as well as every stimulus difference must already have reached a certain finite magnitude before it can be noticed at all—that is, before our consciousness is aroused by a sensation or before a difference between sensations becomes apparent. Conversely, the ability to notice a stimulus or a stimulus difference disappears before its value has diminished to zero. The zero-point of sensations or sensation differences is therefore found to lie above that of the occasioning stimulus or stimulus difference. This fact will now be examined in detail.

The point at which a stimulus or a stimulus difference becomes noticeable or disappears will be called a threshold, for short. This expression can be applied equally well to the sensation or difference between sensations that can just be noticed as well as to the stimulus, stimulus difference, or stimulus ratio that is the cause of the sensations at this point. One can therefore refer to the threshold of a sensation or of a difference between sensations as well as to the threshold value of a stimulus, a stimulus difference or a relationship between stimuli. In short, we may speak of stimulus threshold, differential threshold, or relative threshold. When two stimuli are given, their relative values are apparent from their differences, and vice versa; it is, therefore, generally sufficient to mention only one or the other of the last two kinds of thresholds.

Since extent and differences in extent also have to reach a certain value in order to become apparent to touch or vision as a distance or a difference between distances, we will be able to apply our concept of threshold also to this kind of magnitude. We will call thresholds applicable to intensive sensations, intensive thresholds, and those applicable to extensive sensations, extensive thresholds.

Finally, since other general higher phenomena of consciousness also have a point of expiration and a point of origination, we will be able to generalize the concept and expression of threshold to them. Examples of this type of phenomenon would be the level of total awareness with respect to sleeping and waking, the way single thoughts become conscious, and the focusing of attention in a given direction. In these instances we cannot speak of a threshold value of an external stimulus responsible for lifting consciousness above threshold. But the question may be raised whether we would not have to assume a threshold value of the underlying psychophysical processes and whether stimulus thresholds, differential thresholds, and relative thresholds do not exist as far as sensations are concerned only to the extent that they can be translated into such processes. This question will be taken up when we undertake to discuss inner psychophysics. For the moment we will deal only with purely empirical relationships, which may be substantiated directly. In this chapter I shall endeavor to demonstrate and explain the factual natures of the stimulus threshold and differential threshold. I shall also discuss the deductions and the use to which the existence of a threshold in the area of experience may lead. Next I shall take up each type of threshold determination separately.

1. THE INTENSIVE THRESHOLD

a. Stimulus Threshold

For intensive light sensations we cannot prove directly that there is need for a certain stimulus intensity in order to arouse our sensations, or in other words, that a threshold for visual sensation exists for any finite value of a light stimulus. As we have noted several times, the eye is always above threshold because of its internal excitation, so that each external light stimulus can only add to the excitation already present. The facts which show that this addition must have a given strength to be noticeable belong in the section on differential thresholds.

Concerning those modifications that we call colors, however, the following conditions can be said to obtain as far as visibility is concerned: (1) the degree of refraction and therefore the frequency must be above certain limits; (2) the intensity or amplitude must be above certain limits; (3) the color must cover a sufficient area, the more the further it falls on the periphery of the retina; (4) there must not be too much white mixed with the color.

As far as the first point is concerned, it is well known that beyond the red end of the spectrum no colors are visible, nor can they be made visible, notwithstanding the fact that effects of heat prove the presence of rays beyond this limit. Red light has the slowest frequency and our inability to become aware of infrared rays must be attributed to no other cause than that their frequency is too slow.[1] On the other hand the so-called ultraviolet rays, which one cannot normally make visible when using a conventional prism and whose presence used to be deduced in the past only from their chemical action, have recently been made visible by suitable means. All that was necessary to cause them to be perceived was to bring them up to sufficient strength. This fact serves at the same time as evidence for the second condition.

The visibility of the ultraviolet part of the prismatic spectrum can indeed still be maintained by use of quartz prisms, which pass these colored rays more easily than glass prisms. Whereas if glass prisms are used, nothing can be seen, particularly if the spectrum formed by a quartz prism is isolated by a slit in a screen and observed through a telescope with glass lenses with a second glass prism attached. Proof that ultraviolet rays pass through the glass prism also, and are not recognized only because of their low intensity, lies in the fact that these spectra can still cause a visible fluorescence, as first discovered by Stokes.

As far as the third point is concerned, E. H. Weber* discovered that a green surface would no longer appear green when viewed through a very narrow slit. He concluded that a colored surface had to have a certain extent to appear as of its specific hue. One might argue that some fixed stars appear to have a slight color. However, this color is not very noticeable and one should consider also that the star's image is somewhat extended through diffusion (as is, of course, also true for the light shining through a slit), so that it cannot be thought of as a true point source.

Thorough and careful studies on this topic with respect to the behavior of the periphery of the retina have been carried out by Aubert.† These specialized results cannot very well be taken up in this general exposition, however.

In respect of the fourth point, we may note that it is always possible to thin a colored fluid to such an extent that the coloration becomes impossible to see. Similarly, white can be mixed with a pigment to give the same result. This case will be taken up in detail in a future chapter on the phenomena of mixture.

[1] Trans. Note: Fechner chooses to characterize the spectrum in terms of frequency. Modern usage expresses the visible part of the spectrum in terms of wavelength, although frequency is used for other parts of the electromagnetic continuum, for example in the case of radio frequencies. This terminology also shows that he visualized light waves in terms of the speed of their vibrations. This quaint usage had been preserved in preference to the more modern terms low or high frequency.

* *Müller's Arch.* 1849, p. 279.

† *Gräfe's Arch. f. Ophthalmol.* III, pp. 38 ff.

Concerning the intensity of sound, the factual nature of the threshold can be easily demonstrated.

If a source of sound is moved further and further away, we eventually do not hear it at all, in spite of the fact that the sound waves which reach our ears have not been diminished to zero. Bringing the source of sound closer amplifies the sound, allowing it to make an impression, where before it had not been noticeable because of its weakness and not because of its absence.

Thus we cannot hear a distant single bell. But should 100 bells at the same distance ring together, we would hear them, though we do not hear any single one. Each and every bell at that distance must make its contribution to our hearing, although none is sufficient by itself to arouse a noticeable auditory sensation.

A single caterpillar feeding in the woods cannot be heard, but a mass of caterpillars feeding can be heard quite well; yet the sound made by many caterpillars is only the sum of the sounds of each individual caterpillar. Therefore each caterpillar must contribute something to our hearing all the caterpillars, in spite of the fact that a single one cannot be heard because by itself its sound is not enough to stimulate our auditory sensations.

There is always a certain amount of noise in the air, but unless it reaches a certain point we think that we do not hear anything.

In homeopathic dilution we do not taste the most bitter substance, but sufficient concentration of the solution brings out the bitter taste.

Undoubtedly there are at all times many odorous substances in the air, which we do not smell because they are too diluted, yet the dog or the savage with his sharpened sense organ smells the trail which we can no longer smell, though we could smell it just as well, were it but stronger.

A single pair of galvanic plates gives no noticeable sensation, but the column made up of single pairs of plates gives us a shock.

Any pressure on our body need only be distributed sufficiently in order to become unnoticed, although it has still not become nothing.

b. Differential Thresholds

In general, no one will doubt that a stimulus difference must have a certain magnitude to be noticed as a difference. The method of just noticeable differences, which is applicable to all sense domains, rests completely on this fact.

There is no more beautiful, simple and striking way of demonstrating the existence of a differential threshold in the field of visual sensations than the shadow experiment which we cited as proof of Weber's Law. Let us recall the circumstances of that experiment:

One places two lamps next to each other in front of an object that will throw a shadow. Each of the lamps throws a shadow which is illuminated by the other lamp, whereas the surrounding background is illuminated by both lamps. If one now turns down the wick of one of the lamps or moves it away from the object that is throwing the shadow, the shadow is seen to become weaker and weaker, while the surrounding illumination becomes less and less different from it. Finally the shadow disappears, apparently absorbed by the general illumination of the background, in spite of the fact that both light sources are still present. I was most astonished when my attention was first drawn to the sight of two lights throwing but one shadow. Both lamps were clearly lit, but only one shadow was seen. In a word, when the difference between the illumination of the shadow and that of the surrounding background falls below a certain amount, the difference in sensations disappears completely and can no longer be perceived by any means.

This experiment is particularly striking because one has the components in view simultaneously and the gaze can be fixed sharply, quietly, and steadily on the boundary between them as their difference is made to disappear. There is no chance of forgetting the previous impression or of overlooking the difference. In other modes of experimentation one might be inclined to blame the inability to perceive or the vanishing of the difference on these factors, but not here.

This experiment may be modified in many ways. Generally: if a shadow can just be seen, one needs only to turn down one of the lamps or turn up the other one to make it disappear; and if it cannot be noticed, one merely has to turn up one lamp the necessary amount or turn down the other by a corresponding amount for it to become noticeable. Instead of turning a lamp higher or lower we might just as well move it closer or further away.

We have already noted how, even with the greatest degree of attention, we cannot see any stars in the daylight sky. From this experience we can learn the same lesson as from the above-mentioned experiment.

The increase of the differential threshold with increasing stimulation is as widely known as is the existence of a differential threshold itself. To the extent that Weber's Law holds, the size of the just noticeable difference and therefore of the differential threshold is directly proportional to the magnitude of the stimuli that are to be compared. Where the law does not hold, there still exists a functional relationship to stimulus magnitude, although it is no longer a direct proportion.

Since relative stimulus differences remain constant as long as the stimulus proportions remain the same, and vice versa, we can say just as well that identically just noticeable differences in sensations are associated with the same relative stimulus differences as with the same stimulus pro-

unconsciousness becomes lower. Thus distant sounds or the olfactory portions, independently of stimulus magnitude. But even if both of these relationships turn out to be the same in fact, it may still be more pertinent sometimes, from a formal point of view, to use one rather than the other mode of expression. From now on we shall accordingly refer to the absolute stimulus difference as the absolute differential threshold, which means the same thing as a just noticeable difference. We will designate by relative differential threshold or differential constant the relative difference between stimuli, and by relative threshold or relative constant the stimulus proportions at which a sensation of difference reaches its threshold. The letters α, ω and v will be used to identify these thresholds. Thus the differential constant ω for light intensity equals $\frac{1}{100}$, the relative constant equals $\frac{101}{100}$ according to Volkmann's procedure.

In general one has

$$v = 1 + \omega \quad \text{and} \quad \omega = v - 1$$

In many places in what follows we shall use the logarithm of v. Since the magnitude of ω in the expression $v = 1 + \omega$ will always be very small, its higher powers can be neglected. One can then substitute $M\omega$ for log $(1 + \omega)$ according to well-known mathematical proofs, where M is the modulus of the logarithmic system. We may therefore put

$$\log v = M\omega$$

It is important to keep in mind that while the relative stimulus difference and the stimulus proportion, and therefore also the differential constant and relative constant, both remain constant with changing stimulus levels, it is not true that when one of these values is changed, the other changes proportionally. Instead, the logarithm of the relative constant behaves, according to the above equation, proportionally to the differential constant. We can therefore substitute log ω for v at any time that only relative values are important.

2. THE THRESHOLD OF EXTENT

If a white circle on a black ground, or vice versa, is too small or looked at from too great a distance, it cannot be recognized. When two points or parallel threads come too close together or are observed from too great a distance, they flow into each other and their separation becomes unrecognizable. The limit in the first case can be called the threshold of the recognition of size; the latter instance is an example of the threshold of recognition for distance.

We know that two compass points which touch the skin too closely together give the impression of one. We are dealing then in this situation with a threshold of distance.

Two impressions are felt as one when they occur too rapidly one after the other. There exists then also a threshold of extent with regard to intervals of time.

When an object such as the hour hand of a clock or a star in the sky moves too slowly, we cannot recognize its movement, but when the movement is accelerated sufficiently we can notice it. There is, therefore, also a threshold for movement.

In this case both space and time are concerned. Presumably movement becomes noticeable when the thresholds for time and space coincide, that is, when a separable space is covered in the smallest duration which does not register in the mind as a simultaneous moment of time.

3. GENERAL CONSIDERATIONS CONCERNING THRESHOLDS

There is a certain paradox inherent in the nature of the threshold. A stimulus or stimulus difference can be increased up to a certain point without being felt; above that point it is felt and its growth is noticed. How can something that does not reach consciousness when it is weak begin to affect the mind when it is strengthened? It appears as if the sum of nothing adds up to an effective something. However, though this relationship can make trouble for a metaphysician, there is no difficulty from the mathematical point of view. The fact may point to the conclusion that the mathematical point of view, according to which the magnitude of a sensation can be regarded as a function of stimulus magnitude (or of the inner processes released by a stimulus), is also the correct metaphysical point of view. Indeed, when y is a function of x, y can vanish at certain values of x or change into the negative or become imaginary. We know that it suffices to increase x beyond this value to see y again reach positive values.

The following phenomenon is inherent in the nature of the threshold. The farther the stimulus or stimulus difference falls below the threshold, the less chance there is for the stimulus or stimulus difference to be perceived and the greater must be the amount added before a sensation can be felt. As long as the stimulus or stimulus difference remains below threshold its perception is, as one says, unconscious. As stimulus and stimulus difference fall deeper and deeper below threshold, the level of stimuli in the atmosphere stay below threshold and the corresponding unconsciousness becomes lower. Thus distant sounds or the olfactory sensations remain unconscious until their intensity exceeds a given magnitude, their threshold. We are naturally led to the use of negative values to designate these unconscious sensations, if we call the threshold zero and the conscious sensations positive. We will take up this concept more precisely in the future.

The fact that small differences cannot be perceived leads directly to a fine point of no mean importance when measuring sensitivity by the method of right and wrong cases.

Let us assume that the difference between two weights or, in general, between two experimental stimuli, is so small that it falls below the point where it can be consciously recognized. The question is now: can it influence the number of right or wrong cases? Is not the relationship between them as though no difference existed at all, until the difference has exceeded the boundary where it is perceptible as such; and from there on is not the influence to be evaluated, not by the absolute size of the difference, but by the difference from the value where it begins to become truly perceptible?

At first this conclusion seems obvious, for how can a difference which does not affect our consciousness determine our judgment? Nevertheless it is not admissible without destroying the principles of this method of measurement and at the same time the principles by which one calculates the probability of error with respect to the errors' magnitudes, which is the whole basis for this method of measurement. Also, a more searching examination will lead to conclusions opposite to this apparently obvious assumption. In spite of the fact that a difference is itself unnoticeable, it will nevertheless allow us to find a preponderance of right cases in favor of the heavier weight, or more generally in favor of the greater stimulus, provided a sufficient number of comparisons is made.

We must take into account that, simultaneously with the difference which we are trying to apprehend, there are at work random effects which would on the average make the judgment come out equally often in favor of one or the other. The difference creates an additional tendency to throw the judgment in one direction, partly by causing tendencies which would have been subliminal without it, to become noticeable in favor of one direction, and partly by strengthening the already noticeable tendencies in that direction and prevailing over the contrary tendencies. This effect occurs regardless of the fact that the influence of the added increment, together with the fluctuations which are present at the time, often remains below threshold, in which case judgment remains ambiguous. These cases very frequently appear in this type of experiment, but can be reduced to the other kind of case by counting them half with the right and half with the wrong cases.

One can see how in this way differences that are themselves subliminal can become effective in one direction by summation with the other influences. The level of probability (the relative number of right and wrong cases for a very great number of experiments) depends on the size of the difference so as to allow us to deduce a measure of sensitivity from it, as we have already seen.

The threshold values of both stimuli and stimulus differences vary widely due to conditions of fatigue, adaptation, practice, internal causes of excitation and inhibition, drugs, the periodicities of life, the individual's constitution, and so on, and can therefore be considered as constant only insofar as conditions do not cause any variations of these states. The investigation of these conditions is one of the most important tasks of psychophysics. It falls into the same category as do general inquiries into the functional relationship of absolute and differential sensitivity or of excitability and irritability, in that the absolute sensitivity is the reciprocal of the threshold stimulus and differential sensitivity is the reciprocal of the difference threshold.

Should it be possible—as we shall try to prove later—that the real nature of the threshold can be considered as due to the psychophysical processes released by the stimulus rather than the stimulus itself, then the threshold of the psychophysical activity which corresponds to the beginning of a certain sensation should also be considered to be constant, according to our general premise that there is a fixed relationship between bodily and psychic changes within us. Thus, the sensation would certainly emerge when the associated processes reach their threshold level. However, since a stimulus may find it more or less difficult to release psychophysical processes of this intensity, depending on the changing state of the organism, the threshold value of a stimulus, which is a function of this state, is not unchangeable but depends on the excitability of the organism. The threshold would be high at a low level of excitability and low at a high level.

It would be well to keep our eye on this distinction between a threshold value, where sensation disappears, associated either with the stimulus or with the processes it initiates. Only the threshold in the latter sense can actually be constant, while, in the first sense, the threshold changes with stimulus sensitivity and the manner of application of the stimulus.

4. INFERENCES BASED ON THE EXISTENCE OF THE THRESHOLD

The existence of a stimulus threshold and of a differential threshold gives rise to a number of deductions of interest and importance.

If even the slightest stimulus were effective, we would have to feel an infinite mixture and an unending variety of mild sensations of every kind at all times, since minimal stimuli of all types constantly surround us. Such is not the case. The fact that each stimulus must first reach a certain limit before it arouses a sensation assures to mankind a state undisturbed to a certain degree by external stimulation. It is not necessary to bring the stimulation down to zero, something man is not capable of doing, in order for him to remain undisturbed by them. All that he needs to do is to move far enough away from those stimuli that are weakened by distance, and in general to bring stimuli down below a given limit.

Besides the fact that we are saved from disturbances by unwanted and strange perceptions, because any stimulus escapes notice when it falls below a certain point, there is also the fact that a uniform state of perception is assured because stimulus differences cannot be noticed below their threshold.

Stimuli are never quite uniform in time and space due to inner and outer causes, but this does not prevent us from seeing light and colored surfaces at the same time or hearing uniformly sustained tones, and so on.

A simple demonstration of these phenomena is given by the well-known experiment with a color wheel having white and black sectors. If turned sufficiently fast, it appears a uniform gray. Now, the intensity of the impression made by each of the edges of a sector cannot really be equal since stimulation progressively becomes less as a black sector passes and increases with the passing of a white one. As soon, however, as the difference at both edges falls below the differential threshold, a uniform gray makes its appearance. This gray, as a matter of fact, appears so uniform, when the speed of revolution is sufficiently high, that it is no longer possible to detect any alternation, even when paying the sharpest attention.

An analogous case exists when one holds a finger against the edge of a rapidly revolving toothed wheel (spur gear). While individual teeth can be distinguished when the wheel is turning slowly, this is not the case when it is revolving quickly. Valentin* has carried out thorough studies on this

---

* *Vierordt's Arch.* 1852, pp. 438, 587.

topic. Among other things he noticed that no major disturbances are caused if the widths of the teeth vary slightly, whereas when a gear of 160 teeth has 3 or 5 adjacent teeth which are three or four times smaller than the rest, uniformity cannot be completely achieved, even at high speed.

A black and white sector disk revolving at a sufficiently high speed appears a uniform gray; in just the same way, a surface of alternating white and black squares appears a uniform gray when viewed from sufficiently far away. There may be two reasons: either the distances subtending too small a visual angle cannot be perceived separately, in which case the phenomenon would depend on thresholds of extent, or the blurring of the white squares at a small visual angle makes them merge into each other, in which case the phenomenon would depend on intensity difference thresholds. Possibly both causes may act together; it seems to me that observations so far have not enabled us to decide.

Let us look ahead again briefly to the meaning that the facts of outer psychophysics may hold for inner psychophysics. Even if a stimulus can be translated into psychophysical processes, the mind can operate in a state that is free of sensations and uniform in spite of the presence and play of these psychophysical processes, as long as certain limits are not exceeded. The first case, as I shall show, is exemplified by sleep, the second by the fact that psychophysical processes cannot, by their nature, be uniform. Probably they are oscillations. But the changes of these processes are not felt, as long as they do not exceed their limits. Thus uniform sensations on the basis of unequal processes are made possible.

Thus it becomes easier for us to grasp to what different qualities of sensations are related. Although the nonuniformity of psychophysical processes does not make itself felt as inequality of sensations, the quality of sensation can still depend on these processes. A discussion of these suggestions does not, however, belong here. Even in inner psychophysics one can, at present, look into this matter only with great caution and circumspection.

We have mentioned a number of times that the eye, because of the presence of a weak inner excitation, stays above threshold at all times with respect to intensive visual sensations. This fact gives occasion for some special teleological arguments.

If it would need an external light stimulus of a given strength in order to lift the internal activity on which our visual sensations depend up to its threshold, then we would not even see weakly illuminated or black objects. Thus in the dark there would be the same effect as that of the blind spot on the retina, a fact which would undoubtedly be very disturbing. If, on the other hand, the eye's threshold be exceeded greatly due to internal excitation, then according to Weber's Law, small increments of light should no longer be noticeable with any degree of precision. The color black seen by the unexcited eye is therefore undoubtedly the most advantageous way by which a very weak degree of light could be represented. This is the best possible way in which our sense of vision could be arranged.

There is no corresponding teleological need, as far as the ear is concerned. In fact, in hearing it would rather seem disturbing, if every tiniest sound could be heard. Normally, we have indeed nothing analogous to the color black that we see with the eye, even though we direct our attention to the ear, but only a feeling of silence.

In abnormal conditions the ear may be subjected to internal excitation which exceeds its threshold. We then hear buzzing or ringing and similar sounds. On the other hand, the ear may be in a state far below threshold, due to lack of stimulation. Now it becomes possible to interpret correctly observations on those cases who suffer from a torpor of the auditory nerve. These people are able to understand speech well, only when there is some other noise, like a drum or when traveling in a carriage. It seems as if the loud noise serves to bring hearing up to its threshold, where the additional noise becomes audible. By itself it would not have been sufficient to reach threshold.

There is still another application of the differential threshold, which I want to take up now.

If, as is now generally acknowledged, so-called irradiation in the eye depends more on the optical aberrations and phenomena of refraction than on spread of light on the retina, as Plateau assumes, then we should find that this physical irradiation should increase only in its intensity and not in its extent with an increase of intensity of the light. Plateau's experiments* showed, however, that the irradiation effects, while not at all proportional to the intensity of the light, did increase by a not inconsiderable amount with this intensity, up to a specific maximum, which represented an upper limit.

In his experiments the visible spread of irradiation J [in seconds of arc] corresponded to the following light intensities i, observed against black background; where the maximum i of 16 equaled the bright sky reflected from a mirror at a 30° angle (measured from the mirror surface):

$$i = \quad 1 \qquad 2 \qquad 4 \qquad 8 \qquad 16$$

$$J = 40.9'' \quad 47.6'' \quad 55.7'' \quad 56.0'' \quad 56.0''$$

With respect to the differential threshold, these results of Plateau's

* *Pogg. Ann. L. Suppl.*, pp. 412 ff.

show that visible irradiation increases in extent with light intensity, but in less than directly proportional amounts, and not beyond a certain limit. This result would be necessary for a truly constant physical spread of irradiation.

The outermost limits of visible irradiation must necessarily coincide with the boundaries of physical irradiation. However, when the irradiating light is of weak intensity it becomes so similar to the background black, near the edge of its diffusion field, that it can no longer be kept apart from it. Therefore the boundary of the visible irradiation must come closer to the edge of the diffusing field as the irradiating light becomes weaker.

Babinet* points out, in a paper on the density of the mass of comets, that some reliable astronomers, whom he identifies, were able to observe stars of the tenth or eleventh magnitude or even less through the nucleus of a comet without noticeable weakening of their brightness. On the other hand, according to an observation by Valz, a star of the seventh magnitude almost completely obscured the brightness of a comet. He then takes up the following considerations, referring to Bouguer's difference constant:

Since the interposing of a comet lighted by the sun does not perceptibly weaken the brilliance of the star in front of which it forms a luminous curtain, it follows that the brilliance of the comet is not $\frac{1}{60}$ of that of the star, for otherwise, the interposition of a light equal to $\frac{1}{60}$ of that of the star would have been perceptible. We can therefore grant that, at the most, the comet was equal in brilliance to $\frac{1}{60}$ of the light of the star. Thus, in this hypothesis, by making the comet 60 times more luminous, it would have had a brilliance equal to that of the star, and if we had made it 60 times more luminous than it was, that is to say, 3600 times, the comet would then have been 60 times more bright than the star, and, in its turn, it would have made the star disappear by the superiority of its light. . . . We may grant that the light of the moon makes all the stars below the fourth magnitude disappear; thus the atmosphere lighted by the full moon acquires enough brilliance to render invisible the stars of the fifth magnitude and below.

In this connection Babinet considers further the density and mass of comets, for which he finds, in agreement with other lines of thought, a negligible magnitude. However, we are not further concerned with this problem. I cited this discussion only as an example of possible applications of the difference constant. However, I do not consider the application of Bouguer's values to stars permissible for reasons which are discussed in the following chapter. For this reason doubt is thrown also on the results of Babinet's calculations.

* *Compt. rend.* 1857, p. 357.

XI.

Further Details on the Magnitude and Relationship of the Threshold in Various Sense Domains

Absolutely certain and universally valid determinations of the magnitude of the absolute and differential thresholds cannot be given for any sense domain. The threshold depends too much on the experimental procedure and the state of the organism for that. Both of these elements are too variable. In addition there is the difficulty of determining precisely the value at which a sensation or sensation difference begins. In the meantime, what I said on page [44] in this connection, with respect to measurement of sensitivity in general, remains valid. The determination of mean values (even if only approximate) for common conditions on the one hand, and for extremes on the other hand, is always of interest and is often indispensable. Their functional relationship to the circumstances under which they were obtained can itself often be looked upon as a subject for investigation.

The lower the threshold, the greater the sensitivity, other things being equal. Undoubtedly the human organism is so constituted that there exists a limit in this respect which cannot be passed. There are, on the other hand, many conditions, such as a deviant constitution, the abnormality of organs, or chance effects of all sorts, that can increase the threshold. All thresholds obtained in practice are to be regarded as upper limits, below which lies the ideal threshold, so to speak, which would be found under the most favorable circumstances. The lowest threshold values are therefore the most interesting, provided that they are based on valid observations, since they bring us closest to the real limit.

The following account unquestionably does not represent a complete collection of all that is known of reports on threshold values in the various areas. I mention them, however, as a start toward future completion. Most of these reports concern only the differential threshold, since as yet, little knowledge is available for absolute thresholds.

1. INTENSIVE THRESHOLD

a. Light and Color

As noted previously (p. [200]) there is no way of experimentally determining an absolute threshold for brightness. What is known about the differential threshold so far has been mentioned in Chapter IX, of which the following is a recapitulation.

Bouguer found a differential threshold equal to $\frac{1}{64}$ of light intensity in experiments on shadows. There is some question whether movement was present. Arago found a ratio varying from $\frac{1}{39}$ to $\frac{1}{71}$ on different individuals when there was no movement, and $\frac{1}{58}$ to $\frac{1}{131}$ with movement present (see p. [144]). Volkmann's results for various observers were about $\frac{1}{100}$ in experiments on shadows, with movement allowed (see p. [124]). Masson, in experiments with a spinning disk, found a ratio of $\frac{1}{50}$ to $\frac{1}{120}$ and higher on a number of different observers (see p. 126).

According to Masson the value does not change for different colors, but does vary from person to person.

In the experiments by which these determinations were made, lighted surfaces and shadows of a given extent were viewed directly. However, it is certain that the difference threshold also depends on the extent of the visible area, at least up to a certain limit, and on whether the peripheral area of the retina or the center is employed.

In general a small black surface on a white background, or vice versa, disappears the more easily against this background (that is, can no longer be distinguished from it), the smaller its visual angle and the more peripheral the area of the retina it stimulates. Lines of the same width as points are still recognized, where the points are not. Color also makes a difference.

As far as size is concerned, irradiation alone must be responsible for the fact that objects of small dimensions disappear more readily into the background at equal viewing distances than larger ones. Sufficient attention has not always been paid to this point. It should be noted, in this respect, that a black line or point on a white background tends to become wider as its blackness decreases, as does a white one on a black background with decreasing brightness. These facts and theory have been stated and developed more precisely by Volkmann.*

Of course, light which has been scattered and therefore diluted by irradiation, or black on which some light has been superimposed, can be

---

* *Berichte der Leipz. Soc.* 1858, pp. 129 ff.

distinguished less readily from a black or white background, respectively. This condition also must affect points to a greater extent than lines. There is no question, then, that the differential threshold for fixed stars must be considerably larger than Bouguer's value, on which Babinet bases his calculations (see p. [211]). This means that a fixed star will not be distinguished from the background sky even if the difference of intensities is much more than $\frac{1}{64}$ and it would be most important for many astronomical problems to determine this threshold directly by experiments with artificial stars.*

The foregoing discussion suffices to show that intensive and extensive thresholds for light can be determined only in relation to one another. I shall therefore leave this topic for the time being, to return to it once more when discussing thresholds of extent, where the influence of irradiation will also be discussed again.

It has been said that colors also must be presented to the eye as a minimum area before they are recognized as colored. This is surely the case for direct view, and is still more important with indirect view. Irradiation and induction (in the sense used by Brücke) of the background undoubtedly play a role in the disappearance of small patches of color. However, this disappearance has not yet been completely explained. The most careful observations of this fact have been made by Aubert.† However, before drawing more definite conclusions, one would have to add observations on the behavior of white and black squares on a colored background in the peripheral part of the visual field to these studies on the behavior of colored objects against black and white backgrounds.

b. Intensity of Sound and Pitch of Tones

Schafhäutl‡ has carried out experiments on the limits of audibility, using appropriate procedures of measurement. Sound was produced by allowing a small ball§ to drop from a known height onto a rectangular plate made of ordinary plate glass and held on its nodal point by screws. The ear was positioned rigidly against the glass that was the source of sound. The horizontal distance from the middle of the plate, which was the point of impact of the small ball, to the middle of the opening of the ear selected to receive the sound, was 55 mm, the vertical distance was 74 mm, while the direct distance was 91 mm. "Experience has taught me,"

---

* It would be useful here to refer to Stampfer's experiments on a related matter in the *Sitzungsber. d. Wien. Akad.* 1852, pp. 504, 511.

† *Gräfe's Arch. f. Ophthalmol.* III, pp. 30 ff.

‡ *Abhandl. d. München. Akad.* VII, p. 501.

§ Held by tweezers which could be opened by means of two latches.

writes the author, "that this is the best distance at which the ear can hear with certainty the least sound which it is still capable of receiving." The essential results of these experiments (which are not described in detail) are, in the author's words, as follows:

"In my experiments on determining the quantity of sound which my ear could still perceive, I have found that on the average the sound of a cork ball of 1 mg [milligram], falling through a distance of 1 mm, was still audible during complete silence, in other words at night. In 30 trials of this kind at 12 o'clock at night, when the wind was completely calm, I was able to hear sound generated in the above manner with complete certainty 25 times. A similar condition was found with some young people, whose ears had been musically trained. I found that only few older persons were still able to hear this sound, unless they had a practiced ear; however, some succeeded after practice in perceiving the above-mentioned sound with certainty.

"I state therefore without hesitation that the sound intensity produced by the fall of a small cork sphere, 1 mg in weight, from a height of 1 mm, can be taken as the acoustical energy which marks the average limit of sound intensity just perceivable by the healthy human ear subject to the influences of our civilization."

There is no doubt that studies with more impressive sound intensities at greater distances from the ear would be desirable, since, naturally, small disturbing influences and errors of measurement would thereby be minimized. One should also take into account that, according to the procedure of the above-mentioned experiment, hearing could take place only with one ear, while in general both ears are utilized in hearing.

There seems to be much less sensitivity for differences in the intensity of sound than for differences in the intensity of light, according to the experiments of Renz and Wolf cited on page [146], as well as those of Volkmann. Intensities at a ratio of about 3 : 4 can be differentiated with certainty, but become less dependable as the ratio becomes smaller.

As far as pitch is concerned, there is general agreement on a lower limit of hearing. It is usually placed at 30 (Chladni) or 32 (Biot) vibrations per second. In the meantime, according to some recent experiments of Savart's,* using a siren, a tone corresponding to 14 to 16 vibrations a second still is supposed to be audible. He is inclined to believe that, depending only on the ability to prolong single impressions as long as necessary, even lower tones could be made audible, so that there would be no real lower limit. However Despretz,† who carefully repeated

---

* *Ann. de Chim. et de Phys.* XLVII, p. 69. or *Pogg. Ann.* XXII, p. 596.
† *Comp. rend.* XX, p. 1214; *Pogg. Ann.* LXV, p. 440.

Savart's experiments, categorically denies his assertions and concludes "that it is at present not proven that the human ear is able to perceive and determine tones of less than 32 simple vibrations" [16 double vibrations]. Savart was probably led astray by the great intensity of the tones produced by his apparatus, which are indeed very strong but which are neither musical nor determinable as to pitch, and would therefore have more of the characteristics of noise.

If, indeed, Despretz is correct, it was the noise made separately by each single pulse of the siren, heard as continuous because of the duration of the pulses, which gave the mistaken impression of a tone.[1]

Whatever may be the case, as far as the difference between Savart and Despretz is concerned, it would be absurd not to assume the human ear to have a lower limit for tones. A tone generated by vibrations of an hour's duration would obviously not be perceived as a tone by man—perhaps by beings of different make-up, but certainly not by man.

The audibility of tones appears not only to have a lower, but also an upper, limit.

Sauveur, in the *Mém. de l'Acad. Ann.* 1700, puts the upper limit at 12,400 vibrations per second. Wollaston believes the voice of the bat and the cricket represent the upper limit of audible tones. The frequency of vibrations is supposed to be 600 to 700 times higher from the lowest tones of the organ to the highest of the insects, which would bring the upper limit to 19,000 to 22,000 simple vibrations. Biot assumes only 8192, Chladni 12,000, Olivier* 16,000, and Young 18,000 to 20,000 as upper limit.

Savart discovered in the meantime that if one generates very high tones of sufficient loudness, as he did with a toothed wheel whose teeth struck against a thin material, tones corresponding to 48,000 simple vibrations (24,000 strokes) could be heard. Also Despretz concludes from experiments of his with small tuning forks that the ear can still perceive, determine, and classify (*entendre, apprécier, classer*) tones up to 73,000 vibrations, "that, however, the hearing of very high tones does not occur quickly enough, for one to include them in the musical scale."

One might after all pose the question whether the limit of audibility of high tones has already been reached, or if still higher tones might not be audible with greater amplification. On the other hand, it is quite possible that either the nerves themselves are incapable of perceiving tones which are too high or that the eardrum and its appendages might be incapable of receiving them.

---

[1] Ed. Note: Maybe Savart used double vibrations and thus agreed with Despretz. Germans generally use double, French simple.

* *Urstoff der m. Spr.*, p. 12.

The preceding discussion concerned the absolute audibility of tones. As far as the discrimination of pitch is concerned, our sensitivity appears to be incomparably greater than it is for the discrimination of loudness.

A. Seebeck[*] was able to observe on two tuning forks which were almost precisely in tune, so that one vibrated at 1209, the other at 1210 vibrations per second (as determined by beats when both were sounded together), that one was a trace lower "than the other."[†] "One could (Seebeck states) just differentiate this small interval from tones that were completely in tune. One does not have to be reminded that this discrimination does demand a well-practiced ear; although I have reason to trust my own hearing to be quite sharp in this respect, I cannot doubt that the ear of a piano tuner or a violinist, and so forth, could do still better. Two excellent violinists, to whom I presented these two tuning forks, did not doubt in the least which of them was the higher one. The fact that both tones sounded alike in this case may well have been a favorable condition for discriminating their pitch; perhaps the same precision could not be reached at all levels of pitch."

Earlier data on the ear's sensitivity to differences in pitch did not reach so high by any means. W. Weber[‡] remarks in passing that under favorable conditions the ear could judge tones directly (that is, without the aid of beats or averaging) exactly enough for the error never to amount to more than one in 200 vibrations.

Delezenne[§] has not only determined just noticeable differences from the consonance of two like tones, as others have done up to the present time; but also for other intervals, such as the octave, the fifth, the major third, and the major sixth. One may note that the task is here to determine a difference or ratio between two notes rather than the just noticeable difference between one tone and another. Here each pure interval between two notes that are struck successively represents a difference, and each impure interval a difference that varies slightly from it. However, the case in which the just noticeable difference from the purity of a consonance is determined can be regarded as a special instance of the general case: that is, the one where deviations from a null difference between two tones are determined.

The experiments were carried out in this way. A string, vibrating at a frequency of 120 cycles a second was stretched on a monochord (*sonomètre*) between two bridges, exactly 1147 mm apart. It was subdivided at one point of its length by a

* *Pogg. Ann.* LXVIII, p. 463.
† Undoubtedly when he allowed one to sound after the other, although he does not expressly mention it.
‡*Pogg. Ann.* XIV, p. 398.
§*Recueil des travaux de la soc. de Lille.* 1827, p. 4.

movable bridge in such a way that the sounds of the two parts of the string yielded one of the tonal intervals. The movable bridge was sharp. It was placed under the string without increasing its tension and pressed against it by another sharp edge. Delezenne first made sure of the purity of the tone interval. The movable bridge was then moved a little, up to one or a few millimeters, to the right or left. The observer now judged when impurity in the sound of the interval became noticeable. At other times the bridge was moved, out of sight of the observer, until a pure interval seemed to have been reached and it was determined how much of an error was made.

Although these experiments appear to have been carried out very industriously and carefully, there is unfortunately, a lack of exact method, so that one cannot have too much confidence in the comparableness of the numbers found. It is very desirable, therefore, that these determinations, which are important to both musical practice and the theory of musical sensations, should be repeated. The method of right and wrong cases and the method of average error should be used, keeping everything strictly comparable and using various observers with poor and with good hearing, since the method the author used, that of just noticeable differences or limits, cannot guarantee a sufficiently precise result.

Delezenne's results were as follows.

Taking a string, 1147 mm in length, vibrating at 120 vibrations a second, and slightly moving a bridge so that the consonance of the two parts of the string was disturbed, it was found that it took an excellent ear to recognize the difference between the two parts, sounded successively, if the bridge was moved as little as 1 mm from the center. One part of the string was now $(^{1147}/_2) + 1$ and the other $(^{1147}/_2) - 1$ mm in length, thus the ratio of their lengths and at the same time of their frequencies amounted to 1149 : 1145. At a ratio of 1151 : 1143 this difference could be recognized by quite unpracticed ears. [He writes:]

If we move the mobile bridge 2 mm to the right or left, the difference becomes perceptible to the least trained ears, as I have assured myself in the case of several persons. If the displacement of the bridge is only by 1 mm, one must have a rather delicate ear in order to become immediately aware of it. The person subjected to this test closes his eyes, either not to be distracted by surrounding objects, or not to be aware of the feigned or real displacements of the bridge and thus to avoid being forewarned of the direction of the change he would see being made. So an extremely delicate ear is sensitive to this slight difference. Let us assume that this is the extreme limit of sensitivity of the human ear, and let us calculate the relationships between these two senses having such slight difference. We shall see:

$$\frac{(1147/2) + 1}{(1147/2) - 1} = \frac{1149}{1145} = \left(\frac{81}{80}\right)^{0.2807}$$

The best organized ear is thus sensitive to a difference of 4 vibrations out of 1149!

To compare this interval with that represented by the comma [musical interval]

$^{81}/_{80}$, and which we shall take everywhere as a unit, we shall say that the ear is barely sensitive to one quarter of a comma, upon unison.

We have seen that a displacement of 2 mm was perceptible to persons who had never attempted to compare sounds. We find for the sounds thus compared the interval:

$$\frac{(1147/2) + 2}{(1147/2) - 2} = \frac{1151}{1143} = \left(\frac{81}{80}\right)^{0.561}$$

Those persons are thus sensitive to a difference of 8 vibrations out of 1151, or to an interval slightly superior to a half-comma.

If we list also the corresponding results for the other intervals, we find that according to Delezenne a very sensitive ear is just able to discriminate a deviation from the following intervals when the ratio of frequencies is as shown and the tones were heard in succession.

$$\text{Unison } \frac{1149}{1145} = \left(\frac{81}{80}\right)^{0.2807}$$

$$\text{Octave* } \frac{2/3 \times 1147 + 1}{1/3 \times 1147 - 1} = 2\left(\frac{81}{80}\right)^{0.31}$$

$$\text{Fifth } \frac{3/5 \times 1147 - 1/2}{2/5 \times 1147 + 1/2} = \frac{3}{2}\left(\frac{80}{81}\right)^{0.1461}$$

$$\text{Major third } \frac{5/9 \times 1147 + 1}{1/9 \times 1147 - 1} = \frac{5}{4}\left(\frac{81}{80}\right)^{0.284}$$

$$\text{Major sixth† } \frac{5/8 \times 1147 + 1}{3/8 \times 1147 - 1} = \frac{5}{3}\left(\frac{81}{80}\right)^{0.291}$$

or

$$\frac{5/8 \times 1147 - 1.5}{3/8 \times 1147 + 1.5} = \frac{5}{3}\left(\frac{80}{81}\right)^{0.441}$$

As one can see, perception of the deviation for the fifth is relatively the most distinct.

* For persons completely unpracticed in tonal comparisons it was found that the ratio was $1151/1143 = (81/80)^{0.561}$.
† Depending on whether the bridge was moved to the right or to the left.

c. Weights

Kammler, in conjunction with some collaborators (Aubert, Förster, Trenkle), has carried out a series of experiments on the least absolute weight that can be felt on various skin locations. His results are published in his dissertation: *Experimenta de variarum cutis regionum minima pondera sentiendi virtute. Vratislaviae* 1858. His procedure consisted of taking light weights of pith, cork, or cardboard, each about 9 mm² in size, but weighing different amounts and capable of being loaded further if needed. The weights were lowered very slowly and as vertically as possible onto the region that was to be tested. A fine arched brass wire or bristle was attached to two diagonally opposite corners, so that the weight took on the form of a stirrup on whose upper bend a cotton thread was fastened to hold the weight.

It would lead us too far afield to report all the results here in detail, since the whole surface of the human body has been measured in experiments by various observers. I shall only mention the following: The order of sensitivity of the various regions has nothing in common with that which Weber determined in his experiments with compass points. The order agrees closely, but not completely, among the four observers. Forehead and temple, eyelids and the dorsal side of the forearm are in the category of the most sensitive, where 0.002 gm was felt most of the time. The fingers were generally much less sensitive.

In general, the following are the particulars about the most sensitive regions where the lightest weights were just felt:

Aubert felt 0.002 gm on the forehead, temple, right and left forearm and joint (both on the volar and dorsal sides), and the outer region of the metacarpal of the thumb and the back of both hands. By Kammler this weight was felt on the forehead, temples, dorsal side of the right forearm, and the back of both hands. By Förster on the forehead, temples, upper and lower eyelids, and nose. By Trenkle on nose and lips.

Aubert felt 0.003 gm on the outer part of the metacarpal of the right thumb. Kammler on the volar part of both forearms and the dorsal surface of the left forearm and the outer surface of the metacarpal of the left thumb.

Kammler felt 0.004 gm on the outer surface of the metacarpal of the right thumb.

Aubert felt 0.005 gm[1a] on the nose, lips, chin, lower and upper eyelids, center of the stomach, and so on. Kammler, on the nose, lips, chin, lower and upper eyelids, center of the stomach, and so on. Förster, on the lips, stomach, and so on. Trenkle, on the forehead, lips, lower and upper eyelids, stomach, forearm, and so on.

[1a] Trans. Note: The original citations read 0.04 and 0.05 respectively. Although Kammler's dissertation was not available for checking, it seemed very probable that a zero had been omitted through a printer's error.

One gram was cited as the heaviest weight that could just be felt, on the fingernails, and (according to Aubert) on the right heel.

We have already cited on page [115] the results that Weber found, incidental to our test of Weber's Law, regarding differences of weight. His treatment* includes, however, more detailed experiments on the least noticeable difference of weight, depending on pressure only or on pressure and the muscle sense combined, and according to the regions on which pressure was applied.

In the following experiments the two weights that were to be compared were lying on the two hands and their just noticeable difference was determined by the method given on page [115]. Comparisons were made between pure pressure sensations, when the hands were kept lying on the table (column a) and combined pressure and muscle sense, when both hands were lifted (column b). While at the start there was always an initial weight of 32 oz in each hand, the difference became noticeable, when the weight on one hand was reduced by the following amounts:

		a	b
(1)	Merchant, unpracticed	6	1
(2)	Mathematician	6	2.5
(3)	E. H. Weber himself	16	2
(4)	Merchant, unpracticed	8	4
(5)	Young girl	16	2
(6)	Woman	16	4
(7)	Woman	12	2
(8)	Student	8	3
(9)	Student	12	2
(10)	Student	8	1.5
(11)		15	1.5
(12)		10	1.5
(13)		18	8
(14)		12	6
(15)		6	4
(16)		8	1
(17)		8	4
	Mean	10.88	2.93

In the following experiments† the observer hefted two weights alternately with the same hand. The weights hung in two folded pieces of cloth whose ends were held together in the hand. "Among a total of ten persons, half of them male, who compared 78 and 80 oz lifted in pieces of cloth in the manner described, there were only two unable to distinguish the heavier from the lighter weight. Seven judged correctly every time, in three trials each, which weight was the heavier. Some of them were given

* *Progr. coll.*, pp. 81 ff.
† *Tasts. und Gemeing.*, p. 546.

four to seven trials, making the correct determination every time. One of the ten observers was right seven times and wrong once in eight trials given to him."

Weber holds that in this procedure the muscle sense alone is involved. I am not in complete agreement, as my remarks on page [166] have shown

In the following experiments* the constant weight of six stacked *Thaler* coins, each one weighing a little less than 2 oz (for a total of close to 12 oz), was placed on the corresponding body regions bilaterally (and on the median line in the two last named areas). One after the other of the *Thaler* coins were then taken away on one side, until the weight difference could be felt. The following table (p. 69) lists the number of coins that had to be taken away before the difference became noticeable. (The subject of the experiment is not specified.)

Volar surface of fingers	1
Volar surface of the hand†	2
Dorsal surface of fingers	2
Inner surface of arm	4
Sole of foot (*capitulis metatarsi*)	1
Concave part of sole of the foot	4
Heel of the foot	3
Gastrocnemii (calf of the leg)	4
Temporal parts of forehead	1
Hairy region in back of the head	4
Frontal region of chest	4
Shoulder blade	2
Side of the abdomen	4
Median line of the back near the shoulder blade	5
Median line of the abdomen	5

These experiments can also be related to those carried out with the method of equivalents, cited in Chapter XII.

d. Temperature

E. H. Weber‡ has published some accounts on the magnitude of the just noticeable temperature difference. According to him one can discover the difference between two temperatures only $\frac{1}{5}$° to $\frac{1}{6}$°R apart using the method of alternately dipping the whole hand into two containers of water of unequal warmth, while paying strict attention. However, he did not determine exactly the temperatures at which the differences may be noticed. I found that in the middle range of temperatures even smaller

---

* *Progr. coll.*, p. 96.
† *Superficies volaris metacarpi manus.*
‡ *Der Tastsinn und das Gemeingefühl, Wagner's Wört.*, p. 534.

differences can be detected, and that they may vary widely depending on temperature. Compare this with the remarks in Chapter IX (pp. 168–175).

Experiments and discussion of painful degrees of heat and cold by E. H. Weber may be found in the same report (pp. 571 ff).

2. THRESHOLD OF EXTENT

a. Vision

Basically, all distances that our retinas detect are limited by the field of vision, and one might ask how many sensory circles are needed in general to produce a visual field of noticeable extent. This question should be distinguished carefully from that concerning the fraction of the amount already present that is necessary to recognize a part of the general visual field as different from the rest, when it is stimulated in a different manner from the remainder. There is so far no possibility of solving the first question. I shall therefore stay away from this question, in spite of the fact that it is really fundamental to the problem of a threshold of extension, only to return to it in a later chapter with some items of a theoretical nature, and turn now to the investigation of the threshold of extent as follows.

What are the smallest magnitudes, distances, and differences of magnitude and distance that the eye can just perceive?

The task of finding the smallest recognizable distance coincides with that of determining the smallest possible magnitude, since one can, after all, consider the diameter of any magnitude that is just noticeable as a just recognizable distance between two limiting points, and, vice versa, a just recognizable distance as a just noticeable magnitude. However, the experiments can be divided into those in which a point, a line, a thread, or a small surface are regarded against an extended uniform background, in order to determine at what ocular distance (and therefore at what visual angle), this small magnitude is still visible (or vanishes), and those other cases where two or more distant points, lines, threads, or small surfaces are viewed against a given background. The task is to see at what visual angle of separation they fuse uniformly with each other. Let the former be called, for our purposes, experiments on smallest recognizable magnitudes, and the latter experiments on smallest recognizable distances. The experimental conditions differ here insofar as in the former the irradiation, which is so essentially concerned with the outcome of the experiments, of only two edges is involved, while in the latter it is four edges.

Any magnitude that is to be recognized visually must appear on a given background and can therefore be recognized only to an extent depending on its contrast with the background. The question of an extensive visual threshold is therefore connected with the question of difference threshold for intensity and has already been discussed on page [104] from this point of view. A visual object will be easier to discriminate, per unit extent, the greater its relative contrast with its background. On the other hand (at least up to certain limits), if contrast is held constant, the object is seen better the greater its visual extent. Whether the ground is black and the surface to be discriminated white or vice versa, this fact remains valid.

Twining* has made experiments with the purpose of finding a lawful relationship in this regard. He determined the distance from the light source at which regular black round spots on a white background, illuminated only by this light, ceased to appear as separate, when the eye was placed at various distances. These studies led him to the law that while the distances to the eye decrease in geometric progression, the corresponding distances to the lamp increase in arithmetic progression.†

If one defines the intensity of illumination J as the reciprocal of the square of the distance of the lamp L, and the apparent diameter D of the black spots as the reciprocal of the ocular distance A, one can substitute $\sqrt{1/J}$ for L and $1/D$ for A. The law can now be expressed in the form: equal ratios D'/D correspond to equal differences $\sqrt{1/J} - \sqrt{1/J'}$. Such a law is of itself not very probable and Twining's assumption that A is the reciprocal of D is undoubtedly not valid because of the influence of irradiation under the conditions of this experiment, a matter which we will take up immediately. Therefore in spite of the fact that this author's experiments fit the law very well, as one can see below, his is most probably only an empirical expression, whose general validity under other experimental conditions one might doubt, rather than a true natural law. In the meantime, these experiments are not without interest insofar as they show that the relative intensities of illumination at which clear recognition of the spots begins or ends increases at a rapid rate when a large viewing distance is increased by a given ratio, whereas the relative increase is only slight, when a small viewing distance is increased in the

* Twining, Enquiries concerning Stellar Occultations by the Moon and the Planets—Experiments upon Light and Magnitude in Relation to Vision, in *American J. of Sc.* 1858. July V. C. XXVI, [2], p. 15.

† The author himself formulates the results of these experiments in the following manner (p. 23): "That while the distances of the eye diminish in a geometrical ratio, the corresponding distances of the light increase in an arithmetical ratio. In other words, the distance of the light is a logarithm of the linear magnifying effect.

"One remarkable result of this law is that a small fractional change of a faint light possesses as great efficacy to balance a given magnifying effect as a large fractional change of a much brighter light."

same ratio. Thus the two largest viewing distances of 107.29 and 134.11 English in., employed by the author, which have a ratio of 4 : 5, correspond to distances from the lamp of 29.5 and 15.5 English in., that is, an illumination ratio of 1 : 3.62. On the other hand the two smallest viewing distances used, 28.12 and 35.16 in., also in a ratio of 4 : 5, correspond to lamp distances of 131.6 and 110.5, a ratio of intensities of 1 : 1.419. This result will always remain stable.

Essentially the author's apparatus consists of a box, painted black inside and outside. The box is completely closed except at the front, where it has a square opening through which light enters on one side, and through which one looks on the other side. The illuminating lamp and the eye are only as far apart (at the opposite sides of the opening) as is necessary to prevent them from interfering with one another when providing both illumination and viewing. On the back wall, inside the box, there is some paper, marked with small, round, black spots equidistant and regularly arranged,* which receives the light and is viewed by the observer. When the eye is placed at different distances from the back wall of the box in the various experiments, the lamp is moved each time, either closer or farther away, until the black spots can just be resolved or until their clear resolution just ceases.† The lamp was covered except for the hole necessary to provide for the beam of light, and the viewing was carried out by the eye looking through a tube fastened to a framework (eye-tube). The tube had a circular aperture of 0.16 in. and a length of 3 in. Tube and lamp could be shifted on graduated long boards or planks, which converged at the box at a small angle. The slide for the eye-tube was graduated in a geometric progression with a ratio of 5 : 4. In front of the square opening of the box there was placed a blackened screen with a corresponding hole, in order to keep out the stray light of the room.

The following table contains the results of the observations in English inches.‡ According to the original account, four pairs of observations were taken at each viewing distance, but the table gives only four numbers for each. Each, therefore, probably is the average of two observations. The sequence of viewing distances are in a geometric ratio of 4 : 5. The last column, "calculated," lists the lamp distances calculated under the assumption that an arithmetic difference between them of 16.0 in. would correspond to this geometric progression of viewing distances.

---

* "A paper regularly marked with small black round spots equidistant and regularly arranged." Nothing is said about the size and the distance of the spots from one another.
† "Till the cluster of black spots became just resolved—or was just ceasing to be visible as a distant cluster."
‡ The author remarks concerning the last and smallest viewing distance: "At the nearest station (and greatest corresponding lamp distance) the faint illumination and consequent straining of the eye created occasional brief paroxysms of distinct and magnified vision which introduced uncertainty."

DATA OF TWINING'S EXPERIMENT

Distance from Eye	Distance of Lamp				Average Distance	Calculated
134.11	14.5	14.8	18.2	14.5	15.5	14.8
107.29	34.3	29.5	27.6	26.4	29.5	30.8
85.83	40.5	51.7	50.6	46.5	47.3	46.8
68.66	57.4	69.2	61.9	64.7	63.3	62.8
54.93	74.9	77.1	74.7	79.1	76.5	78.8
43.95	99.0	90.5	88.3	90.2	92.0	94.8
35.16	114.1	106.5	110.0	111.4	110.5	110.8
28.12	138.4	122.6	132.1	133.4	131.6	126.8

It had been maintained earlier, that the discriminability of small visible objects was greatly dependent on irradiation effects. This influence will now be examined more closely. We include here under irradiation the physical scattering of the impression of light on the retina due to optical aberration and refraction.

In all experiments on the smallest perceptible size or distance, one diminishes size or distance—or does it by moving far away—so that, apart from irradiation, the retinal image is reduced to a point or a line of negligible width. In general, except for Volkmann in his new treatise on irradiation,* the diameter of the smallest recognizable image, or the least recognizable distance, has been calculated with no regard to irradiation. Volkmann's fine experiments, however, the results of which are given below, have shown without a doubt that even in the best and most thoroughly accommodated eye there occurs a noticeable and measurable spreading of the light impression due to irradiation. If one compares his data on the size of the diffusion circles under best possible viewing conditions with either his or other observers' statements on the smallest noticeable object sizes, one finds not only that the diameter of the diffusion circle is relatively large compared to the diameter of images of the least perceptible magnitudes (or least perceptible distances), calculated without regard to irradiation, but also that generally it actually exceeds this diameter by a considerable amount. The light impression must, therefore, be considerably more extended, although at the same time weaker, due to dispersion, than the size which this calculation of the least perceptible magnitude indicates.

Indeed, according to Volkmann's measurements (quoted later), the edge of a silver thread illuminated by a brilliant light on a black background is broadened by from 0.0012 to 0.0032† mm (0.000532 to 0.001418

---

* *Berichte der sächs. Soc.* 1858, p. 129.
† Half of the value of R, as given later.

Paris line) minimum and maximum, in the direction of the black. These values are based on six observers who had the best possible accommodation. If the thread is seen as black against a light background it spreads by 0.0003 to 0.00185 mm. Yet, according to Hueck, for example, the visual angle at which a white stripe on a black background just begins to disappear and which, therefore, also marks the limits of a just noticeable width of a line, amounts to two seconds, representing 0.000145 mm on the retina.

Now, as noted on page [210], the area of irradiation is dependent on physical conditions and cannot increase with the intensity of the illumination. Therefore, the light from an intensively and a dimly lit point source is spread over the same area. However, the dim point can be weakened to such an extent that it cannot be distinguished from the background, whereas the bright point would remain noticeable.

In general, when a point source of light is not intense enough to differ from the background in the center of its diffusion circle by the amount of its differential threshold, then it can no longer be recognized. In the case of a black spot on a white background analogous considerations are found to hold. The surrounding light diffuses and floods the black spot with light, so that it is found to spread out and its blackness is weakened due to irradiation in exactly the same manner as in the case of the white point on a black background—as Volkmann discusses the matter in detail (loc. cit., p. 120) and as he has proven experimentally.

Bergmann* observes that points or lines which are used in experiments on least noticeable magnitudes appear very pale at distances, so that any slight shadow can easily be confused with them. He noted that every time one gradually approaches a grid composed of black and white stripes, 1 mm in width, from the distance where it was first resolved, the white increases in clearness, the black in depth. These conditions can be explained easily by the fact that at ranges greater than clear viewing distance the spread of the light increases due to optical aberrations.

It has been said that experiments on just noticeable small distances might be suitable for checking the acuity of space perception,† because of the important role played by the intensity of the light, a matter easily explained by the facts just mentioned. Actually, the influence of irradiation is only more complicated here, and by no means absent. When two bright points or lines approach each other closely enough for their diffusion circles to overlap and for the difference between the minimum brightness in the center of the intermediate space and its maximum in the center of

* Henle und Pfeufer Zeitschr. Series III. Vol. II, p. 93.
† [E. H.] Weber, Berichte der sächs. Soc. 1853, p. 141.

the irradiating points to fall below the threshold, they also can no longer be distinguished. Experience has shown that here the light intensity also plays a certain role. I find that Steinheil's treatise on photometry mentions that weakly blackened glasses showed a surprising success with regard to the separation of very close binary stars. I must confess, however, that I cannot deduce this effect from the conditions of irradiation as I know them, for it seems to me, under the assumption that the spread of the diffusion circle does not increase with growth of intensity, that the ratio of minimum and maximum intensity must stay the same with weak or strong light. If this were so, it would leave the ability to perceive the difference unchanged. In fact there should be a certain advantage to discrimination at higher intensities considering the increasing intensity of the background.

Summarizing the foregoing discussion shows that present experiments on the least noticeable magnitudes and distances on the retina are useless for drawing any conclusions on the acuity of space perception or the degree of extensive sensitivity, as long as the question of the part played by irradiation has not been resolved and its role been eliminated. The summary shows that the calculation of the size of very small retinal images from magnitude and distance of objects and the judgment of the relationship they have ultimately to the elements on the retina are illusory and fallacious, when irradiation has been ignored. In this connection, Volkmann concludes his treatise on irradiation (p. 48) as follows: "All statements that have been made so far on the magnitude of the smallest retinal images that can just be perceived are false, for they are in particular too large, since the calculations on which they are based do not consider the influence of irradiation."

This discussion brings up the question of the role played by the dimensions of the objects themselves in the determinations of the difference threshold. Is it all due to irradiation? In this case we would have to assume there is a limit as object-size increases. Unfortunately we are still lacking sufficiently decisive experiments that had been purposely designed to test this question. I am aware only of some related experiments of Förster's[*] which, however, were not made with this specific question in mind. They seem to show that the influence of magnitude on perceptual thresholds actually exceeds whatever could be attributed to irradiation. The experiments were carried out as follows: "A closed box, blackened inside, in the form of a parallelepiped, approximately 36 in. long and about 8 in. wide and high, serves as a darkroom into which is put the

[*] *Ueber die Hemeralopie.* 1857, pp. 5–10.

object that is to be illuminated. On one of the square ends of the box there are two round holes, 2½ in. between centers, for the eyes, and next to them, at the same height, a larger square opening of 25 sq cm for the light source. This hole is covered on the inside wall of the box with good quality white bond paper. At a distance of ½ in. there is a burning wax candle* (allowed to burn as evenly as possible). The square of paper which is illuminated in this way serves as light source for objects placed on the opposite wall inside the box. The size of the light source was changed as needed by diaphragms (cardboard slides with appropriate holes) which were slipped closely in front of it."

The author states (p. 10): "The weakest illumination necessary to distinguish black rectangles, 1 to 2 cm wide and 5 cm long, (with long side vertical) against a white ground, (at a distance of 12 Paris in. = 32.5 cm from the eye) is represented by a light source 2 to 5 sq mm in extent. If the light source falls below this value, then the objects must be considerably larger."

One can calculate that the image of a stripe 2 cm in width amounts to 0.9 mm on the retina at the viewing distance given. This value exceeds by far the amount of blurring of an accommodated eye according to the data given above (p. [226]). If now even larger objects become visible at even weaker illumination, then the influence of size cannot depend only on irradiation. However, extended experiments, directed specially to this topic, tracing changes in size as a function of absolute brightness, are still desirable.

In any event, all that has been asserted is that present determinations of the thresholds for size and distance without regard to irradiation are invalid. It is not suggested that thresholds of extent do not exist independently of intraocular irradiation. Granted that the extent of an impression on retina or skin may be diminished at will and still give rise to a sensation, as long as an active nerve ending has been stimulated or the threshold of intensity has been exceeded. However, this impression is not necessarily one of extent (that is, one in which several points can be discriminated) when the extent of the impression falls below a certain limit. In other words, it cannot be said to satisfy the closely related criterion, that a distance on the retina may be reduced by any amount and still be appreciated as a distance, since such a sensation presupposes the perception of a difference between two edges and thereby also the stimulation of several points.

Indeed, present-day nerve physiology generally accepts the assumption

---

* Twelve per pound, 4½ in. high and ¾ in. in diameter.

that impressions can only be discriminated if they fall on different sensory circles, if we understand by the term sensory circle the terminus (or in case of branching, the terminals) of the simplest nerve fiber. A sensory circle, however, necessarily possesses a certain diameter, whether it belongs to an unbranched or a branched fiber, and impressions that fall side by side on the same sensory circle therefore cannot be distinguished. In the field of vision, it is true, experimental proof that this really is so appears to face unsurmountable difficulties because the diffusion circle of a point of light would always be expected to be larger than a sensory circle. However, we might look to the skin as an organ of extensive sensations analogous to the retina. We must admit that diffusion also plays a role in experiments on touch, since the pressure of a point against the skin must necessarily be propagated more or less to adjacent parts of the skin. But it is impossible to make this fact responsible for Weber's observation that two compass points, 30 lines apart, on the back, the upper arm, or the upper thigh, merge into a single impression, nor to think that differences between various regions of the skin with respect to the just noticeable distance would depend on it. The analogy between sensations of extent on skin and on the retina has been so well established by Weber in other respects, that we would doubt whether it would not also hold here.

It is clear, from what has been said, that the evaluation and explanation of our topic needs, on the one hand, knowledge of the absolute degree of diffusion that can occur when the eye is accommodated as much as possible, and on the other hand, knowledge of what retinal elements may be thought to represent sensory circles, and what their dimensions might be. With respect to the first point, I shall include parenthetically the results which Volkmann found on himself and some other persons. As far as the last is concerned, I shall remark briefly that the so-called cones are nowadays looked upon as most probably the elements on the retina that perceive sensations. According to Kölliker's measurement of a cone in the macula, where clearest vision takes place, it has a diameter of 2 to 3 thousandths of a line. Bergmann[*] was able to confirm the smaller of these values when measuring toward the outside of the fovea lutea.

Silver threads, 0.445 mm in diameter, were fixated at the clearest viewing distance S (in millimeters). The following results were found, depending on whether the threads were viewed (a) as black threads against a light background, such as the sky, or (b) as white threads against a black background when shining in reflected light. The results are given as an

* *Henle und Pfeufer Zeitschr.* Series III. Vol. II, p. 37.

average of Z trials, where the first number of trials refers to (a), the second to (b), in the form of diffusion circles of diameters R (in millimeters).

VOLKMANN'S EXPERIMENTS ON IRRADIATION

Observer	Z		S	R	
				a	b
A. W. Volkmann (author)	39	24	333	0.0035	0.0046
His son Otto V., 23 years old, good eyes	10	15	250	0.0037	0.0064
His son Edmund V., 26 years old, good, well-practiced eyes	15	12	250	0.0024	0.0058
Dr. R. Heidenhain *	?	40	100	?	0.0051
E. Appel, student, very sharp eyes	20	20	300	0.0006	0.0025
Young girl, 16 years old, very nearsighted, vision otherwise good	10	15	112.5[†]	0.0017	0.0024

*Heidenhain's results were not uniform under condition (a) and are therefore omitted. The majority of trials were unfavorable to the hypothesis that irradiation played a role. Volkmann calls this case an exception, unlike any other in his experience.

[†]S was equal to 115 under condition (a) and 110 under condition (b).

Source: *Berichte der sächs. Soc.* 1858, p. 129.

Volkmann mentions that he has in his possession many single observations by Professors Knoblauch, Hankel, Ruete, Czermak, and others (done on occasion at his instigation), with corresponding results (that is, proof of the presence of diffusion), in addition to the results of the experimental series here communicated. These results were obtained as follows. The observer places the micrometric instrument, mentioned on page [183], containing parallel silver threads, 0.445 mm in diameter, at a distance from the eye that provides the clearest appearance of the threads. He then seeks to put the parallel threads at a distance apart that equals their diameter, by turning the micrometer screw. It appears that the distance selected is always greater than the true diameter of the threads, because this diameter appears wider due to the diffusion effects. One can calculate this result in the following manner: the intersection of the principal rays falls 9 mm behind the foremost point of the cornea and 15 mm in front of the retina on the optical axis of the eye. Given these data, one can calculate not only the diameter $2r$ of the retinal image of each thread of the micrometer, but also the distance ϵ of the axis of one wire from the other on the retina, apart from their dispersion due to irradiation effects, as long as the distance from the threads of the micrometer to the eye and their distance apart are known. Simple consideration of the case when the distance δ between the dispersed images of the wires equals the diameter 2ρ of a wire, as realized in this experiment, gives the diameter of a diffusion circle $= \epsilon/2 - 2r$, since $\epsilon = \delta + 2\rho$ and $2\rho = \delta = \epsilon/2$. In an average of 39 trials, Volkmann found that a clear distance between threads of 0.207 mm appeared equal to the 0.445 mm width of the dark thread at a viewing distance of 333 mm. Therefore $\epsilon/2 = 2\rho = 0.0055$ mm; $2r = 0.00199$ mm, and consequently $\epsilon/2 - 2r = 0.0035$ mm. As a check, Volkmann carried out another ten trials in which he sought to make the distance between the threads twice the apparent size of their diameter. One can calculate from the results of the previous experiment (p. [144]) that this distance should amount to 0.328 mm. The average result of his ten trials gave 0.337 mm, agreeing remarkably well and proving that this procedure warrants confidence.

The following points also deserve attention: irradiation effects differ in vertical and horizontal direction. When Volkmann viewed the wires in horizontal position at the same viewing distance as in the previous experiments (when the wires' position was perpendicular), a very indistinct image appeared, so that weakly convex glasses had to be employed in order to keep the viewing distance the same at 333 mm. An average of ten observations against a light background resulted in a diameter of 0.0047 mm for the diffusion circle, compared with the value of 0.0035 mm in perpendicular position (without glasses).

The details regarding brightness for the five days on which experimental sessions took place follow for method (*a*). Volkmann's finding of the distances D that appeared equal to the diameter of the wire is given below (the subscript to D refers to the number of trials).

First day (no details) $D_9 = 0.1897$
Second day (overcast) $D_{10} = 0.2271$
Third day (bright sky) $D_{10} = 0.2153$
Fourth day (very bright sky) $D_{10} = 0.2074$

Heidenhain's experiments, using method (*b*), yielded the following results:

First day (no details) $D_{20} = 0.111$
Second, very bright light $D_{20} = 0.153$

No definite influence of the degree of illumination can be noticed.

Special determinations of the smallest perceptible magnitude

Although, according to the preceding discussion, previous determinations of least perceptible magnitudes and distances do not appear to allow us to draw valid conclusions of any kind, they are important with respect both to the lower limits of the eye's efficiency (which they establish) and to their practical interest. A summary should therefore not be unwelcome.

Unfortunately it is true that this summary shows only little agreement between the results of various investigators. And since the precarious value that these results might have would disappear entirely if the conditions of observation were not specified exactly, I shall give them as much as possible in the observer's own words.

Since it is essential to translate visual angles into magnitudes on the retina, and vice versa, I havetaken the distance of the intersection of the principal rays as 15.1774 mm = 6.735 Paris lines in front of the retina and as 7.4696 mm = 3.315 Paris lines from the cornea, based on Listing's determinations. I have therefore substituted 0.00007357 mm or 0.00003265 Paris line for a visual angle of one second.

One finds that the following statement in Smith's Optics is about the most frequently used. I shall cite it here from the French translation of the work,[2] which is at my disposal (Part I, p. 40):

Dr. Hook assures us that the subtlest eye is unable to distinguish well a distance in the sky, such as a spot in the body of the moon, or the distance of two stars, which subtends at the eye an angle less than a half-minute (see his remarks on the celestial machine of Helvetius, p. 8). If the angle is no greater, the stars will appear to the naked eye as a single star. I was present at an experiment where a friend of mine who had the best eyes of the company, was scarcely able to distinguish a white circle on a black background, or a black circle on a white background or against the light of the sky, when it subtended at the eye a lesser angle than two thirds of a minute; or what amounts to the same thing, when its distance from the eye exceeded 5156 times its own diameter; which rather agrees with Dr. Hook's observation.

Tobias Mayer* cites the results of several experiments as follows:

The first experiment took place in a shadowy place with open windows facing away from the midday sun. Objects, drawn in India ink that they call "Tusche," were placed on very white flat paper. (1) A black dot whose diameter was ¼ Paris line could be distinguished very well at a distance of 10 Paris ft, by a myopic eye which was corrected by a properly fitted lens. At a distance of 12 ft it was seen dubiously. Indeed, at a distance of 13 ft it disappeared completely. (2) A similar dot, but with a diameter of 0.44 lines, was still visible to the eye at a distance of 14¾ ft. At a distance of 17 ft the mark was scarcely seen, and at a distance of 18 ft the object was not visible to the eye at all. (3) A third dot whose diameter was 0.66 lines, was still distinguished at a distance of 24½ ft, but at a distance of 26 ft it was seen with difficulty and dubiously. A little further away from the eye, it could not be seen at all.

After recounting further experiments on grids, which will be mentioned below, he adds:

[2]Ed. Note: Or look up original English in Robert Smith, *A Compleat System of Opticks*, 1738.
*Comment. Soc. sc. Gotting. Vol. IV, 1754, p. 101.

Dots and figures placed higher than eye level, and in the light of the midday sun (where color and illumination were greatest), began to appear blurred at approximately the same distances as above. Discrepancy, if there was any, became apparent as the experiment was repeated more often with the measurement of the larger distances, and the smaller distances thus became clear.

This result, that the degree of illumination had no influence on the recognition of the points, directly contradicts Plateau's experiments, whose results follow.

If one puts the viewing distance, which according to Mayer's expression (p. 101) made the points *e conspectu eripere*,[3] at 12, 17, and 26 ft, then the diameter of the image in the eye becomes respectively 0.000973, 0.001126, and 0.001186 Paris line. The corresponding visual angles are 30, 35, and 36 seconds, which are in remarkable agreement for these different distances.

Plateau* in his experiments, simultaneously took into account color and degree of illumination. Small targets of colored paper, 1 cm in size, were fastened to a board erected out of doors. Plateau gradually moved away from them until the colored target appeared only as a tiny, hardly noticeable cloud, and disappeared a few steps beyond. He then measured his distance from these objects and calculated the corresponding visual angle. The results in two cases follow:

	In the Shade	In Sunshine
White	18"	12"
Yellow	19"	13"
Red	31"	23"
Blue	42"	26"

The difference introduced by the colors probably reflects merely their different degrees of brightness.

Hueck† carried out experiments of the following kind: A clearly visible mark is fixated sharply by, a normal eye. The observer gradually moves away from the object until it vanishes, and the board to which the spot or stripe is fastened appears completely clear.

"Several hundred observations from different individuals showed that a dull white spot in a black field disappeared at 10 seconds visual angle." This result corresponds to a distance of 0.00033 Paris line or 0.00074 mm on the retina. A white stripe in a black field was still visible, according to him, at a visual angle of less than 2 seconds. On the other

[3]Ed. Note: Barely visible.
* *Pogg. Ann.* XX, p. 327.
† *Müller's Arch.* 1840, p. 85.

hand, the visual angle at which a black spot disappeared against a white field amounted to 20 seconds. The former corresponds to 0.0000652 Paris line or 0.0001470 mm, the latter to ten times this distance on the retina. Further details, regarding the number of trials and the agreement of observers, are not given for the last statement. Nothing is said, either, respecting the conditions of illumination under which the experiments took place.

Volkmann* was able to recognize a simple thread from a spider web at a distance of 21 in., and another person was able to see the same thread up to a distance of 22 in. A hair 0.002 in. thick was recognized by Volkmann† at a distance of 30 in. A student of Bär's recognized‡ a hair of a thickness of ⅟₆₀ line at a distance of 28 ft.

A more thorough account, with some interesting sidelights, is given by Ehrenberg§ but I have rarely seen his work taken into account. It relates, not to observations with a changing eye distance, but to the clearest viewing distance (4 to 6 in., according to Ehrenberg) at which small objects can be seen at all. I shall quote his own words.

"At the many opportunities," he states, "that I have had to observe curious people who liked to learn about the wonderful structure of infusoria through their own observations in my laboratory, I found to my amazement that the diversity of their visual acuity was much less than I had expected and than has generally been said to be. Once I had focused the instrument (microscope) on the delicate object or once I had directed my naked eye carefully onto some very small object, 15 to 20 persons to whom I demonstrated these objects at different times, simultaneously saw the same item that I saw myself, equally well and with equal clarity. They rarely felt the need to change the distance of the object from the eye by even a trivial amount. In order to be quite sure that I was not being led astray by the courtesy or embarrassment of those who did not want to confess not seeing anything, I have often had the observers draw the objects they saw or I had them describe them to me in detail. I became convinced that they saw exactly the same thing, just as sharply as I had done, and mostly without it being necessary to change the focus of the microscope in the first place. These observations, which were carefully continued on a large population with various viewing distances, made me think it probable that there existed a more or less fixed general limit for the acuity of the unclouded and healthy human eye, which should

* *Volkmann Beitr.*, p. 202.
† *Wagner's Wört. Art. Sehen.*, p. 331.
‡ According to Volkmann in his article on vision, p. 331.
§ *Pogg. Ann.* XXIV, p. 35.

allow us to draw a conclusion about the highest power of microscopes. I made many observations in order to find to what extent the variations of myopic and presbyopic eyes influence the manifestation of this capacity, and have convinced myself many times that the opinion—by no means rare—that myopic persons see more or more sharply than others is unfounded. The result of my experiences is twofold:

"(1) There seems to be a normal capacity for perception of very small details by the human eye. Deviations from this capacity appear to be much more rare than is commonly believed.

"Of course, only those capable of clear seeing at some distance can be considered. Among more than 100 persons whom I observed, those who saw most clearly under normal viewing conditions were not capable of distinguishing more than I could myself. Those who considered themselves nearsighted or farsighted were usually able to see whatever I did, but they needed specific instructions and, especially when viewing with the unaided eye, they had to move the object somewhat closer or farther from the eye than I.

"(2) The smallest area usually visible to the unaided human eye has a diameter of $\frac{1}{36}$ of a Parisian line, whether it is white on a black or black against a white or a bright background. It is still possible to recognize magnitudes between $\frac{1}{36}$ and $\frac{1}{48}$ of a line, by using the greatest concentration of light and strictest attention, but only in an unclear and dubious way.*

"This then is the limit of the capacity of the unaided human eye for seeing colored objects, as anyone can easily check by themselves, in the same way as I have done. One takes some very fine black dust particles, for example, dried ink or india ink, and puts them on very white paper. One then picks up the smallest of them with a very fine point and places it on a glass micrometer that reads directly to at least $\frac{1}{48}$ line. Sun or lamp light permits easy observation of the black particles or similar objects, with or without a mirror, on the glass micrometer in a light field. Objects smaller than the ones mentioned cannot by themselves be recognized by the unaided eye, in spite of all efforts, although they can be seen if arranged in a row. Further, if some of them are found close together or lined up in rows, they make a common impression on our eye and fool us, as if we saw a larger single object or surface.† The usual distance at which people

* "It is obvious that it would not be worthwhile to claim 1/49. The next conditions which would be worthwhile are 1/60 or 1/72 line, and I have never found that they have been seen by anyone."

† "I am accustomed to recognize the very fine cilia of infusoria in this way. As soon as they are moved they form a small apparent surface, which is visible. But as soon as they are at rest, their dimensions are so fine that they are out of reach of visual acuity with the microscope."

with good vision had to observe in order to recognize these very small objects was 4 to 5 in. and sometimes 6 in., the latter being the usual distance for persons with very acute vision. Myopic individuals seldom come closer than 4 in., and still less often 3 in., to these objects, and then they are usually as good as the others. Someone who sees most clearly at 4 in. cannot increase his acuity by moving his eyes closer to the object, but will feel pain and experience unclear vision. Once the object has been fixated, one can move it considerably farther away, without losing sight of it. I, myself, cannot see $\frac{1}{24}$ of a line at 12 in. in black on white, but if I have first looked at it at a distance of 4 to 5 in. I can move it away to 12 in. and still see it clearly. This phenomenon depends on the well-known capacity of the eye to accommodate somewhat for distance vision. Often one recognizes small objects at a great distance, as soon as one's attention has been drawn to the spot where they are, or if they move. Similar phenomena are found when a balloon is seen against a bright sky or a ship on the horizon. One sees them easily as soon as they catch one's attention, but this capacity to orient oneself quickly depends on habit and intelligence, and does not allow us to make general conclusions about acuity. When one person is more easily excited by visual impressions than another, he is orienting himself more quickly, but he does not see any more than one who orients himself more slowly because he perceives less vividly. I often look for very small objects first with the magnifying glass, which is a help when I want to recognize them with the unaided eye in order to change their position with a fine point. All that this does is to help in finding the place of the object and to speed up orientation. Myopic eyes have an easier time in orienting themselves because they are less distracted, since their visual field is smaller. Finally we should probably add one condition under which there is potentially a higher human visual acuity, and that is in the recognition of luminous objects. It is well known that luminous objects appear larger than they are and are easily able to affect the human eye when much smaller than $\frac{1}{48}$ line, depending on their brightness, whether they are self-luminous or shine in reflected light. I have never had the opportunity to observe self-luminous objects myself with a true diameter so small that they could have called my attention to a limit in this respect. . . . Metallic shine, which reflects light quite strongly, can be recognized down to $\frac{1}{100}$ line, according to observations of mine on gold dust with the unaided eye in normal daylight. This is half the size of colored objects. . . .

"Lines behave differently when viewed against the light. One can recognize opaque threads $\frac{1}{400}$ line thick with unaided eyes. Spider webs measure $\frac{1}{300}$ to $\frac{1}{2000}$ line; threads of the silkworm $\frac{1}{200}$. The latter are double in the cocoon."

If one transforms the $\frac{1}{36}$ line, at a viewing distance of 4 to 6 in., which Ehrenberg gives as the limits of visibility for nonlinear targets, into distance on the retina, one finds 0.0039 to 0.0025 line, which is ten times Hueck's 0.00033 line—this, in spite of the fact that both results were based on a large number of trials. It is also more than twice Mayer's result. Hueck and Ehrenberg also differ, in that for Hueck black dots on a white ground need a larger visual angle than the other way around, whereas according to Ehrenberg they are equal.

One difference in conditions may be the fact that Ehrenberg's experiments were conducted by viewing tiny particles from as close as possible, whereas Mayer and Hueck used targets of considerable size at greater distances, since both had the observer move away from the point of clearest vision to the vanishing point of the target. It is true that according to Mayer's experiments distance is not an important factor, but since his distances amounted to 12 ft and more, a much lesser distance (as in Ehrenberg's experiments) might make a difference after all. This point warrants further investigation.

When it is a question of not only recognizing the presence of a visible target, but also of determining its shape, a much larger visual angle is necessary. According to Hueck* a square of 1.2 lines diameter was still recognized as a square at 11 ft, equivalent to a visual angle of 2 minutes 35 seconds of arc. Similarly, an oblique stripe, 1.5 lines long, was recognized as inclined at 13 ft, equal to a visual angle of 2 minutes 45 seconds of arc. Printing, in which the width of letters was 1.5 lines and the spaces between letters were 0.5 line, was read by Hueck at a distance of 13 ft with the use of glasses suitable for his eyes.

Bergmann† found "that short stripes were seen at closer distances than longer ones of equal width."

E. H. Weber‡ remarks: "A white line on a black background can be seen three times as far away as an equilateral rectangle as wide as the line, according to my investigations, and a very contrasting background made the distance even larger, if anything."

Special determinations of the smallest perceptible distance

Experiments on this subject have been carried out in various forms and their results vary accordingly.

---

*Müller's Arch. 1840, p. 88.
† Henle und Pfeufer Zeitschr. Series III. Vol. II, p. 92.
‡ Berichte der sächs. Soc. 1852, p. 142.

(α) *Two distant dots or squares*   Smith's statement with respect to two stars has already been mentioned on page [233].

Volkmann* allowed the images of two lights, 4 in. apart, to fall on the small bulb of a thermometer, 0.15 in. in diameter, which was 8 in. away. . . . He perceived, with the aid of glasses, complete separation of the images up to 20½ in. and clearly double images, touching in the center, up to 26 in: . . . One of his friends repeated the experiment and recognized the images up to 37 in. away. Without his glasses Volkmann had to come as close as 12 in. in order to recognize the complete separation of the mirrored images.

According to Hueck† two black dots, 0.45 line apart, against a white background, fused when the observer was 10 ft away. This distance corresponds to a visual angle of 1 minute 4 seconds of arc. Stripes, the same distance apart, gave the same result.

E. H. Weber‡ adds to his determination of the distance at which white lines and rectangles on a black ground disappear from view, mentioned on page [238]: "On the other hand, two white, equilateral rectangles on a black background were separated by a black space of equal width. They were still seen as separated at a distance which was almost equal to that at which two white stripes on a black background, just as wide as these rectangles, and separated by a black space of equal width and of the same shape as the stripes, were seen as separate."

(β) *Two distant threads*   Volkmann§ stretched out two parallel threads from a spider web, at a distance of 0.0052 in. from each other, and found that he distinguished them as two at a distance of 7 in., but not farther. The most sharp-sighted among his friends recognized the doubling at a distance of 13 in. Two black parallel stripes on a white background, 0.016 in. apart, were distinguished by Volkmann with the help of his glasses at 27 in.

Valentin¶ was able to separate two lines whose images on the retina were only 0.0009 line apart.

Hueck found the same results for stripes as for dots. (See p. [234].)

(γ) *Striped and checkered figures*   Tobias Mayer# describes

---

* *N. Beitr.*, p. 202.
† *Muller's Arch.* 1840, p. 87.
‡ *Berichte der sächs. Soc.* 1852, p. 142.
§ *Wagner's Wört. Art. Sehen.*, p. 331.
¶ Valentin, *Textbook of Physiol.* II, p. 428.   Cited here from Weber's article on the sense of touch, p. 534.
# *Comment Soc. sc. Gotting.* Vol. IV, p. 102.

experiments in diffuse daylight as follows:

1. A striated figure whose black lines alternate with equal white ones, and whose width was 0.36 Paris line, immediately appeared considerably blurred when viewed directly at a distance of 11 ft, to the extent that one could discern only with effort the intervening white space between the white and black lines. At a distance of 12 ft, all space between the different stripes disappeared. Certainly, the intervening space was perceived with great difficulty. With the eye further away, the entire figure gave the illusion of a homogeneous grayish color.

2. In the same manner, a striated figure whose black stripes were twice as wide as the white ones, that is, the breadth of the latter was 0.2 line, of the former 0.4 line, began to appear blurred to the eye at a distance of 9 to 10 ft.

3. At the same distance, another striped figure whose white lines were twice as wide as the black ones, that is, changing the order of the above measurements, failed to be seen distinctly. The width of the white stripes was 0.4 line; of the black ones, 0.2.

It must be noted that these two figures (no. 2 and no. 3 also in the following experiments*) always required the same distance of the eye. Therefore, it will be convenient to refer to these two concurrently in the future.

4. A figure crossed by alternating white and black lines, whose width was 0.44 line, when seen from a distance of 15½ ft, began to give the appearance of being equally black everywhere, so that it was doubtful whether any whiteness was contained in it.

5. A figure similar to a die (we will call it a die for the sake of brevity), with alternating black and white squares, each side of which measured 0.52 line, allowed the form to be seen with the eye at an extreme distance of 12 ft, for by placing the eye a little further away, the white squares seemed to be confused with the black ones.

After comparing no. 1 with no. 2 and no. 3, and no. 4 with no. 5, Mayer concludes that inequalities of light and dark intervals facilitate recognition.

MAYER'S EXPERIMENT

L	A			
Distance	Distance of Eye			
of Light	No. 1	No. 2 and 3	No. 4	No. 5
½	7½	6½	12	9½
1	6½	5½	9½	7½
2	5¾	4½	7	6
3	4¾	4¼	6½	5¼
4	4½	3¾	6	4½
5	4¼			
6	4			
7	3¾			
8	3½	2¾	4½	3¼
13	3	2¼	3¾	3

* Made by candlelight.

The experiments on the striped and checkered figures no. 1 to no. 5 were later also repeated in the dark with direct illumination by a tallow candle at different distances L of the light from the figures. The tabulated distances from the eye to the figures were found to be the limiting values of perception (*termini visionis*, in units of Parisian feet).

Mayer represents the law according to which A varies with L by the following equation

$$A = n\sqrt[3]{L}$$

where n is a constant which depends on the nature of the figure. He takes it to be as follows for the various figures:

No. 1	2 and 3	4	5
79	52	73	99

He gives a summary of calculations and observations according to which the formula holds close enough within the limits of these experiments.

Hueck* observed coins, medals, and gems, line-engraved by machine, in the *Trésor de Numismatique et de Glyptique* (Paris 1834), and was still able to resolve intervals of 0.727 line at a distance of 22 in. 3 lines, in other words at a visual angle of 56.8 seconds of arc. Indeed, some that were printed very clearly with sharp strokes on a clean, smooth white surface could still be resolved at a visual angle of 44.3 seconds of arc. At somewhat greater distances the striated area appeared gray. Yellow striations on a red surface had an orange appearance when their retinal image was 0.001 in., similarly yellow striations on a blue surface appeared green.

Marie Davy† drew some black stripes on white paper in such a way that the space between the stripes was as wide as the stripes themselves. He made up a number of such pages with stripes of various widths and then tried to find out at what distance from the eye each one became a uniform gray, instead of a pattern of black and white stripes. He discovered that this occurred, with each of the pages, at a distance which gave a calculated width of the retinal image of about 0.0011 mm. Specifically it was 0.00109, 0.00113, 0.00113 and 0.00112 mm at distances of 5.8, 0.75, 0.53, and 0.41 m. His mode of calculation is not given.

E. H. Weber‡ used black stripes that were machine engraved, very closely and regularly spaced, and printed on white paper. They were

* *Müller's Arch.* 1840, p. 87.
† *Instit.* XVII, p. 59.
‡ *Berichte der sächs. Soc.* 1853, p. 144.

0.025 Paris line wide, separated by intervals of equal widths. His son, T. Weber, still recognized the lines at a distance of 9 Paris in. 2½ lines, when the visual angle subtended by a space amounted to 45.3 seconds. He also tried the same experiment on a few other persons. The greatest acuity was found for two individuals, of which one (No. 9) also saw the stripes at 9 in., the other at a distance of 11 in., corresponding to visual angles of 45.3 and 36.5 seconds respectively or 0.00148 and 0.00119 Paris line.

Bergmann* employed lithographed gratings, with stripes and spaces each 1 mm wide, in the following manner. A hole about 20 mm in diameter was cut into the cover of a small round cardboard box and the grating fastened to the inside of the cover, so that only a round portion appeared on the outside. "One can now give the grating any inclination by turning the cover, so that the individual whose eyes are being tested can prove by telling the direction of the stripes whether he really can see them."

"The success of a considerable number of trials consisted in the fact that the exceptionally good eyes of various individuals never had to come closer than the corresponding distance of E. H. Weber's experiment no. 8. The grating, with its 1 mm spacing, was always recognized at a distance of 5.5 m. . . .

"Frequently, incidentally, the direction of the stripes was identified correctly several times at greater distances, sometimes from as far away as 7 m. Often the subjects remarked also that if they knew the direction of the stripes beforehand they were able to see them from these greater distances. In an earlier experiment it even happened that a 10-year-old boy, whose excellent vision the experimenter had noticed before, identified the direction of the stripes (changed each time) correctly three times in succession at a distance of 8 m. Then followed an incorrect report."

Bergmann (p. 97) emphasizes as remarkable "that at a distance of 5.5 m, at which reasonably good eyes regularly recognize the direction of the stripes with assurance, the images of the stripes are somewhat wider than half the diameter of a retinal cone. One might suspect that there might well be an essential relationship between these dimensions."

At distances beyond 5.5 m, where correct identification of stripe direction often occurred, the errors that were committed frequently had the peculiarity that the direction of the stripes was described as exactly perpendicular to the true direction. At the same distances the gratings at times also appeared checkered. One man, who had no knowledge of the object, took it to be checkered at a distance of about 6 m; a second

---

* *Henle und Pfeufer Zeitschr.* Series III. Vol. II, pp. 94 ff.

person, standing about 2 ft behind him, commented at this point, that he also saw the same thing.

Bergmann relates these circumstances ingeniously to some probable hypotheses on the form and arrangement of the retinal cones, but these views are too complex to take up here.

Certain directions of the stripes appeared to favor recognition of the gratings more than others, but this seemed to be a matter of individual differences. (See Bergmann, p. 104.)

Properties of the periphery of the retina in perception of very small objects and distances.

My accounts so far have been based on the interpretation of visible objects and distances by the central parts of the retina, which have the clearest vision. The power of perception decreases toward the periphery with regard both to objects and to distances, but by no means equally in all directions. Observations on this point have been made by Hueck and by Volkmann with Hüttenheim; some others have been made by Bergmann, but the most thorough are those of Aubert in collaboration with Förster. Among other things, these studies have shown that the fact that it is impossible to distinguish two dots at some distance from the axis of the eye can by no means be attributed to the optical aberrations of the eye. They have also shown that numbers or squares, subtending the same visual angle at various viewing distances, can be recognized closer up by more peripheral parts of the retina than they can farther away.

I believe it would be best to refer to the original papers, regarding the particulars of the experiments, so as not to draw out the details in this chapter too far.

Hueck in *Müller's Arch.* 1840, p. 92.

Volkmann, in *Wagner's Wört. Art. Sehen*, p. 334.

Aubert and Förster, in *Gräfe's Arch. f. Ophthalmol.* III, p. 14, and Moleschott, *Unters.* IV, p. 16.

Bergmann, in *Henle und Pfeufer Zeitschr.* Series III. Vol. II, p. 97.

One can relate to this problem experiments to determine the part of the retina with which one can see clearly enough to read printed matter. (See E. H. Weber in the *Berichte der sächs. Soc.* 1853, pp. 128 ff, and Aubert and Förster in the above-mentioned paper.)

Differences in distance (estimates of visual size)

We find in E. H. Weber* the following statements on estimates of visual size:

* *Progr. coll.*, p. 142.

I divided a sheet of writing paper, of the largest standard size, into eight equal parts. On each part I inscribed a straight line, being careful at the same time that all the lines were of equal width and blackness, though of different lengths. The shortest line was 100 mm; the next longer, 100½ mm; the next, 101 mm, and so forth. Thus the different lines were extended to a length of 105 mm.

Now two sheets, juxtaposed, were shown to men whose accuracy of vision I wanted to examine; namely, men who devote themselves to the art of drawing and therefore enjoy excellent vision. These men were able to distinguish the vertical line 100 mm long from the vertical line 101 mm long. In the ensuing experiments three, four, and five, they always indicated the longer line correctly. Nevertheless, as they tired, they sometimes made errors. Indeed, several could not distinguish between the 100 and 104 mm lines, but could distinguish with certainty only between the lines 100 and 105 mm long. These experiments showed that some of the men could perceive, by virtue of excellence of vision, a difference of a hundredth part in the lines, while others could only perceive a difference of a twentieth part in the lines, when the second line was parallel to the longer one.

A few of my own experiments on just noticeable distances between compass points have been cited on page [195].

b. Touch

As is well known, E. H. Weber was the first to investigate the just noticeable distance of compass points placed on the skin. He found that this distance is exceptionally variable on different parts of the skin. Sensitivity was found to be highest on the tip of the tongue, where the compass points could be recognized as double if they were only ½ Paris line apart. Next came the volar side of the finger tip (1 Paris line), the red parts of the lips (2 lines), the volar side of the second phalanx of the finger, and so on. The least sensitive was the upper part of the spine and the middle of the upper arm and the thigh (30 Paris lines). The tabulated results of his observations are given most thoroughly in his *Progr. coll.*, pages 50 ff. A shorter version may be found in his article on touch and common sensibility in *Wagner's Wört.*, page 539, and reproduced in his paper in the *Berichte der Leipz. Soc.* 1853, pages 85 ff.* In the latter place he gives also various supplements on general concepts of space perception and methods of determining its acuteness. Weber's observations have been confirmed first by Allen Thomson (in *Edinb. Med. and Surg. Journ.* no. 116), later by Valentin (*Lehrb. d. Physiol.* 1844, Vol. II, p. 565), and finally by Czermak (*physiol. Studien* or *Sitzungsber. der Wien. Akad.* XV, p. 425; XVII, p. 563, Moleschott, *Unters.*, p. 183), and have been enlarged by the latter in various respects.

---

* An abbreviated version, but without tables, can be found in *Fechner's Centralbl.* 1853, No. 31. The table is also reproduced by Czermak in his *physiol. Studien*, p. 54.

Some very interesting observations, according to which narcosis and the administration of chloroform make the just noticeable compass distances on the skin very much larger, have been made known by Lichtenfels in the *Sitzungsberichten der Wien. Akad.*, 1857, VI, page 338. Paralytic conditions of the skin have the same effect. One might compare Landry's experiences in *Archiv. gén. de méd. XXIX. Juill. Sept.* (*Cannst. Jahresber. f.* 1852, p. 189) and especially Wundt in *Henle und Pfeufer Zeitschr.* 1858, page 272, and also Brown Séquard in *Cannst. Jahresber.* 1853, page 202. The last also reports a case of diminution of the just noticeable distance in a hyperesthetic condition. Findings that practice makes the just noticeable distance smaller have been published by Hoppe in his medical letters, 1854, issue 2, by Czermak in the above papers, and especially by Volkmann in the *Sitzungsber. d. sächs. Soc.* 1858, page 38.

Theoretical discussions of dermal space perception may be found in the publications of Weber and Czermak (already cited), in Lotze's *medicin. Psychol.* 1852, in Meissner's *Beitr. z. Anatom. u. Physiol. der Haut.* Leipzig 1853, and in Wundt's *Abhandl.*, which contains a particularly thorough summary of this subject.

c. Perception of Time and Motion

When two impressions arrive too quickly one after the other, they fuse into one uniform sensation, and one might ask how great the interval between them would have to be, so that they could still be perceived as distinct.

One cannot give a purely experimental answer to this question for reasons analogous to those which apply to other thresholds of space perception, for each impression leaves an aftereffect, just as each impression is surrounded by an irradiation circle. If this aftereffect of the first impression is still strong enough when the second comes along, so that its difference from the second one does not reach the differential threshold of intensity, then one impression must uniformly fuse with the other.

One might ask whether the inability to perceive two discrete impressions when they follow each other too quickly depends solely on this circumstance. There is no empirical answer to this question, and it is difficult to make any decision. Probably it is simply impossible in the case of temporal conditions, as in the analogous spatial conditions, to still perceive temporal impressions as discrete when they are too close to one another.

Of course one cannot claim the presence of sensory circles in the sense discussed on page [230], but perhaps the point may be made that the subjective measure of time is tied to psychophysical oscillations within us just as the objective measure of space is related to the sensory circles, and that everything which falls within the duration of such an oscillation can be as little differentiated in time as whatever falls within a sensory circle in extension can be discriminated in space. It would be idle in the meantime to pursue this hypothesis any further, without the chance of basing it on something more precise.

The question with which we are concerned here arises, among others, with regard to the experiments on a spinning disk of white and black sectors. During the time that a white sector passes by, the impression increases; during the time that a black one passes by, it decreases. Does the appearance of uniformity only depend on the fact that the difference between maximum and minimum does not reach the differential threshold of intensity, as it exists for light stimuli perceived at rest, or is the appearance of uniformity aided by the fact that minimum and maximum impressions follow each other so quickly that we cannot keep them apart in time? Can, therefore, a difference be larger than when perceived at rest, without endangering the uniform appearance?

There appears to me to be a possibility to decide the first question by means of an experiment, once one has determined some data.

In connection with the question of a temporal threshold, there is the question of the time that is necessary to perceive a given stimulus with a given degree of clarity. I find some remarks and experiments on this matter by Valentin in his textbook of physiology, Vol. II, page 471:

"The minimum time," he states, "which is needed for satisfactory perception of known objects, after thorough practice, we can best see by reading familiar letters. Reading only a line at a time of large print in this volume (Valentin's text), it took a maximum of 4.21, a minimum of 2.34, and an average of 3.330 trice[4] for each letter, in ten trials. Reading a whole page of large print, without a paragraph, 2629 letters and punctuation marks were found to take 1 minute and 32 seconds. On the average this is equal to 2.1 trice per image. Repeating the same experiment on a running page of fine print of this work, I needed 2 minutes and 12 seconds for 3944 letters and other signs, or 2.01 trice for each impression. We can therefore say in general that during rapid reading the perception of a single character takes only 2 to 4 trice on the average."

I find the following statements on the smallest just perceptible movement in *Gehler's Wörterbuch* in the article on sight, page 1457, by Muncke.

"One can explain why some very slow movements cannot be perceived

---

[4] Trans. Note: Trice (German *Terz*) equals 1/60 second, with respect both to second of time and to second of arc.

by determining the duration of the light stimulus in conjunction with the above-mentioned size of the visual angle. To make this point clear G. G. Schmidt* chooses the example that the stars, even at the equator, where their movement is fastest, nevertheless appear to stand still. If, as an example, one takes as high a value as 0.5 sec for the duration of a light stimulus on the eye, then the star only covers an arc of 5 seconds in this time, and since this distance is less than the smallest visual angle for a spatial object, it seems to stand still. If, on the other hand, the star is observed through a telescope with a magnification of only 100 times, the visual angle will amount to 50 seconds and its movement will be perceived, although with difficulty. However, the larger the magnification which one uses, the faster its movement appears. In this case the vivid impression that the star makes on the eye also comes into play, for Schmidt found another result in observing the motion of the minute hand of a pocket watch. He was just able to perceive this movement when employing a tenfold magnification. Since the length of the hand amounted to 4.5 Paris lines, and the visual angle of one of its divisions came to 13.5 minutes (at a distance of 10 in. for clear vision of the observer), its velocity appeared to be 13.5 seconds of angle in 1 second of time, and at tenfold magnification 135 seconds of angle or 2 minutes 15 seconds. Meanwhile we have to consider many variables, particularly visual acuity and the illumination of the object to be examined, in this admittedly clever method of measuring the tiniest movements. This is also the reason why the two just-mentioned values deviate so much from each other. In order to check the latter value, I observed the minute hand of my pocket watch myself. It is 9.1 lines long and steel blue, moving against a dazzling white face. As long as it passed over the latter, I was able to perceive its advance with the unaided eye at a viewing distance of 8 in. However, it seemed to stand still when it happened to be over one of the black division marks, so that this velocity may be looked upon as the limit of perception for my eye. One has therefore only to double the stated magnitude of 13.6 seconds, and adjust it by a ratio of 10 : 8, in order to get the smallest visual angle in the neighborhood of 34 seconds† which, however, would not come out quite so small under less favorable circumstances, particularly if the measurement of the distance of the tip of the hand from the two minute marks were omitted. These circumstances also explain why the motion of stars in the telescope becomes visible at a visual angle of 50 seconds. It is due, in part, to the strong light they give off in a relatively dark space and, in part, to the fact that the visual field of

* *Hand-und Lehrbuch der Naturlehre. Giess.* 1826, 8, p. 471.
† Exact calculation gives 34″ 50‴. [‴ = trice]

a telescope is somewhat illuminated, while its surrounding is completely dark, since the tube is blackened on its inside. In this way the variable distance of the star from the edge of the visual field can also be measured."

One can go to Valentin in his textbook, Vol. II, page 465, for the following additional information:

"Although I am still unable to see with the unaided eye, in daylight, the movement of the gilded minute hand (of a pocket watch), 14.5 mm in length, I do see it if I use a magnifying glass of 1½ power. On the other hand, when the length of the gilded hand of another watch amounted to 18 mm, I was just able to perceive its travel with good fixation at a distance of 4 in. from the eye, in good light. However, I would have considered the whole thing stationary at a fleeting glance. If I put a magnifying glass in front of it, however, which likewise enlarges 1½ times at 4 in., then I can perceive its travel very clearly. . . . All these determinations of the velocity per second of the smallest alterations of the visual angle will give only approximate estimates, even if the preliminary measurements are correct, because a great number of minor conditions also play a role and these cannot always be taken into account. Not only the light intensity, luster, and color of the item to be viewed, the distance, the field of vision and acuity, but also the nature of adjoining objects have considerable influence on the perception of the slightest motions. If the hand of the watch, for example, goes right up to some fine lines, it makes it easier to perceive the slight motions than under other conditions, because these fine ornamental lines serve as fixed reference points and the least relative progress of the tip of the hand draws one's attention to the movement."

XII.

Parallel Law in Relation to Weber's Law

There remains a fundamental question, which we encountered when we sought to prove Weber's Law and which we must now examine more closely. To what extent does differential sensitivity parallel absolute sensitivity? In particular, do the variations in sensitivity to stimuli that arise from the action of the stimuli themselves account in part for the sensitivity to differences between them?

A white disk on black paper when viewed without interruption is seen as veiled by a gray film which up to a point becomes darker as time goes on. This effect is proof that sensitivity to light is blunted by the light's effect. Many other examples could be added. On the other hand, after tiring from carrying or lifting a burden, a weight is felt as heavier, so that the sensitivity for weights is increased by the previous influence of a load. In one case it takes a stronger light stimulus, in the other case a lesser load, to produce equally strong sensations.

The question is: does the just noticeable or equally noticeable light difference or weight difference become respectively larger or smaller, or will the fatigued organ be as sensitive to the same difference between physical forces as it was before it became fatigued?

At first glance it may seem quite natural that when each of the stimuli is felt as weaker or stronger by itself, their difference would also be perceived as weaker or stronger. But Weber's Law has taught us that a difference is felt as strongly as before, when two stimuli are really weaker or stronger, provided that the difference has decreased or increased in proportion to the stimuli. Therefore, the change in the stimulus impression, altered as it is by internal conditions, might have the same effect as the real objective stimulus change, and the difference might still be perceived equally strongly.

What, in fact, is the psychophysical meaning of a statement such as: "the stimulus sensitivity is changed"? If there is a fixed relationship between psychophysical processes and sensation, it can mean nothing but: "another intensity of the stimulus is needed to bring about the same sensation," that is, the identical psychophysical processes. If Weber's Law fundamentally refers to the relationship of sensation to internally released effects of the stimulus, instead of merely the relationship of sensation and stimulus, then it does not matter in the end whether the external stimulus is weakened or its internal effects are weakened, since the weakening of the external stimulus can only be considered in the light of the weakening of the internal effects. In short, blunting the stimulus effect internally and weakening it externally result in the same thing. The difference in sensation remains unchanged, as long as the components are affected in the same ratio.

Admittedly, if Weber's Law could not be transferred from external stimuli to internal effects, (that is, to the psychophysical processes), then the sensation of difference would not remain constant, when the relative difference (or the ratio) of inner effects, measured somehow, stays constant, but would change as some function of the absolute difference. In this case the corollaries of the law cannot be transposed from the external to the internal realm. Thus we see that the question with which we are concerned here has indeed a fundamental meaning for our theory. It is the question of a bridge between outer and inner psychophysics.

Apart from these considerations, there is the important question of the extent to which there exists an essential relationship between absolute and differential sensitivity. Findings on this problem would be most suitable to help us clear up the murky theory of irritability and excitability.

I shall call the law with which we are mainly concerned the law parallel to Weber's Law, or, in short, the parallel law, since we can look at it as a transposition of Weber's Law from the external to the internal realm. It can be formulated in this way:

When the sensitivity to two stimuli changes in the same ratio, the perception of their difference will nevertheless remain the same.

It can also be rephrased in the following equivalent manner:

When two stimuli are both perceived as weaker or stronger than before, their difference appears unchanged, if both stimuli would have to be changed in the same ratio to restore them to their previous absolute sensation level.

The question whether temporal changes in the absolute sensitivity of one and the same sense receptor are accompanied by a change in differential sensitivity is naturally related to the question whether spatial differences in absolute sensitivity (differences in the absolute sensitivity of different parts) are accompanied by differences in their differential sensitivity. The problem is now shifted from a problem of time to a problem of space. The various parts of the retina have demonstrably different absolute and different differential sensitivity to light. Is their function essentially parallel? Different weights are felt when the same loads are placed on diverse parts of the body. Do those parts of the body to which the same weights feel heavier also have an advantage in recognizing a given difference of weight?

It does not seem to me that this kind of question has been clearly framed in the past; still less, that it has been answered clearly and unequivocally, but these are fundamental questions.

Undoubtedly, if differential sensitivity can remain unchanged when absolute sensitivity varies with time, then the same rule could also hold for variation in space, and vice versa. Thus, proving the law in respect of time would also speak in favor of its existence in respect of space, and vice versa. Still, one cannot avoid the task of validating it in both respects.

In fact, one cannot be certain that one can infer the validity of the law under certain conditions from its validity under others. It is possible that there are circumstances under which both kinds of threshold increase or decrease in unison, although this relationship between the absolute and differential sensitivity is not essential—that is, it is not universal, necessary, and fundamental to their nature. Proof that neither depends essentially on the other is not so much a matter of showing that one always stays constant when the other changes, as that they can change just as well without each other, and contrary to each other, as well as with one another and in the same direction. In other words, the parallel law may hold under certain conditions, although it does not hold under all conditions.

It is important not to overlook a requirement of the law that the sensitivity to both stimuli must really change at an equal ratio, if the equivalence of the sensations of difference is to be expected. Let us assume, for example, that the same stimulus strikes two places on the retina that have at the start the same absolute sensitivity. It would therefore be perceived as equal at both places. Let us now assume that there is a change of absolute sensitivity—either plus or minus—in only one part and not in the other. Immediately a sensation of difference between the two is created, even though the parallel law is assumed to hold, and this sensation of difference increases in the same way as the differences between the absolute sensitivities. It is as if the stimulus reaching one area grew while that reaching the other remained unchanged, with the sensitivity of both areas remaining constant.

All questions raised and conditions discussed here with respect to intensity of sensations also apply to extent. One can in this case ask also: are given differences in extent perceived best when and where given extents appear largest? Does the just perceptible spatial difference therefore parallel the just perceptible extent?

The following pages will treat all these problems, as far as our knowledge goes. Certainly we are by no means close enough to the desired relationship and completeness to allow us to report a general, simple, and elegant result. One can state, however, that an essential relationship between absolute and differential sensations generally does not exist, as the following tests of the parallel law in the field of weight-lifting experiments will show.

Success in proving Weber's Law itself does not seem possible without support of the parallel law; it is, so to speak, bound up with its validation. Irritability and absolute sensitivity must necessarily change in the course of continued experimentation, because of the continued, repeated, and changing influence of the stimulation. It does not seem possible to prove Weber's Law over a range of different degrees of stimulation, if transposition to internal effects (the parallel law) does not exist.

I consider this argument binding, though it is indirect. Meanwhile, it does not do away with the need for direct proof, and I shall give now all that is available to me.

1. EXPERIMENTS
IN WEIGHT LIFTING

A series lasting 32 days (June and July 1858) was carried out with a standard weight P of 1000 gm and two additional weights, D, of 40 and 80 gm. The standard weight was lifted $32 \times 8 \times 64 = 16{,}384$ times, and the additional weights were changed from one day to the next. Normal conditions, as noted on page [80], prevailed, except for the variation of the time the weight was held in the hand. Four such times, one half, one, two, and four seconds, were employed. The weight was lifted 64 times with the left hand, followed by the same amount with the right, for each of the four durations, on each of the 32 days that experiments were made, adding up to a total of $8 \times 64 = 512$ liftings each day. Each time the weight was lifted for four seconds the hand felt very fatigued, since the standard of 1 kg [kilogram] had to be held up for so long, whereas at the shorter times, even at two seconds (which I watched specially), I did not feel anything. If this fatigue had influenced differential sensitivity, it would have shown up in the number of cases right and therefore in the values of hD calculated from them by the procedure mentioned on pages [93–96], values which measure sensitivity when D is constant. In any case these values would show if the duration of lifting influences differential sensitivity, for even if fatigue is not clearly felt, it must take more energy to hold the weight up for a longer time and therefore must be more wearying than if it is held for a shorter time. My experiments, however, show no such effect. Taking the sum totals of the four principal conditions, I list below the number right ($n = 2048$ for the special case), and the values for $32hD$ combining both D's, and $64hD$ summing in addition right- and left-hand results. It should be observed that each duration appeared equally often at the beginning and at the end of a trial session.*

TEST OF THE PARALLEL LAW
$n = 2048$

Lifting Time	½	1	2	4
$r\{$ Left	1541	1507	1496	1546
Right	1561	1502	1483	1551
Sum	3102	3009	2979	3097
$32hD\{$ Left	159,509	161,316	155,271	183,353
Right	192,175	172,139	168,915	175,337
$64hD$	351,684	333,455	324,186	358,690

This series can be used as an experimental proof of our rules for calculation (see p. [85]). The sum of L and R for all four durations gave, as can be seen, the following values of $32hD$ according to our rules for calculation:

$$D = 0.04P \text{ gave } 454,399$$

$$D = 0.08P \text{ gave } 913,613$$

or twice the D produced twice the hD.

If we examine the lowest line of the table giving the sums of $64hD$, which summarize the results of all the experiments, then the largest difference might be expected between lifting durations of one half and four seconds, if the time a weight was held and the consequent fatigue made any difference in the differential sensitivity. But the values of $64hD$ are remarkably close, and the values for the intermediate times do not vary to any extent either.

This result is given additional importance by the fact that the duration a weight was held in the hand was shown to be by no means without in-

---

* The number right and values of $32hD$ do not always correspond in the table for the reason given on p. [98].

fluence on the estimations of the weights. For example, the constants p and q varied noticeably because of it, as can be seen in the following table, which shows their average value in grams, determined in the manner described on page [95]:

EFFECT OF LIFTING TIME

Lifting Time	Left		Right	
	p	q	p	q
½ sec	+ 6.73	− 3.17	+31.49	+6.28
1 "	+ 13.07	− 19.46	+43.38	+3.30
2 "	+ 12.38	− 16.00	+38.05	+0.36
4 "	− 7.95	− 3.28	+ 3.43	+6.04

We see from the table that the first container, when lifted with the left hand and held for two seconds, appeared 12.38 gm heavier than the one that was lifted second, but when it was held for four seconds it seemed to be 7.95 gm lighter. Lifting with the right hand resulted in changes in the same direction, without going as far as a reversal, however.

It is no doubt important that the values of p as well as of q at a duration of one and two seconds are almost the same, whereas they depart notably from each other at one half second and four seconds. The explanation is that at a duration of one half second the weight is lifted with a kind of quick jerk, which is not quite comparable to the steady lift applied at the longer durations, while at four seconds strongly felt fatigue introduces a lack of comparability.

The results cited were found incidental to an experimental series carried out for other purposes. Recently (January and February, 1859) I conducted another series of experiments under standard conditions (except for duration) expressly for the purpose of increasing the influence of fatigue, due to the time a weight was held lifted. I used two heavier standard weights than in the previous series. Unfortunately this series remained uncompleted due to a reason stated subsequently. Nevertheless, these fragmentary results deserve mention since they strengthen the results obtained otherwise.

The series totaled only $16 \times 64 = 1024$ liftings of the weight, distributed over eight days, each with two divisions of 64 weight lifts. The series were conducted on successive days with the left hand only, although at other times I constantly changed from left to right. Two P's of 1500 and 3000 gm were employed; they were alternated every two days. D was $0.06P$ for both. The same P and D were continued for two days, but from one day to the next there was an alternation of the two following experimental procedures.

(a) Each weight was lifted for one second. The rest period after each two weight liftings was five seconds (the standard time interval).

(b) Each weight was held for four seconds. The rest interval after two weights had been compared was three seconds.

The time the weight was held suspended in condition (b) was therefore four times as long as in condition (a), and the rest period was shorter in a ratio of 3 : 5.

As a result, whenever procedure (b) was employed fatigue set in strongly in the hand doing the lifting (to a greater extent, of course, when $P = 3000$ than when $P = 1500$ gm), which was not the case under condition (a). Added to this fatigue under condition (b), there appeared—to a certain extent even on the first day—a pain in the region of the spleen. For this reason I limited myself to two series daily (I normally carry out 8 to 12 series). This pain increased with each day on which the (b) condition had to be used and it became so great on the fourth day* that I found it difficult to finish the two divisions of the series. This situation prevented me from carrying the series further. I had intended to repeat the work with a right-handed and a two-handed procedure and to continue it for at least $1\frac{1}{2}$ months.

Judging by my experience in other cases, I do not consider 1024 liftings of the weight nearly sufficient to form the basis of an assured result, and naturally, fractions of this number cannot be reliable by themselves. Yet when it is seen, first, that with $P = 1500$ gm, hD was larger with procedure (a), whereas with $P = 3000$ gm, the larger result was found with proce-

TABLE OF r

	$n = 64$				$n = 256$
	r_1	r_2	r_3	r_4	Sum r
$P = 1500$ (a)	52	46	58	45	201
" " " (b)	52	39	48	51	190
$P = 3000$ (a)	55	43	51	57	206
" " " (b)	46	61	33	60	200

dure (b), and second, that the over-all result showed only a negligible difference between (a) and (b), although great fatigue was present (which showed itself in a large difference in hp), then one also cannot see in this instance any influence of fatigue on differential sensitivity h.

---

* This pain continued for weeks, so that I was afraid of permanent damage. A mustard plaster seemed to be good for it.

Since it can be done without much trouble, I shall give complete specifications in terms of r, from which one can then derive the results. One can see from the table that the sums of r, with both $P = 1500$ gm and $P = 3000$ gm, are smaller under condition (b) than under condition (a). But with $P = 3000$ gm this result depends only on the exceptional increase of the influence of p, due to fatigue. Calculation, on the other hand, shows that hD is larger for (b) than for (a) when $P = 3000$.

One finds, in fact, the following values, when one carries out the calculations by means of the fundamental table and the rules given on pages [93–96]:

RESULTS OF WEIGHT-LIFTING EXPERIMENT

	4hD	4hp	4hq
$P = 1500$ (a)	23,460	+ 7726	− 2724
" " " (b)	18,879	+ 5023	− 2405
$P = 3000$ (a)	25,335	+ 1649	+ 3803
" " " (b)	27,071	− 18,327	+ 4821
Sum (a)	48,795	+ 9375	+ 1079
Sum (b)	45,950	− 13,304	+ 2417

In summary, the totals for ΣhD, with and without intense fatigue, are found to be in a ratio of 48,795 : 45,900 [misprint for 45950]. They differ less than would be expected by the uncompensated effects of chance. The effect of p, when $P = 1500$, has lost only a little of its positive influence, because of fatigue; but when $P = 3000$, it has turned strongly negative, because of the much greater influence of weariness. The effect of q is everywhere too small, compared with D and p, to be reliable.

In the foregoing two series of experiments, fatigue was brought about by the prolonged lifting of the weights themselves. I carried out two other long and laborious series, in which fatigue was induced before the experiments. The first of these, probably because of accidental reasons (as discussed later), did not come out with completely decisive results; whereas the second may be regarded as definitive proof of our law.

The first of these series (January to March, 1856), which had other purposes besides those of testing the effect of fatigue, was carried out one handed, with the left and right hands tested separately. The standard remained at 1000 gm. There were five comparison weights daily, of 15, 20, 30, 40, and 60 gm. During the 72 days of experimentation, the weights were lifted 640 times daily, so that each D was lifted 64 times with the left and the same number of times with the right hand. Each of the five D's formed, in turn, the final condition of a day; but since 72 is not divisible by five, some D's could not be used as often as others in the final session. To make up for this imbalance, the results have been adjusted proportionately. This adjustment makes it appear as if the 64 times each D would have been lifted as the last series of a session would have occurred eight times with the right and with the left hand, and thus as if the whole series would have lasted 80 days.

Every day, after the weights had been raised 640 times in succession, the arm was fatigued in a manner to be described, and an additional 64 weights lifted. This series was nothing but a repetition of the final one of 64 with the last used D. The purpose was to compare the last two series, the first one without fatigue and the second after fatigue had been induced. Thus there were (presupposing the adjustment we have cited) eight sections of 64 weight lifts each. These covered every one of the five D's. These weights were lifted with the left, and in equal number with the right hand, both in a state of fatigue, and could be compared with the corresponding section immediately before the onset of fatigue. In addition, the results of the session, carried out in the state of fatigue, could be compared with the total results that were obtained the same day before the fatigue was induced.

The means by which fatigue was induced has been described by me in the *Berichte der sächs. Soc.* 1857, pages 113 ff, since these experiments also served as studies of the effect of practice on muscle strength, published there.* It is sufficient to mention here that two lead weights, each of about $9\frac{1}{4}$ lb weight, were raised in cadence from a lowered position to above the head until further lifting in cadence became impossible. As the experiments progressed this time became longer and longer. The weights were raised for one second and lowered for one second. About one minute after finishing the last lift, during which the general agitation died down somewhat and the pulse was sometimes taken, I proceeded immediately to the repetition of the last part of the experiment.

There follow in column z the values of hD in the state of fatigue. Those in column u were taken from the section immediately preceding the fatiguing operations. Column U represents the calculations of the day's

---

* It may be of some interest to mention that the strong practice effects shown in this series, carried out from January to March 1856, had disappeared entirely when I took up lifting weights again on two successive days in October 1858, for no practice had taken place in the meantime. The first series started with 104 and 128 weight lifts on the first two days of the experiment and rose eventually to a maximum of 692; on October 19 and 20, 1858, 122, and 118 respectively could be made, using the same procedure.

total before fatigue was induced. Each value was derived from subgroups of $n = 64$, keeping the four principal conditions separate.*

VALUES OF hD

D	Left			Right		
	U	u	z	U	u	z
15	2854	2447	3890	4044	2984	4822
20	4809	3349	4937	5698	4534	5801
30	7171	6570	4400	7593	7776	8233
40	8980	10,485	11,108	9052	13,054	11,693
60	13,092	12,352	11,464	12,112	14,056	16,470
Sum	36,906	35,203	35,899	38,499	42,404	47,019

Considering now the bottom line giving sums of the results, one can see that the values of hD and therefore of h are just about the same for the left hand with and without fatigue. This is not the case for the right hand, where not only the sums, but every single result (except for U [should read u] when $D = 40$, which is clearly too large) shows a larger value under z compared to the results in columns u and U. The results in column z for the right hand certainly have a much higher weight than for the left hand, because they are almost proportional to the D's, as they normally should be, whereas the results are quite irregular for the left hand, pointing to marked disturbances. The results for the left hand in column z when $D = 30$ and 60, particularly, are obviously much too small, relative to the other left-hand results, as well as to the corresponding right-handed values. If these results are omitted, then, for the left hand also, the remaining z's are found to be uniformly too large compared to u and U. It would therefore be reasonable to draw the conclusion from these experiments that fatigue, when pushed to its limits, has somewhat increased the differential sensitivity.

In the meantime, however, this difference seems to be of little consequence, compared to the great fatigue that preceded it; nor does it seem certain enough, considering the results with the left hand, the previous series, and the following series, not to attribute this difference to an accidental reason, as stated later on.

* Although this series was carried out mainly to explore the influence of the size of D, the results were much less regular, in spite of its length, than other, shorter series. Perhaps the interpolated fatigue was itself at fault. Still, the values in column z for the right hand, with the exception of $D = 15$, do agree quite well—that is, they are proportional to D. Here one should remember that reliable results for small D's can only be expected with a large number of trials in any case.

First, however, it might not be without interest to list the values of *p* and *q* for this series also. They are given in grams, averaged over all *D*'s:

VALUES OF *p* AND *q*

	p		*q*	
	Left	Right	Left	Right
U	− 15.15	+ 7.88	− 17.50	+ 0.20
u	− 21.76	− 7.28	− 13.23	− 2.73
z	− 35.81	− 13.92	− 14.69	+ 0.72

The table shows that the influence of *p* has increased as we go from *U* to *z*. The changes in value of 20.66 for the left hand, and of 21.80 for the right hand are remarkably similar, including in the case of the right hand a reversal from positive to negative. The results demonstrate the effectiveness on the conditions of estimation of the means adopted to produce fatigue. They are, at the same time, a noteworthy example of the manner in which such changes take place. One can already see the same directional tendency in the comparison of *U* to *u*, since *u*, correlated with the last section of a series, is already affected by a certain amount of fatigue compared to *U*, when correlated with the average of all trials. (I did not examine the initial sections separately.)

In respect of the question of accidental circumstances, we may note they could be as follows:

The exercise of lifting the lead weights up and down not only fatigued the muscles but also agitated the whole organism, as shown by the enormously increased pulse rate, which became so fast and shallow immediately after completing the exercises that I was unable most of the time to count it. On some occasions I found it to be 150 beats and more per minute. Yet weight-lifting experiments for about an hour, under standard conditions and with containers weighing 1 kg, before the forced inducement of fatigue or without succeeding fatiguing exercises, did not step up the pulse rate in the same way. On the contrary, on 29 days of the present and an adjoining series, when I took the pulse immediately before and after the experiments (in the same position of the body and keeping the arm steady), on 21 occasions the pulse rate was higher before than after the trials, and amounted, on the average, to 87.8 before, 85.2 after the experiment. This reduction may perhaps be due to the slow, uniform rhythm of the method, and a faster cadence might have brought about another result.

The assumption that agitation, as shown by the greater pulse rate, had the effect of increasing differential sensitivity is supported by the following experiences: During the above-mentioned series my pulse rate was quite irregular from day to day. Considering the tranquil mode of my life, this change could only have been caused by the repeated daily violent episode of fatiguing exercise, which extended its influence, in variable amounts, over the whole duration of the experimental series. I had, unfortunately, omitted taking and recording my pulse in the earlier parts of the series, for I thought of it only too late. I did, however, take it during the last 14 days of the series. The pulse was counted just before the start of the daily morning period of experimentation and again immediately after its end, before the fatiguing exercises, and the two readings were averaged. Taking the 14 averages and comparing them with the number right on the corresponding days of observation* there is admittedly no exactly corresponding trend, but there is, nevertheless, a clear preponderance of greater sums of the number right, on the whole, on days with higher pulse rates. The following table lists the corresponding results in the order of the size of the sum of right responses r ($n = 640$):

EFFECT OF EXCITEMENT ON r

r	Pulse Rate*	r	Pulse Rate
411	75.87	446	81.75
416	95.5	453	88
431	84.5	457	86.5
434	79.25	463	90.75
438	74.25	471	96.5
439	75.87	483	93.65
440	88.25	487	82.5
Sum 3009	573.49	3260	619.65

*
   The fractional values of the pulse rate stem from averaging and from the fact that pulse rate was partially determined by counting over a few minutes and reducing to a minute.

The mean of the corresponding results for the seven days with the lowest r are accordingly,

$$r = 429.9, \text{ pulse} = 81.92$$

and during the seven days having the highest r,

$$r = 465.7, \text{ pulse} = 88.52$$

* The number right are summed for the four principal conditions and all D's of the same day.

The average temperatures during the hours of observation were 15.21°C on the first seven days and 16°C during the last seven.

Undoubtedly the number of cases is not large enough to make sure the result is reliable, but a similar outcome in the following series reinforces the findings of the previous trials, as I shall show below.

Since the results of the previous series were indecisive with regard to the question of our law, I conducted another comparable series of experiments with and without fatigue and in another form (November 1858). The series lasted 16 days—or including idle days, since trials took place only every second day, 32 days. Both hands were used. P was equal to 1000, D to 60 gm. Standard conditions were employed. The total number of weight lifts was $16 \times 10 \times 64 = 10,240$. Fatigue was induced in this case by slowly lifting heavy loads, in the manner to be described, so that even when fatigue was very great there was incomparably less of an increase in the pulse frequency than in the previous series. In this case, too, not only both arms but also each arm by itself was subjected to the same fatiguing exercises as before, and the results were compared. The method follows.

Every day of experimentation began, after the pulse had been taken for one minute, with 4 two-handed sections of 64 trials each. The pulse was then taken again for one minute. Then one of the arms was fatigued and a two-handed session of 64 trials, identical with the first, was carried out. The other arm was then fatigued, and there followed two sections using both hands. Finally both arms were exercised together, and again there followed two sessions of weight lifting. After each section the pulse was taken again, but each time only for one-half minute. The addition of cases came only before the next exercise period, so that the two sections after each exercise period, which belonged together, were interrupted only by one-half minute of counting the pulse. Altogether there were four sections daily, of 64 trials each, without fatigue, and six sections after exercising. The four sections before the induction of fatigue constituted the beginning, the two sections after both arms had been fatigued the end of each day's session. In between there were four sections in which one arm had been exercised. In these the arms were alternated, so that if in one session the left arm had been fatigued first, the next session commenced with the right.

The interval between the exercise and the initial lifting always amounted to the half minute of pulse counting and a few additional seconds needed to put away the lead weight or weights and to switch to the containers. The exercise itself was carried out as follows.

To induce fatigue on one side, a lead weight of 9¼ lb was lifted slowly from a completely lowered position to a horizontal position at shoulder height in four seconds, by the metronome, and was then lowered again in four seconds. During the exercise the arm was stretched out in front more than to the side. Work was continued until the arm could no longer be lifted, then there was a pause of one-half minute, then some more exercise, until it again became impossible to lift the arm, and so on for five times in succession, each time with an interpolated rest of one-half minute. I count these five exercise periods (fractional periods) as one single operation for the purpose of inducing fatigue. The slow pace at which the lifting was done had the purpose of keeping down the rise in pulse rate, and the repetition was meant to cause the fatigue to summate. The number of times it was possible to lift the load decreased during the five fractions of an exercise period because of the increasing fatigue, steeply from the first to the second and only a little during the following periods. The left arm could lift the weight considerably less often than the right, especially at the beginning of the series, but it came more to resemble the other arm during the course of the experiments. Practice also appeared effective in other ways. The simultaneous induction of fatigue in both arms was carried out in the same way as with one arm, except that two weights of $9\frac{1}{4}$ lb each were lifted simultaneously. Since the left arm was weaker than the right one, lifting by both arms was always limited by the earlier tiring of the left arm.

It might perhaps be of some interest to give the details of the observations made during the onset of fatigue in these experiments, which were carried out methodically and comparably from day to day. I shall also have occasion to use some of these details later on. All that it is essential to mention here is that in each of the three daily fatigue sessions the exercises were repeated five times, each time with a rest period of one-half minute, and that one-half minute after the end of the exercise the lifting of the containers commenced. I shall also note that since the exercises started on alternate days, first with either the left or the right arm, it could be seen that the fatigue of one arm did not lessen the number of times the heavy equipment could be lifted (some 12 minutes later) with the other arm. The number of times it was possible to lift the heavy weight was the same, on the average, regardless of whether an arm was fatigued first or second. Finally, the number of times both heavy weights could be lifted was only slightly less when both arms were fatigued simultaneously than when the left arm alone was fatigued.

The following fact should be noted with respect to pulse rate: That pulse rate increases momentarily through vigorous bodily exertion is well known; but it seemed strange to me, and of some interest, that this elevated pulse rate, brought on by strenuous effort, also continued, to a certain extent, throughout the days on which no experiments were made. It could thus be found even before the start of work on the days of experimentation. This continued elevated pulse increased its frequency during the month of experiments, and continued long after the end of the series, decreasing very gradually. The pulse rate's growing higher and higher during the course of the series was the main reason why I discontinued these experiments on fatigue, which I had planned to continue with further variations. In particular, I believed that I could not stand any further elevation of pulse without harm, since I started to feel that my head was being affected by the violent exercise periods. This was no great wonder, since during the last, exhausting phases of every exercise my blood rushed to my head, which is one of my weaker parts, due to some earlier ailment, whereas my very healthy chest suffered no ill effects. This effect on the head showed itself by some sensations I cannot characterize exactly, and by an intensification of a ringing in my ear from which I habitually suffer. There was, however, no lasting ill effect after I ended the series of experiments.

The gradual elevation of pulse rate during the course of the experiments was correlated with a gradual increase in the number right, r, under the four conditions which preceded the exercise periods, although again, not in a regular way but rather clearly indicating a mutual relationship. After all, since I had been carrying out experiments on sensitivity for years, this change cannot be attributed to a practice effect.

There follows a summary of pulse rate and the number right for the 16 days of the actual experimental series, divided into two parts, I and II. Added to this are the results of the seven preliminary and two additional days of experimentation. These may well be compared with the four sections of weight lifting before the exercise period during the 16-day series, whereas the subsequent inducement of fatigue took another form and was carried out mainly for preliminary and additional orientation. The results after the tiring effort are therefore not given. On the first two of the seven preliminary days, the pulse was taken before the exercise period, but no trials, the lifting of containers for judging sensitivity, were carried out. The number of right cases, r, is as always summed for the four principal conditions.

SEVEN PRELIMINARY EXPERIMENTAL SESSIONS

Date	Pulse Rate before Fatigue	r ($n = 256$)
Oct. 19	87.5	no experiment
" 20	85.5	no experiment
Oct. 21	89.25	154
" 23	91.5	155
" 25	97.5	165
" 27	102.5	152
" 29	81	153
Mean	92.35	155.8

SIXTEEN MAIN EXPERIMENTAL SESSIONS

	I			II	
Date	Pulse Rate before Fatigue	r ($n = 256$)	Date	Pulse Rate before Fatigue	r ($n = 256$)
Nov. 1	97	158	Nov. 17	86	172
" 3	93.75	163	" 19	100.5	199
" 5	103.5	204	" 21	89.5	178
" 7	75.5	180	" 23	94.5	191
" 9	97	169	" 25	103.5	198
" 11	87.5	165	" 27	102.5	177
" 13	91	177	" 29	94	191
" 15	95	183	Dec. 1	107	183
Mean	92.53	174.9	Mean	97.19	186.1

TWO ADDITIONAL EXPERIMENTAL SESSIONS

Date	Pulse Rate before Fatigue	r ($n = 256$)
Dec. 3	98	175
" 5	100.5	170

If one takes the average of the seven smallest, the eight middle, and the eight highest values of r with the correlated pulse rate (adding the average temperature) one finds,

r	Pulse	Temp.
157.1	93.1	16.6° C
172.9	95.5	16.7° "
191.1	96.7	16.2° "

After December 5, the date of the last fatiguing effort, I did not take the pulse rate again until I started another series of experiments, without exercise periods, on December 19—the one- and two-handed series at $P = 2000$ and 3000 gm reported on pages [162–164]. When I examined my pulse at this occasion (and in the next series) before and after the experimental run each day I still found an unusually high frequency, in spite of the fact that there had been no experiments whatsoever between December 5 and 19. This rate later decreased slowly but continuously, as seen by eight-day averages determined as the mean rate before and after the lifting of containers, as follows:

	Pulse	Temp.
Dec. 19 to Dec. 26	104.16*	17.16° C
" 27 " Jan. 3	101.11	16.81° "
Jan. 4 " " 11	98.79	15.49° "
" 12 " " 19	98.78	16.49° "
" 20 " " 27	89.46	18.10° "
" 28 " Feb. 4	87.78	17.18° "

*The following were the rates on each of the eight days: 92.75; 109.5; 103.5; 106; 107; 113.5; 97; 104.

During this subsequent series a tabulation of pulse rates for the 16 largest and the 16 smallest number right, found under comparable experimental conditions, also showed an advantage, though small, for the faster pulse rates, as shown here ($n = 8192$) by the totals:

r	Average Pulse Rate
5732	96.88
6147	98.18

Accordingly, some correlation between the increase of r and the increase in pulse frequency seems to me at least very probable.

All of the following again pertain to the 16 central days of the series, which are our main concern at the moment. The pulse rates before and after the four first sections of the experiment, which preceded the presence of fatigue, were found to be practically identical as appears from the fact that their sum amounted to 1517.5 for the 16 days before, and to 1518 for the days after, or on the average to 94.84 before and to 94.88 after the daily session. Thus the lifting of a 1 kg load exerted no effect on pulse rate.

The rate immediately following the three periods of exercise, separated by two sections of experimentation (adjusted from one-half to one minute) was on the average:

	After the First Exercise Period	After the Second Exercise Period	After the Third Exercise Period
In I	100.4	106.5	112.1
In II	108	105.1	115.4

The pulse rate had therefore increased (in comparison with the values in the table on p. [264]) only some eight to ten beats after the first exercise period, and somewhat more during the following intervals, compared to the state before fatigue was induced—in any case very little compared to the tremendous increase in the previous series. Here there also seemed to be, on the whole, an increment from subgroup I to subgroup II. The average pulse, finally, marked (1) and (2), respectively, after the first and second section of experimentation, following the exercise periods, was as shown below:

	1. Exercise Period		2. Exercise Period		3. Exercise Period	
	(1)	(2)	(1)	(2)	(1)	(2)
I	96.5	97.5	98.3	97.5	101	99.9
II	100	99.9	100.9	101.5	101.8	101

Let that do for the pulse rates.

Since in the previous series of experiments (p. [256]), in spite of exceptionally great momentary elevation of pulse rate through exercise, there had not been even a completely certain increase in the values of r, and correspondingly in hD, one could expect even less from the much smaller momentary increase of pulse rate in the present series. The effect of fatigue could thus be judged uncontaminated by the effects of pulse. We shall now compare our results in this respect, before and after fatigue. All results are adjusted to $8hD$; however, those values taken prior to the fatigue period were derived from double the total. The four sections

8 hD BEFORE EXERCISE

1.	Series	28,096
2.	"	35,273
3.	"	32,613
4.	"	30,930
Mean		31,727.4

are specified according to their daily sequence. With the totals for each arm it is indicated whether the left or the right hand was the first or the second to be fatigued.

8 hD AFTER EXERCISE OF ONE HAND

			Left	Right
First	1.	Series	34,681	26,760
"	2.	"	30,063	31,288
Second	1.	Series	30,888	40,731
"	2.	"	34,602	30,175
	Mean		32,558	32,239

It can be seen that the results before and after fatigue do not differ in any substantial way, so that the parallel law can be considered confirmed.

8 hD AFTER EXERCISE OF BOTH HANDS

I.	Fraction	1.	Series	26,425
		2.	"	31,322
II.	Fraction	1.	"	30,932
		2.	"	30,827
		Mean		29,877

It must be pointed out that, on the other hand, the values of $8hp$ and $8hq$ underwent very considerable changes as a result of fatigue (hp as usual in the negative direction). I must omit the details, however, since their listing and discussion would take us too far astray.

Nevertheless, I feel that the following point should be singled out, since it was so unexpected. Since when fatigued one does, generally speaking, feel a given load as heavier than usual, it might be expected that one-sided fatigue would only affect one side in this way. Therefore we would expect that when the left arm had been exercised *hq* would be changed in a positive direction and that after the right arm had been fatigued *hq* would change in a negative direction, compared to the experiments without fatiguing exercises. In addition, it would be expected that these changes would be greatest on those days on which one specific arm was exercised before the other, on which, therefore, prior fatigue in the opposite arm could not have induced a counteracting change. In addition, the effect should have been greatest in the first part (half) that followed the exercise period (after the one-half minute interval), since this part occurred closest to the fatiguing exercises. Examination of these experiments, however, shows that *hq* changed in the positive direction in both instances, after one-sided fatigue of the right as well as of the left arm, although incomparably more after tiring the left than after tiring the right side. Even after the final two-sided fatigue period, *hq* shows a change in a positive direction compared to the resting state, which, while less than after one-sided fatigue of the left arm, is greater than after one-sided fatigue of the right arm. In my opinion these facts are to be interpreted in the following way. Fatigue had the general effect of increasing *hq*; this effect was increased by one-sided fatigue of the left arm and decreased by one-sided fatigue of the right arm. The cause of the general effect is unknown, but the tendency of the increase and of the decrease correspond to what was to be expected from the start.

All the foregoing results have referred to temporal changes in sensitivity through fatigue. The question to what extent parts with greater absolute sensitivity for weights also possess greater differential sensitivity can be considered in terms of E. H. Weber's experiments. One has to compare his results obtained by the method of just noticeable differences* on a given part with those obtained on the same part by the method of equivalents† since the first is concerned with differential sensitivity, and the latter with absolute sensitivity.

When a column, 6 *Thaler* coins high, was placed bilaterally on various regions of the body, a weight difference was perceived, when the following number of *Thalers* were taken away from one side, thereby denoting the just noticeable difference.

Volar surface of the fingers	1
Sole of the foot (at head of metatarsal)	1
Shoulder blade	2
Heel	3
Back of head	4

On the other hand, the following weights were equivalent, that is, were perceived as equal in weight on the respective body regions (in ounces):

* *Progr. coll.*, p. 96.
† *Ibid.*, p. 97.

Volar	surface	of	fingers	4	and sole of foot	10.4
"	"	"	"	3	and shoulder blade	8
"	"	"	"	4	and heel	8.8
"	"	"	"	4.5	and back of head	5

It is obvious that there is not the least correspondence between the two scales. The just noticeable difference is the same on the finger and the sole of the foot, while weights of a ratio 4 : 10.4 are felt to be equal on these same spots. Yet, on the contrary, the equally noticeable weights on finger and back of the head are almost the same, while the just noticeable difference is found to be in ratio of 1 : 4.

Such experiments can be considered decisive only when carried out under strictly comparable conditions, a requirement which cannot be assumed in this case, since there had been no intention of comparing the results obtained by both these methods, and the experiments were carried out at different times, perhaps also on different persons. Nevertheless, we can hardly believe that if there were really a parallel course of absolute and differential sensitivity such discordant results would be possible.

2. EXPERIENCES IN THE AREA OF VISUAL SENSATION

In the area of visual sensation direct experiments regarding the validity of the parallel law are admittedly still lacking, but a good number of facts that are related to this question are available. They will be discussed here, by asking partly whether they fit in with the law, partly to what extent they can validate the law, and partly what light the law can throw on them.

One might be inclined at first to count a generally known fact against the parallel law, a fact which had already been touched upon in the chapter on Weber's Law, but whose further discussion had been postponed until now. A lengthy stay in the dark gives one the capacity to see in the dark; by staying in the light for a time one loses this ability. But what does it mean, to see in the dark? It means that one can still distinguish from darkness a light, which photometrically differs very little from the dark of night.[1] Indeed we have to consider here not so much an

---

[1] Ed. Note: Every time this topic comes up Fechner is stumped. He had experimented and written on afterimages in 1838, but he did not know about adaptation. Thus he was confused about the self-light of the retina. Hermann Aubert, *Physiologie der Netzhaut*, 1865, introduced the concept of adaptation. Hering used it in 1872, but not Helmholtz in 1866. See E. G. Boring, *Sensation and Perception in the History of Experimental Psychology*. New York: Appleton-Century-Crofts, 1942. Pp. 160–164.

absolute sensation, as a difference, since the nocturnal darkness still has its own photometric intensity. Thus it appears as if the tiring of the eye by the stimulation of light also blunts its sensitivity for differences.

In spite of the fact that this phenomenon itself is so widely known that it needs no thorough documentation, I shall nevertheless collect here, parenthetically, some of the evidence showing these circumstances in particularly striking or interesting cases.

"Buffon tells of an officer, held prisoner in a jail, where light entered only rarely from above when food was handed down to him, who after a few months was able to see mice. When freed, after some months, he had to get used to light very slowly. A person who had been a prisoner for 33 years, could see the smallest objects by night, and nothing by day. (Ruete, *Ophthalmol.*, after Larrey, *Mém. de Chir. méd.* Vol. I, p. 6.)"

V. Reichenbach mentions in his writings about the so-called od[2] that certain persons, the so-called sensitives, were able to perceive a flamelike radiance at the poles of strong magnets in complete darkness. These lights appeared blue or blue-gray at the north pole and red, reddish yellow, or reddish gray at the south pole. They also perceived a glow from the tips of crystals, from live bodies of human beings (especially at their fingertips), animals, or plants, from metals, sulphur, and fluids undergoing chemical activity or crystallization, and so forth. The author concludes (*sensit. Mensch.* II, p. 192) that all earthly bodies give off light, which sensitives can perceive, although in varying degrees.

This is not the place to enter into a discussion of the extent to which there really exists such a thing as Reichenbach's od. There seems, to me, to be nothing to contradict his experiences of the light that some individuals can perceive in the dark. I mention them here because Reichenbach not only prescribes as an essential condition the complete darkening of the experimental room, but also that persons who were less sensitive had to stay in the room a long time before they could see anything. According to Reichenbach's statements it was not rare for very sensitive persons to begin to see an od light immediately or after five to ten minutes, whereas it might take persons of medium sensitivity one-half to two or three hours.

I, myself, and older people in general, remember quite well that in former times one used to be satisfied with a tallow candle to provide light in the evening around the family table or at the writing desk. Nowadays, since the brighter lamp light has become common, one would think one is spoiling his eyesight; one is no longer able to see by a candle without strain.

I have heard the following tale about a factory where part of the work was done by the workers at home. A brighter kind of illumination was installed in the factory in place of the former poor lighting. It did not take long before the workers asked for the restoration of the former poor lighting, since they could not manage with the ordinary weak illumination which they could obtain at home.

---

[2] Ed. Note: The Odlehre of 100 years ago was like ESP today. Dowsers used the od to find water. Fechner wrote reminiscently about the Odlehre in 1876. (*Erinnerungen an die letzten Tage der Odlehre und ihres Urhebers.* Leipzig: Breitkopf & Härtel, 1876.)

Aubert in his *Beitr. z. Kenntniss des indirecten Sehens** makes the following remarks: "If one spends a couple of days in a very much darkened room, one estimates it to be as bright as a room which was perhaps ten times as bright. I can tell of a striking example that happened to me. Once, in my fourteenth year, when I had to spend eight days in a darkened room because of the measles, the room was so dark that people coming in had to grope about as if blind. To me after a few days it appeared quite bright, and since I was suffering greatly from boredom, I was glad to get a fairly small map with fine printing. I was able to see the colors quite well and read all the fine printing as well as in normal daylight. I fetched some books into my bed, and was never caught, since those who entered were quite unable to see the book, even when they had been in the room for a few minutes. Let me say that my eyes were not at all affected by the illness."

Förster† remarks with respect to the use of the photometric apparatus described on page [228], where one seeks the lowest illumination at which a small black rectangle on a white ground can be recognized: "At the start of investigation everyone, unless he has previously avoided bright light for quite a long time, needs a greater quantity of light than after a quarter hour, to recognize the same object. If the observer now looks at a brightly lighted surface or at a flame for even a second, his acuity sinks by a number of degrees during the next minute, until rest with light excluded again restores the energy of the retina. It is very remarkable that the center of the retina is particularly easily affected."

All these experiences seem to contradict the validity of the parallel law in vision, in that reduction of the light stimulus weakens differential sensitivity, for, as noted already, a recognition of weakly glowing lights or of dimly lit objects in the dark is nothing other than discrimination of them from a darker background, and does not take place when the eye sensitivity is dimmed.

It is, however, readily seen that these deviations from the parallel law occur under conditions completely analogous to those of the deviations from Weber's Law at its lower limits. As soon as one or both components approach blackness, Weber's as well as the parallel law cease to hold. We do not claim validity for the parallel law, within wider limits than those for Weber's Law.

The question is now: (1) Can we find a reason for the lower boundary of the parallel law corresponding to the one we found for Weber's; and (2) does this disagreement vanish at higher degrees of illumination, just as it did in the case of Weber's Law?

The answer is yes, in both cases, as far as I am concerned. Taking up the first question, I look at it in the following way.

The eye becomes dulled to the effects of the external light stimulus,

* Moleschott, *Unters.* IV, p. 224.
† *Ueber Hemeralopie*, pp. 13, 32.

but the intrinsic light inside the eye darkens relatively little. Therefore the relative difference between it and the effect of the external light becomes less by comparison. Indeed, the intrinsic light can only deepen to a certain extent, as in the case of an afterimage of a bright object, but it cannot disappear. Even with complete amaurotic blindness, when the strongest external light no longer makes any impression, black is still seen; indeed at times it even seems possible to see colors. It makes sense, actually, that the retina, the nerves, and other parts which transmit the stimulus to the brain, may be paralyzed by a number of reasons and become blocked. Now the stimulus will effect only minor or no internal excitation, but the central regions on which arousal of the sensation of intrinsic light depends do not substantially suffer because of this.

If, now, the intrinsic light does not become weaker by being dulled or at least does so to a much lesser degree than the external impression, then this must be equivalent to a relative brightening of intrinsic light with respect to an unchanged light sensation. Even in complete amaurotic blindness, which can be looked upon as the greatest degree of desensitization, the strongest visual impression can no longer be distinguished from intrinsic light, because there is no such impression, while the intrinsic light remains. Just so the perception of the difference between lights disappears together with the perception of the lights themselves, through the use of very dark glasses.

Proof of the validity of this explanation would entail the following consequences: the same persons who see poorly in the dark or in dim light because of being desensitized to the light stimulus—that is, those who discriminate poorly—must be able to discriminate as well as persons who have not been desensitized, if the component lights are strong enough for the self-light of the eye to become vanishingly small compared to them. One can cite positive evidence that confirms this view. This evidence is all the more convincing since it was published not in connection with the above theory and without knowledge of it.

Förster declares in his treatise on Hemeralopia (p. 33): "Look at a white sheet of paper with one eye, while the other is closed and covered, some evening by lamp light. In an illuminated room one will not find a striking difference, even when the other eye is opened. As soon as one moves to a dark room, however, such a difference clearly appears. A kind of fog seems to form in front of the straining eye, which partially or completely covers objects, which the other eye still can clearly perceive. A very strange uncertainty in orientation comes over us in the dark with such differently functioning visual fields, but vanishes immediately on return to a bright room. In the second series of experiments with Aubert on the spatial sense of the retina (which took place by lamp light), I often had occasion to notice this artificial monocular hemeralopia. Sometimes one kept on being blinded for ten minutes or longer. The gas lanterns appeared to the affected eye at some distance like the dim reddish glow of some burning oil lamps and my surroundings appeared so dark that I could orient myself only with difficulty. Closing each eye, one at a time, made the differences in energy of the two retinas stand out particularly strikingly, without, however, making vision in the straining eye more acute in the darkness. Aubert found the artificial hemeralopia still so strong one minute after the end of desensitization, that he could hardly discriminate 1.32 mm stripes with a light source 24 sq mm in area, whereas his unaffected eye, as usual at this illumination, was able to perceive a separation of 0.21 mm. In my own case this blunting of vision reached an even greater degree and lasted longer."

These observations pertain to healthy eyes. Still more instructive, perhaps, are observations of cases of the disease, hemeralopia, with which Förster compares the state of the desensitized eye.

The two conditions, that the eye, after a lengthy stay in bright light, will briefly see poorly in the dark, and after a longer stay in the dark, will for a time see poorly in bright light, are found as a constant condition in two diseases, hemeralopia and nyctalopia. Förster's valuable treatise, based on exact observation, is available on the former. Förster explicitly identifies (p. 32) the state of the healthy retina desensitized by light with the habitual state of the hemeralopic retina because of their similarity in all essential points. In some, but not in all cases a previous lengthy stay in very bright light was actually the cause of hemeralopia (p. 30) and a lengthy stay in the dark for 24 to 56 hours had been the most effective remedy (p. 40).* But the characteristic symptom of hemeralopia is precisely that the patients see incomparably worse in dim light than do persons with normal vision, whereas they see as well as healthy people in bright light. The hemeralope in fact cannot distinguish anything, after the fall of darkness or when entering a dimly lit room, whereas the healthy eye is still able to see quite well, and thus the hemeralopic eye needs a greater brightness of objects or, if brightness stays the same, a larger size, in order to distinguish them, as Förster shows in his experimental results. On the other hand, according to his statements as based on his measurements, "the hemeralope sees small objects with increased light or daylight, just as sharply as the healthy person. But this difference with respect to very small objects disappears only at the brightest illumination.

"In a few cases only, when the disease had been of long standing, or

---

* Ruete has confirmed this point by his own experiences.

great severity, was a deterioration of vision apparent also in daylight, showing itself either by the fact that the patient was in need of very bright light in order to recognize small objects or to read, or by the fact that he was, in general, only able to recognize coarse objects."

This property of hemeralopia is not, as one might believe, a matter of the time of day, because, according to Förster's observations (p. 16), a hemeralope will see just as poorly in the daytime, if the illumination is weak, as he does at night. Up to a point the hemeralope, like a healthy individual, is able to adjust slowly to dim illumination, when going from the bright light into darkness, so that he will recognize objects, which he could not see at first. There is a difference in that he (a) initially sees worse than a healthy person, (b) he needs much more time (four to ten times as much) for adjustment, and (c) he sees worse even after the greatest possible adaptation, than a healthy dark-adapted person. All this has been discovered by Förster by means of the apparatus described on page [228].

As regards the further, very worthwhile details of observations on this disease, I must refer to the paper itself.

It would be very desirable if observations of the same thoroughness were available on nyctalopia; but none are known to me.

With respect to location, it seems that the central regions of the retina, insofar as they are not more dulled through fatigue than the periphery[3] as easily happens due to normal use of the eyes, see objects both as brighter and clearer than the peripheral regions. We are far, however, from being able to report adequate researches on the subject. A bibliography on this topic with some pertinent observations can be found in my paper: *Ueber einige Verhältnisse des binocularen Sehens*, in *Abhandl. der sächs. Soc. math.-phys. Cl.*, Vol. IV., page 373.[4]

3. EXPERIMENTS IN THE AREA OF SENSATIONS OF EXTENT

I have carried out some comparative experiments by the methods of average error and of equivalents, once on chin and upper lip, another time on the five fingers, in order to find out whether the appearance of a difference between two sets of compass points would vary according to the region of the skin, or if no essential relationship exists in this comparison. My experiments speak against any essential dependence of one on the other. Since my observations in this respect were neither complete nor fully discussed, I shall, for the present, refrain from giving further details.

---

[3] Trans. Note: Fechner writes "center" in error.
[4] Trans. Note: The correct reference should read Vol. V, p. 337.

XIII.
Laws of the Phenomena of Mixture

Our discussion of Weber's Law, of its parallel law and of the threshold have so far been concerned only with the simplest aspect of a very general case. It has always been a matter of the extent to which a sensation increased or decreased, began or disappeared, with a stimulus increment or decrement, under the assumption that whatever grew or diminished was of the same quality as the original stimulus. The nature of the stimulus, therefore, was not altered by its increase or decrease. But of all possible cases where a stimulus increment or decrement—or in fact any change—is concerned, the case where that which is added or subtracted is of the same nature as that to which it is added or from which it is subtracted is only the simplest. A stimulus of white light, for example, can be changed in that colored light is added or in that one takes away some spectral color or mixture, other than white, from the mixture that is white light, instead of increasing or decreasing the intensity of all spectral colors in equal proportion. Corresponding reasoning can, as is easily seen, be applied to other than mixed white light, to mixtures of tones and sounds, smells, and substances that arouse taste sensations. For brevity's sake we shall call phenomena eventuating from such changes *mixture phenomena*, as opposed to *homogeneous phenomena*, designating those previously discussed, and we shall limit our discussion mainly to the example of colors.

It is easy to overlook the fact that we have to expect not only quantitative, but also qualitative, changes in sensation, since mixture phenomena pertain not only to purely quantitative but also to qualitative changes of the stimulus. Empirically it can be shown that such changes occur, and the problem will be to bring them into line, in respect of their measurement, with the procedures which have been used for quantitative changes.

In general we find the following:

When two simple or compound stimuli *A* or *B*, each of which is able to arouse a separate simple sensation, *a* or *b* respectively (for example, two colors), are presented as such a mixture or compound that a single perception is produced, it will be found that this resulting impression, or this resulting sensation, will in general agree neither with the impression *a* which *A* would have produced by itself, nor with the impression *b*, which *B* would have produced by itself. Depending on whether *A* or *B* predominates, or whether they balance each other, the resulting impression will approach closer to a or to b, or else neither of the two impressions will appear to predominate—as is the case, for example, when two complementary colors are mixed to form white or when yellow and red coalesce to form orange. If we start now with A acting by itself, then the admixture of B must reach or surpass a certain level before a discrepancy from pure a becomes noticeable, and conversely with b, when we add A to B. Should we commence by letting A and B act together in such proportion that neither a nor b appears to predominate, then we must increase A or B by a given amount before the resulting impression seems to approach the characteristics of a more than those of b.

Quite generally, with whatever simple stimulus or stimulus combination —and therefore with whatever resulting impression—we might start when we add more of the stimulus, regardless of whether it is simple or compound, or when we subtract something from one of the stimuli, we find that the addition or subtraction will have to transcend a certain limit, before the simple or any other resulting impression appears qualitatively different.

These are the conditions that bring us back to the concept of the threshold as related to mixture phenomena. This is the phenomenon that we are able here as "mixture threshold" to contrast with the previously found "homogeneous threshold," as we may now call the threshold of homogeneous phenomena.

The homogeneous stimulus threshold and differential threshold of our earlier interpretation now become only the simplest special cases of the general case of a mixture threshold. In fact, when stimulus B joins stimulus or stimulus mixture A, and one asks at which value of B the admixture begins to be recognized as such or begins to make its effects felt as a difference from the mere effect of A, we can take, from among all the possible values which A could assume, the case where A is null. We then have the case of the ordinary homogeneous stimulus threshold. We can equally well take the case where, among all the possible qualities that A could have, the one where B is of the identical kind. We then have the case of the ordinary homogeneous difference threshold.

Let us now take the case where the addition of stimulus B to stimulus A brings about a just noticeable or generally perceptible change, of a certain degree, in sensation a, caused by A alone. The question is now whether when A is raised or lowered to a given degree, B must also be increased or decreased by the same ratio in order to bring about an equally noticeable change in a. Should this be the case for any given quality of A and B, then we would have in addition to the above-mentioned generalization of the threshold also a generalization of Weber's Law, which represents only the case of the general law where the difference between A and B vanishes.

So far I am still lacking data on this point, but I have carried out a few experiments myself* from which I conclude that, at least for slight admixtures of color $(=B)$ to white $(=A)$, the law holds within a range similar to that of Weber's Law and with analogous limitations.

One can easily generate just perceptible traces of color on white surfaces, either by means of colored pigments or by leaning colored sheets of glass, at an angle against a window, over a page of white paper. On repeating the experiment and its control, described on pages [117–122] (on nuances in cloud shadings), on color tints, using dark glasses, as neutral as possible, I found that one can greatly increase the density of the dark glasses—so that, for example, only $\frac{1}{14}$ of the daylight is passed through—without causing color differences are just perceptible to the free eye to disappear; yet it is always possible to cut out so much light by means of these glasses that color tints, visible to the naked eye, do disappear. On the other hand, I myself have found in the past†—and Helmholtz‡ has found again in more recent experiments—that the impression created by any color, whether homogeneous or mixed, approaches that of white at high intensities.

This exception from the law at its lower end might, however, be only an apparent one, and rest on reasons analogous to those for corresponding deviations from Weber's Law for homogeneous phenomena. When I regard a tinted shadow on a white ground with my naked eye, and then place a dark filter in front of the eye, so that the white ground comes close to the black of the closed eye, I have reduced both the color and the external light falling into the eye at an equal rate, but the intrinsic ocular blackness (which, as colorless, represents a low degree of white light) has not been weakened. The extra color, therefore, is now at a lower ratio to the white than before, and must therefore become less noticeable.

The reason for the upper limit of the law is unknown.

In common experience, strictly speaking, we rarely have to deal with completely homogeneous phenomena, or, therefore, with pure thresholds, difference thresholds, or the simplest form of Weber's Law. Rather, the more common case will be that of the mixture threshold, or of the law as applied to mixtures. Homogeneous phenomena, however, can be approximated. Observation of the simplest, though only approximated, cases is at present the most important task, and will therefore remain our preferred

---

* *Abhandl. der sächs. Gesellsch. der Wissensch., mathemat.-phys. Cl.*, Vol. V, p. 376.
† *Pogg. Ann.* L, p. 465.
‡ *Pogg. Ann.* LXXXVI.

target, especially in view of the fact that few investigations on the regular relationships of mixture phenomena are as yet available.

Even when one allows a very simple spectral color to fall into an eye, otherwise in the dark, and asks at what intensity it would be recognized, one is not dealing with a pure stimulus threshold but with a mixture threshold, since one actually asks what intensity the spectral color would have to have, for its characteristics to be noted as an admixture to the intrinsic light of the eye, which represents a mixture of light rays of all colors. The question is, therefore, of the same nature as if one asks at what intensity color would have to be mixed with white for the white to accept a noticeable tint. The only difference is that in the first case one deals with a very low intensity, whereas in the second case, where one simply speaks of white, one deals with a high intensity of the white or rather a neutral mixture with which the color is mixed. One does indeed find that in the first case the black appears merely as black, with only a trace of color, and in the latter case the white seems to be white, with only a trace of color, at the moment when the admixed color becomes just perceptible.

There is no doubt, therefore, that ultraviolet light would be easier to perceive, that is, at a lower intensity than is the case, were it not for the fact that it must occur as an admixture to the faint white light inside the eye.

The question whether (and to what degree) a mixture phenomenon varies, when all stimulus components contributing to the mixed sensation rise or decline at the same rate, is plainly only a subclass of the more general question of how mixed sensations behave and vary, when their stimulus components change at will and at any given rate.

To bring this question into clear focus, three main cases can apparently be distinguished: (1) when B increases to the point where its addition to A changes the quality of the mixed sensation just perceptibly as compared with a; (2) when B increases to the point where the effect of A just disappears, and the impression can no longer be distinguished from that of pure b; and (3) when A and B are so balanced that the impression is found to be closer neither to a nor to b. All variations that can arise by mixtures of A and B must necessarily fall within these three threshold cases, and the problem is now to find laws that represent these thresholds and the intermediate variations of sensation as a function of the laws of stimulus mixture. No data are available, thus far, and if it is true that the experimental determination of homogeneous threshold values will always remain an approximate one, it is even more likely, it seems, to hold of mixture threshold values.

An important distinction should be made between these mixture phenomena. On the one hand the stimuli which give rise to the mixed impression may themselves be mixed at the time they fall upon the end organ, as is the case when blended hues hit the eye or when a combination of noises and tones strikes the ear, that is, as happens in normal seeing and hearing. On the other hand, the stimuli may fall upon the end organ separately and combine their effect into the mixed sensation only through mediation of the end organs themselves, as is the case when different colors fall on corresponding points of each eye or when different tones strike each ear separately. We will distinguish between these cases by calling one a conjunctive and the other a disjunctive mixed impression.

We have indeed learned by experience that one can receive mixed impressions via two eyes or two ears from separately acting stimuli, impressions which correspond to those we would feel if the stimuli arrived at the same eye or ear already mixed. Although we do not know the anatomical or physiological mediation on which this phenomenon is based, we can be sure that disjunctive impressions depend on more complicated circumstances and can be affected in many more ways by secondary conditions than conjunctive impressions. For the conjunction of two different light impressions, A and B, varying in intensity or color, on the same spot on the retina can at any time take place only in one way; but the disjunction of these stimuli on corresponding points of the retina can take place in an infinite number of ways. The stimulus, for example, might be null on one side, and $A + B$ on the other, or A on one side and B on the other, or $A/2$ might affect one side and $B + A/2$ the other. In the disjunctive case there may also occur differences in the relationship of stimuli on each retina to neighboring impressions, which cannot happen in the conjunctive case on the same retina. Experience has shown that differences in the resulting mixed impression may depend on these differing effects of conjunctive and disjunctive mixing. The distribution of the components on corresponding retinal elements can therefore by no means be replaced by the meeting of the same components on a single identical element. The ear reacts in an analogous way, up to a point. I have treated this subject more extensively in my paper, *Ueber einige Verhältnisse des binocularen Sehens* in the *Abhandlungen der sächs. Soc. der Wissenschaften, math.-phys. Cl.*, Vol. V, pages 339 ff.

Index of Names

Subject Index

Aberrations, optical, 210
Absolute sensitivity, 42, 43
  measurement of, 59, 108–111
Acoumeter, 149
Acuity, visual, 235, 237, 242, 243
Adaptation, 136
  to darkness, 268–273
Afterimages, 138, 268n, 271
Amaurotic blindness, 271
Anatomy, 10
Angles, visual, 223, 233–235, 238, 239,
  241–243
Astrometer, 135
Astronomy, 56
Augenschwarz, 136n
Average error, 102
  method of, measuring differential
    sensitivity, 60–64, 65, 66, 72, 75
    applied to visual span and touch,
     100–107
    mathematical relationship to
     other methods, 107–108
    quadratic, 102, 104, 105
    simple, 102, 104, 108

Biophysics, 29
Body, mind and, relationship of, 1–6
Brightness differences, 118–119

Calculus, application of, 51–52, 53
Carcel lamp, 128, 129
Circle, aspects of, 2
Color, intensive threshold for, 213–214
Components, 40
Conductor, neural, 8
Consciousness, 46, 48
Constant errors, 67n, 73–77, 100–102,
  104, 111
Continuity, principle of, 51

Differences, *see* Brightness differences;
  Just noticeable differences

Differential sensitivity, 40–45, 57
  concept of, 18
  measurement of, methods of, 60–108
    average error, method of, 60–64,
     65, 66, 72, 75, 100–107
    breaking experiments into parts,
     69–70
    chance fluctuations, irregular, 64–
     65
    checking of results, 72
    considerations and precautions,
     64–73
    constant errors, 73–77
    control, repetition or other means
     of, 71
    data, use of, 71
    date of observation, 72
    different conditions, consideration
     of, 67–69
    general description, 60–64
    judgment and power of imagina-
     tion, 71, 73
    just noticeable differences, method
     of, 60–64
    mathematical relationship of the
     three methods, 107–108
    measurements taken at different
     times, comparability of, 69
    multiplicity of observations, need
     for, 65–67
    ordering of experimental condi-
     tions, 71
    pooling of investigations, 72
    preliminary trials, 67
    recording of observed values, 71–
     72
    relative, 59
    right and wrong cases, method of,
     60–64, 65, 66, 68, 71, 72, 75,
     77–100
    secondary conditions, 72
    simple, 59